Biotechnology
Laboratory Manual

Second Edition

Ellyn Daugherty

EMC Publishing® ░ PARADIGM
EDUCATION SOLUTIONS

ST. PAUL, MINNESOTA

Managing Editor:	Brenda Owens
Senior Production Editor:	Bob Dreas
Cover Designer:	Tammy Norstrem
Text Designer:	Leslie Anderson
Production Specialists:	Tammy Norstrem, Ryan Hamner

Care has been taken to verify the accuracy of information presented in this book. However, the authors, editors, and publisher cannot accept responsibility for Web, e-mail, newsgroup, or chat room subject matter or content, or for consequences from application of the information in this book, and make no warranty, expressed or implied, with respect to its content.

Trademarks: Some of the product names and company names included in this book have been used for identification purposes only and may be trademarks or registered trade names of their respective manufacturers and sellers. The authors, editors, and publisher disclaim any affiliation, association, or connection with, or sponsorship or endorsement by, such owners.

Acknowledgments: The author, editor, and publisher wish to thank the following individuals for their insightful feedback during the development of the first and second editions of this text.

- Dr. Jim DeKloe, Co-Director, Biotechnician Program, Solano Community College
- Dr. Toby Horn, Co-Director, Carnegie Academy for Science Education, Carnegie Institute of Washington
- Simon Holdaway, MS, Molecular Biology & Microbiology Instructor, The Loomis Chaffee School
- Brian Robinson, PhD, Cell Biology, MD candidate, Emory University School of Medicine

We have made every effort to trace the ownership of all copyrighted material and to secure permission from copyright holders. In the event of any question arising as to the use of any material, we will be pleased to make the necessary corrections in future printings. Thanks are due to the aforementioned authors, publishers, and agents for permission to use the materials indicated.

ISBN 978-0-76387-299-1

Contents

1 Introduction to Biotechnology Methodologies 1

2 Basic Biology for the Biotechnician ... 13

3 Basic Chemistry for the Biotechnician 32

4 DNA Isolation and Analysis 67

5 Protein Isolation and Analysis 100

6 Assay Development 122

7 Using the Spectrophotometer for DNA and Protein Assays 144

8 Recombinant Protein Production 168

9 Protein Product Purification and Analysis 195

10 Plant Biotechnology 207

11 Agricultural Biotechnologies 239

12 Obtaining Molecules of Pharmaceutical Interest 273

13 Making DNA Molecules 292

14 Biotechnology Research and Applications............................. 321

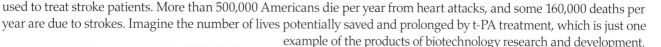

Imagine a world where babies are born without defects, perpetrators of crimes are identified within minutes, diseases are diagnosed and treated right in your own home, and there is enough food to feed everyone. This scenario may sound like the makings of a science fiction novel, but this "fiction" is fast becoming reality. Every day, new advances in the field of biotechnology move us closer to the goals of curing disease, wiping out hunger, and improving the quality of life for all people. Because discoveries and new products are transforming the way we live, some observers say we are undergoing a biotechnology revolution.

As evidence of this revolution, just note the progress in the research and development of biotechnology products over the past 30 years. In the mid 1990s, hundreds of researchers and technicians at one of the largest biotechnology companies, Genentech, Inc, collaborated in producing human tissue plasminogen activator (t-PA), a protein that dissolves blood clots. When given within hours of a heart attack, t-PA clears blockages in blood vessels so that blood can flow more freely. This protein is credited with reducing damage to the heart that is caused by a heart attack. Soon after its release for use in heart attack cases, t-PA was marketed and used to treat stroke patients. More than 500,000 Americans die per year from heart attacks, and some 160,000 deaths per year are due to strokes. Imagine the number of lives potentially saved and prolonged by t-PA treatment, which is just one example of the products of biotechnology research and development.

Now, imagine being a part of this revolution. Imagine working on a team that constructs a vaccine for human immunodeficiency virus (HIV), the virus that causes acquired immunodeficiency syndrome (AIDS). Picture working for a company that produces a high-protein, nonallergenic peanut that can be grown in drought conditions in third-world countries. Envision yourself in the laboratory developing a strain of bacterium that digests petroleum from oil spills.

Imagine the sense of accomplishment and gratification you would feel as a contributor to these breakthroughs. Think of how this type of work could help improve the quality of life for your friends and family.

You could be part of the Biotechnology Revolution. Thousands of employees are needed to staff the hundreds of new biotechnology companies starting up every year. These fledgling companies need scientists and lab technicians to complete research and development on potential products. They also need workers to manufacture and package the products. Since testing has to be done on all products, employees are needed to design, run, and document these tests. Companies also require nonscientific support staff, including those in marketing, finance, and law. Human resource (HR) specialists are needed to choose the best employees. People who work in public relations and corporate communications keep the public informed about product development and keep employees aware of recent news on related items.

Whether you aspire to work in a lab, on research and development, in manufacturing, or in the financial or business end of the biotechnology industry, there is a surplus of jobs to entice people of all interests. No matter what your position, be it entry level or upper management, when a product is released that you have had some part in

developing, you can expect to experience great satisfaction.

The purpose of this lab manual is to introduce the many concepts and laboratory skills you need to master to work in the field of biotechnology. No matter where your interest lies, or which position you may have (science or business), understanding the tools and techniques of basic biotechnology research will help you work effectively on a team charged with developing a process or bringing a product to market.

Best wishes for your success!

Ellyn Daugherty
San Francisco, California

Acknowledgements

I have many people to thank for helping me learn the science I am now sharing.

I might never have started teaching biotech if Jack Chirikjian, PhD and Dr. Carol Chihara hadn't let me into their *Recombinant DNA* workshop in 1998. When Jack gave participants 10 Edvotek, Inc lab kits, a gel box, and a power supply to take back to their classrooms, those 10 labs snowballed over 28 years into this 4-year curriculum.

I gratefully thank Patricia Seawell formerly of Gene Connection and Frank Stephenson, PhD of ThermoFisher Scientific/Applied Biosystems for the many mini-courses over the phone, online, and in the lab to help me get my science "right" and for providing support and reagents when I was testing new curricula. Frank was also the first person to brave the first draft of my manuscript.

Maureen Munn, PhD, Project Director of the Human Genome Program, University of Washington Genome Center, and Lane Conn, former Director of the Teacher Education in Biology program at San Francisco State University, spent many hours helping me bring DNA synthesis activities to my students. Maureen also read and gave feedback on some sections of my manuscript.

I am indebted to Diane Sweeney, formerly of Genencor International and now at Sacred Heart Preparatory, for the extensive teacher training and in-service she has conducted. Two of her Amylase Project labs, which she shared with me in a workshop in 1989, became the cornerstone for a few dozen amylase activities in my curriculum.

Several teachers used the early drafts of the text and lab manual and gave me valuable input. I want to thank Leslie Conaghan, Karen Watts, Josephine Yu, PhD, Tina Doss, and Dan Raffa for their constant and considerable contributions and corrections. Dan and Tina also provided technical advice regarding instructional materials and spent the better part of a summer creating the lab skills tutorials for the Encore CD that was packaged with the first edition of the text and lab manual. I am particularly appreciative of Jimmy Ikeda, my SMBCP teaching lab partner. We worked very closely on all SMBCP program and curriculum matters and he has helped me out of countless jams. In recent years, Jimmy's Independent Research students field tested several of the new lab activities in the second edition lab manual. I thank them all for their efforts testing and improving this curriculum. Regarding technical assistance, the creation of the manuscript would not have been possible without the untiring efforts of my computer technician and exceptional Webmaster, Skip Wagner. In addition, a huge hug and lots of love to my mom, Lorna Kopel, who read every word of the text, lab manual, and instructor's guide and made grammatical corrections.

I am immensely grateful to the science content editors of *Biotechnology: Science for the New Millenium*:

- Dr. Jim DeKloe, Co-Director, Biotechnician Program, Solano Community College
- Dr. Toby Horn, Co-Director, Carnegie Academy for Science Education, Carnegie Institute of Washington
- Simon Holdaway, MS, Molecular Biology & Microbiology Instructor, The Loomis Chaffee School
- Brian Robinson, PhD, Cell Biology, MD candidate, Emory University School of Medicine

I was extremely fortunate to have met Simon Holdaway, bioscience teacher/professor extraordinaire. Simon has shown me how to do biotech better, faster, and cheaper. For this 2nd edition, Simon helped me identify the strengths and the weaknesses in earlier editions and helped me plan the direction to take for this one. Simon created the new pAmylase2014 plasmid used in several of the labs. Simon contributed three new labs to the lab manual and produced the new pAmylase plasmid that makes recombinant alpha-amylase, faster and better. Simon really knows his science and has helped me get that right in this edition.

Many scientists, educators and students have worked on curriculum development with me, or have provided feedback or scientific advice. I would like to thank Katy Korsmeyer, PhD, Maria Abilock, Shalini Prasad, Aylene Bao for their efforts. Aylene Bao was the original illustrator of the manuscript, and her extensive collection of drawings served as excellent models for the illustrators at Precision Graphics who created the beautiful drawings in the text and lab manual. Maria Abilock wrote the original test bank questions and suggested several changes as she read through the manuscript. I am particularly appreciative of Sandra Porter, Ph.D.,President, Digital World Biology LLC. Sandy taught me how to use and teach others to use the molecular modeling applications used in this edition. Sandy also developed a molecular model database to support this curriculum found at **digitalworldbiology.com/dwb/structure-collections**. Thank you to Dr. Timothy Gregory of Genentech, Inc for letting me be the first teacher intern at Genentech, Inc and allowing me to gain real science skills for two summers with Lavon, Allison, Millie, and Dave in the Protein Process Development Department.

Assembling a good working version of the laboratory materials list was one of the biggest challenges in this project. Many individuals have worked hundreds of hours helping me determine the materials that would provide the best performance and value to my teacher users. I appreciate the hard work of all of them but especially Amy Naum who has worked tirelessly to make sure the original materials lists were current and accurate. Amy supported the research and development of several labs in this edition and has been a champion of helping science teachers develop better lab skills.

For this edition, I am indebted to both Colin Heath, of G-Biosciences and Lindsay Kotula of Fisher Science Education. Among other projects supporting the *Biotechnology: Science for the New Millennium* lab manual, Colin and I collaborated to develop *The rAmylase Project* kits that support Chapters 6–9 in the curriculum. These 10 lab kits make it easier to bring a thematic lab experience in recombinant DNA protein production to any high school or college student. Colin has spent countless hours in the lab testing reagents for new or improved lab activities. I appreciate Lindsay's time and effort to create the current *Biotechnology: Science for the New Millennium* laboratory materials list that facilitates educators with the challenging task of finding the right lab materials of good quality and value.

I was extremely fortunate to find the right publisher. I thank Dr. Elaine Johnson of Bio-Link and Kristin Hershbell Charles of City College of San Francisco for all their efforts to support and promote my program, and especially for connecting me with EMC Paradigm. I am so grateful to the publishing teams at EMC School and Paradigm Education Solutions who have agreed with me philosophically about the goals of this project. Mick Demakos, Brenda Owens, Deanna Quinn, Bob Dreas, Carley Bomstad, and Sonja Brown. I appreciate all of your efforts.

Photo by Kainaz Amaria.

About the Author

A 34-year veteran biology teacher, Ellyn Daugherty began teaching biotechnology in 1988. Ellyn founded the San Mateo Biotechnology Career Pathway (**www.SMBiotech.com**) in 1993. Her model curriculum attracts students into an intensive, multiple-year program in biotechnology that leads them to higher education and into the biotechnology workplace.

Ellyn has received several awards for her innovative teaching and curriculum development, including:

- BayBio Pantheon Award, Biotechnology Educator, San Mateo Biotechnology Career Pathway, 2010

- The National Biotechnology Teacher-Leader Award, Biotechnology Institute and Genzyme, 2004

- Presidential Award in Science Education, California State Finalist, 2000

- Intel Innovations in Teaching Award, California State Runner-Up, 2000

- Tandy Technology Prize, Outstanding Teacher Award, 1997

- LaBoskey Award, Stanford University, Master Teacher Award, 1995

- Access Excellence Award, NABT and Genentech, Inc., 1994

- National Distinguished Teacher, Commission on Presidential Scholars, 1992

Ellyn retired from the classroom in 2013 but still works with teachers and schools to improve biotechnology education. Ellyn believes strongly in teacher professional development and conducts several workshops a year in her lab and at national conferences. Her website (**www.BiotechEd.com**) contains a collection of teacher support materials and information about upcoming workshops.

An avid sports fan, Ellyn spends her time outside of the lab at baseball and basketball games, golfing or hiking with her husband, Paul, and their chihuahua, Rocky Balboa.

1 Introduction to Biotechnology Methodologies

A quality control lab technician prepares samples to be tested on a DNA synthesizer. She will report the degree to which the samples meet the required quality standards. Attention to detail is critical in preparing and testing samples.
Photo by author.

From the very first day as a lab technician, you are expected to follow standard laboratory operating procedures (SLOP). SLOP includes skills that are critical for safety such as following written and oral instructions, working in a professional manner, keeping detailed records of all work, and using all equipment and instruments accurately and as directed. Also included are the skills of setting up and running sophisticated instruments, such as spectrophotometers and bioreactors.

In the following laboratory activities, you will begin to learn some of the most basic standard laboratory operating procedures used by lab technicians, research associates, and scientists throughout biotechnology research and manufacturing facilities. These include:

- Setting up and maintaining a legal scientific notebook. All the work you do as a lab technician in this biotechnology course is recorded into your legal scientific notebook.
- Understanding safety concerns, precautions, equipment, and rules for the typical biotechnology facility.
- Setting up experiments, documenting conditions, analyzing data, and reporting results.

In each of the subsequent chapters, you will use these skills and learn additional ones in the areas of measurement, solution and media preparation, sterile technique, cell culture, and electrophoresis.

It is critical to learn to follow testing procedures exactly, and to document the conditions and results of each experiment, test, or reaction. Laboratory instruments and equipment are delicate and expensive. The chemical reagents and biological samples can be dangerous if you do not use them correctly, following specific safety protocols. On the positive side, the results of experiments could lead to discoveries or products that improve human life. You will be able to perform these tasks with confidence because you will have been trained and will have mastered the standard laboratory operating procedures that apply in any biotechnology facility.

Laboratory 1a
How to Set Up a Legal Scientific Notebook

Figure 1.1. **A lab employee receives an official legal scientific notebook from a company. Most companies number notebooks and keep a record of their location.**
Photo by author.

Background

Everyone at a biotechnology company who is involved in research or product design and development must document all work. A laboratory employee documents experiments and other activities in a legal scientific notebook (see Figure 1.1). A legal scientific notebook becomes the historical record of all work done by the biotechnology employee.

A scientific notebook may be required in court cases. Examples of situations in which a scientific notebook may be used in court include the following:

1. To settle patent disputes, such as when someone argues that he/she made a discovery first and says a discovery or process belongs to him/her.
2. To report a specialist's findings from testing, such as in paternity suits or criminal cases.

If the scientific notebook is not maintained in an acceptable fashion, it will be inadmissible as evidence and will not be used. The following protocol will help you set up and maintain a legal scientific notebook.

Setting Up a Legal Scientific Notebook

1. Obtain a bound notebook with sewn pages. A composition-style notebook works well.
2. Use *only* black pen to make *all* entries into the notebook. Be careful when making entries. Incorrect entries may be lined out with a *single line only* and must be labeled with initials and the date. Incorrect entries must still be readable after correction.
3. Graphs and other small sheets of paper may be pasted into your notebook when necessary. When pasting, use a glue stick. Do not use white glue, tape, or staples. There should be no loose papers in the notebook.
4. Number every page of the notebook, at the top outside corner, starting with the front side of the first page as number 1 and the back of the first page as number 2. Continue numbering the front and back of *every* page of the notebook (see Figure 1.2).
5. Make page 1 the title page. In the middle of the page, in bold print, write:

Figure 1.2. **Numbering and Title Page**

[name of course] NOTEBOOK
course section or class period
name of institution
your name
today's date

Also write this information on the front cover of the notebook

6. Make pages 2 through 5 the Table of Contents. Write "Table of Contents" at the top of each of these pages. Record the page and title of each new activity in the Table of Contents (see Figure 1.3).

(Continues)

7. Glue your "Employment Contract" (if your instructor uses one) onto the inside front cover of the notebook. Read the contract carefully before signing it.
8. Glue the "Laboratory Notebook Policy" sheet onto the inside back cover of the notebook. Read the policy carefully before recording information into your notebook. Glue the "Employee Participation Rubric" (if your instructor uses one) onto the last page of your notebook.
9. The record of work begins on page 6.
10. Sign and date the bottom of every page. Also, write, "go to page [number]" on the bottom right-hand side of the page to tell the reader where the rest of the information for this topic is located in the notebook. On the page you "go to," write, "from page [number]" on the top left-hand side of the page showing the page you came from. If you set your notebook up this way, it should be relatively easy for you or anyone familiar with the work you are doing to find the data, observations, and conclusions about a specific topic.

Figure 1.3. Table of Contents

A record of all work performed and data collected is logged into the notebook.
Photo by author.

Laboratory Notebook Policy

Based on the Laboratory Notebook Policy used at Applied Biosystems, a division of Thermo Fisher Scientific, Inc.

Why is proper record keeping in a bound notebook important?

In the United States, the first person to conceive and show diligence to develop an invention, product, or process is awarded the patent for that product or process. Notebooks that are properly prepared, maintained, and witnessed are legal evidence of conception and diligence to practice an invention.

Record-Keeping Procedures

1. Use only your official biotechnology notebook to record your work. All work must be recorded in the notebook and in no other document.
2. Date and sign *every* page. Sign and date at the end of an experiment.
3. Maintain a Table of Contents as you make entries in the notebook. The first page of every lab investigation should be listed in the Table of Contents.
4. Make all entries legibly *only* in *black permanent ink*. No pencil entries are permitted. The use of colored pens or pencils is acceptable in some cases, as approved by the supervisor.
5. *Do not erase, ink over, or white out any errors.* Draw a single line through errors so they can still be read. Place your initials and the date next to the correction.
6. Briefly state the objective or purpose of each experiment, and reference previous work or projects.
7. Use "from..." or "go to..." statements to tie together sections of a lab report or continuous work.
8. Record all directions, materials, and quantities used, plus reactions or operating conditions, in sufficient detail and clarity so that someone of equal skill could understand or repeat the procedure if necessary.

(Continues)

9. Avoid abbreviations and codes when possible. Only the standard abbreviations for metric measurements may be used universally. Any coding or special labeling on samples or in procedural notes should be fully recorded and explained in the notebook.

10. List all persons from whom samples or data were obtained, shared, or transferred.

11. Attach as much original data as is practical in the notebook. Where it is not practical to attach original data, attach examples and make clear reference to where the original data are stored.

12. When procedures, data, conclusions, etc, are continued from previous pages, each page must have a "from page ___" listed. When continuing to another page, there should be a "go to" statement directing the reader to the next page of that work.

13. For important entries, such as key conclusions or new ideas, have a coworker sign and date the entry. Be sure the coworker is not a coinventor, but someone who is capable of understanding the meaning of the notebook entry.

14. Write/print clearly so there is no ambiguity about the information recorded. Skip lines between data tables, graphs, and important conclusions to make it easier to find and read recorded information.

(Continues)

Laboratory 1b
Laboratory Safety: Protecting Yourself and Your Coworkers

Background

A biotechnology laboratory may have several safety hazards. These can put an employee in danger as well as place the safety of others at risk. It is the responsibility of each employee to know and follow the basic laboratory safety rules, to recognize and understand the hazardous materials, equipment, and conditions in a facility, and to work to reduce potential risks.

In the event of an accident, an employee must know what to do to minimize the damage that might occur. Knowing the location of emergency equipment and how to use it is essential for each employee.

Basic Laboratory Safety Rules

1. Follow all posted safety rules and act in a responsible, informed manner at all times.
2. Understand and follow all written and verbal instructions. Ask questions if unsure about any procedure. Be aware of potential dangers that could arise during laboratory work. Before using products or equipment, carefully read labels, experimental protocols, and equipment instructions and literature. Know the location of and how to read Safety Data Sheets (SDS).

Figure 1.4. **A safety shower and eyewash. Do not hesitate to use either one if your clothes are burning or any body parts are exposed to flame or hazardous chemicals.** Photo by author.

3. No eating or drinking in the laboratory. No gum chewing. No makeup application.
4. Wear safety apparel, such as safety goggles, gloves, lab coats, and other protective clothing as necessary. Tie hair back and do not wear dangling jewelry or baggy clothing.
5. Know how to call for emergency help, and the location of a first aid kit, fire exits, fire extinguishers, eyewash, and safety showers (see Figure 1.4). Make sure nothing flammable is within 1 foot of an open flame.
6. Wash hands regularly, with soap and water, especially after working with microorganisms or chemicals.
7. Contaminated samples (chemical, biological, glass, and radioactive wastes) must be disposed of in appropriate containers. Do not pick up broken glass with your hands. Learn the specific methods of waste removal from your lab supervisor.
8. Label all samples and reagents clearly with the name of the item, the name of the person who prepared the sample, and the date of preparation.
9. If you are taking antibiotics, or you are pregnant or ill, report your condition to your supervisor.
10. Report spills, accidents, and injuries to your lab supervisor or safety officer immediately.

In summary, a technician who demonstrates good laboratory practices (GLPs) will:

- Know the location and use of all the personal protective equipment, such as goggles, gloves, hoods, etc.
- Know the location and proper use of all the emergency equipment, such as Material Safety Data Sheets (MSDS), chemical showers, safety eyewash, fire extinguishers, etc.
- Maintain a clean (and sterile, when appropriate) workspace free from clutter.

- Recognize chemical and biological hazards. Know how to handle and dispose of each hazard properly.
- Know who to contact and how to contact emergency services in the case of a fire, chemical, or biological emergency. Know how to contact the Environmental Health and Safety Officer at the worksite (see Figure 1.5).

Purpose

To conduct a safety inventory of the biotechnology laboratory facility. To learn how chemicals are safely used and stored. To learn how to work safely with others in a laboratory.

Procedure

Complete the following tasks, recording all work in your notebook.

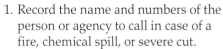

*Environmental Health and Safety Officer

Figure 1.5. **An Environmental Health and Safety Manager,** like Fredric Rosqvist at Sunesis Pharmaceuticals Inc., is responsible for ensuring that employees have the safest working environment possible. To make certain that Sunesis Pharmaceuticals adheres to highly regulated environmental, human health, and safety standards, Fredric provides safety trainings for employees, conducts inspections of the workplace, and reports to federal and state regulatory agencies.
Photo by author.

1. Record the name and numbers of the person or agency to call in case of a fire, chemical spill, or severe cut.
2. Your supervisor will give a tour of the laboratory, pointing out the safety hazards, risk-prevention equipment, and emergency equipment. Record these in a full-page chart similar to Table 1.1. Draw and label a diagram of the room that maps out the hazards and equipment.
3. A safety diamond notifies workers about chemical or biological hazards (see Figure 1.5). Visit biotech.emcp.net/diamond to learn how information is conveyed on a safety diamond. Draw and label a safety diamond that shows the hazards coded within each section.
4. Record the location of SDS sheets available to you. These may be in handbooks, on the Internet, or on a CD. Use SDS information to learn what to do if you get sodium hydroxide (NaOH) on your skin or in your eyes, or if it is inhaled.
5. Go to the website at openwetware.org/wiki/DOs_and_DONTs_of_Good_Lab_Citizenship to learn how to work more responsibily in a shared laboratory. In your notebook, list 3 items from the "Dos" and "Don'ts" list that, maybe you hadn't thought about before, that would make you a better laboratory partner.
*In this manual, the Biotech Ed EHS Officer icon indicates a known safety hazard.

Table 1.1. **Safety Hazards and Safety Equipment Chart**

Potential Safety Hazards	Potential Harm	Safety Equipment Available	Equipment Available
Bunsen burner	burns to person or property	goggles and rubber bands for tying back long hair	fireextinguisher, fire blanket, and safety shower

Laboratory 1c

Cheese Production: The Evolution of Cheese-Making Technology

This activity was inspired by labs developed by Louann Carlmagno, formerly of Genencor International, Inc.

Figure 1.6. **Consumers have many varieties of cheese to choose from. Recently, biotechnology products that make cheese faster than older methods have improved the cheese-making process.**
Photo by author.

Background

The cheese-making industry is huge and has a great number and variety of products (see Figure 1.6). Cheese-making is a good example of how biotechnology has improved an industrial process.

In the past, people made cheese simply by letting the naturally occurring bacteria in milk turn the milk sour. In that process called lactic acid fermentation, the bacteria use milk sugar (lactose) as an energy source and produce lactic acid, a waste product. Lactic acid also causes the mixture to have a mild to slightly bitter taste. Along with other flavorful compounds, the lactic acid gives the cheese a characteristic flavor.

The milk bacteria produce special enzymes (proteins that speed reactions) that convert the lactose to lactic acid. Lactic acid has a low pH (the hydrogen ion concentration, or a measure of the acidity) and causes the milk protein, casein, to denature (unwind) and fall out of solution. Other enzymes, called proteases, may also act on casein. Proteases cleave proteins, such as casein, into smaller fragments that will also fall out of solution. The lumps of denatured casein are called curds. Curds are pressed together to form cheese. The liquid remaining after curdling is called whey.

Quickly, it was realized that new batches of cheese could be produced more quickly and reliably if the cheese makers added just a small amount of a cheese that they wanted. The "starter cheese" contained the bacteria, and their enzymes, that fermented the milk to produce the desired cheese. Many cheeses are still produced in this fashion.

Today, most commercially-produced cheese is made in one of the four ways listed below. In each method, sterilized milk is used as a starting reagent.

1. The milk may simply be left to age, exposed to air and naturally occurring bacteria (see Figure 1.7).

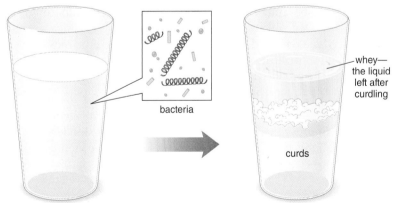

Even "fresh" milk has bacteria in it. The bacteria use the milk protein, casein, as food.

As the bacteria grow, they produce products (lactic acid) that make the protein fall out of solution in lumps. The lumps are called "curds."

whey—the liquid left after curdling

bacteria

curds

Figure 1.7. **Milk Curdling** Milk left exposed to air curdles because of bacterial enzyme activity.

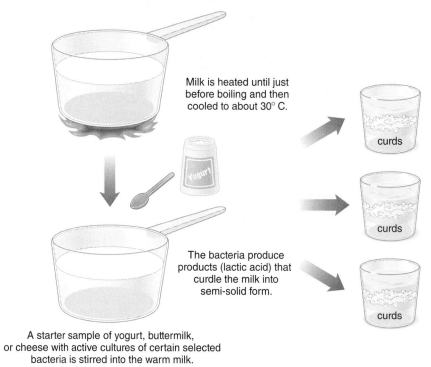

Milk is heated until just before boiling and then cooled to about 30° C.

The bacteria produce products (lactic acid) that curdle the milk into semi-solid form.

A starter sample of yogurt, buttermilk, or cheese with active cultures of certain selected bacteria is stirred into the warm milk.

curds

curds

curds

Figure 1.8. **Milk Curdling with a Starter**   Adding an existing culture of milk-curdling bacteria will speed curdling in a milk sample. Many fermented milk products such as yogurt, sour cream, buttermilk, and several cheeses are made using starter cultures. Adding a starter increases the chances of having a "better" cheese, faster.

2. New batches of cheese are started with specific cultures of selected bacteria. These "known" bacteria also make the enzymes that curdle milk. Buttermilk has a good culture of *Lactobacillus* bacteria and can be used as a "starter" (see Figure 1.8).

3. New batches of cheese may be started by the adding purified enzymes, such as rennin, to milk. Rennin, is a protein retrieved from the cells lining the stomachs of calves (see Figure 1.9). Rennin is of protease, and like other proteases, it cleaves the casein into small fragments that settle out as curds. When calves nurse, their stomach cells produce rennin to digest the milk protein. To retrieve the calves' enzymes for commercial use, companies grind up the calf stomachs and purify the rennin enzyme from all of the other compounds made by the cells. For this reason, some vegetarians do not eat rennin cheeses. There are many rennin cheeses, including Asiago, most bries, most cheddars, and Roquefort.

4. Recently, scientists have learned how to trick bacteria into make calf rennin using genetic engineering techniques (see Figure 1.10). Scientists found the DNA code for the cheese-making enzymes produced by calves in calf stomach cells. They cut out the cow's rennin cheese-making code (gene) and inserted it into fungus cells. Fungus cells then read the cow DNA and synthesized the rennin enzyme, which scientists called "chymosin." Then, cheese makers used the genetically engineered enzymes to speed curdling. Now, fungal cultures produce the curdling enzymes in a faster, cheaper manner, and in larger amounts than can be produced inside big, multicellular organisms, such as cows. Chymosin cheeses include Jack, mozzarella, and most Swiss cheeses, plus many others.

Scientists work to create new and improved versions of cheese-curdling enzymes, as well as to improve the yields and qualities of cheeses. Modern-day cheese makers want to produce large amounts of high-quality cheese in the most economical way.

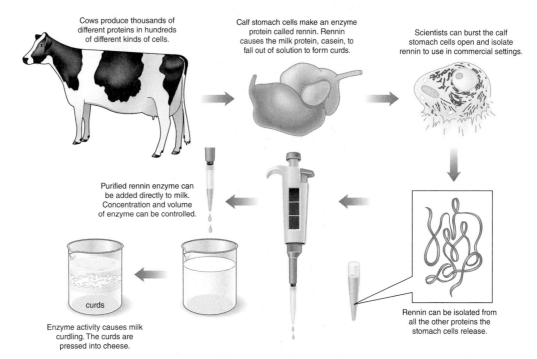

Cows produce thousands of different proteins in hundreds of different kinds of cells.

Calf stomach cells make an enzyme protein called rennin. Rennin causes the milk protein, casein, to fall out of solution to form curds.

Scientists can burst the calf stomach cells open and isolate rennin to use in commercial settings.

Purified rennin enzyme can be added directly to milk. Concentration and volume of enzyme can be controlled.

Rennin can be isolated from all the other proteins the stomach cells release.

curds

Enzyme activity causes milk curdling. The curds are pressed into cheese.

Figure 1.9. **Milk Curdling with the Protease, Rennin**   The enzyme rennin is extracted from calf stomachs. Rennin curdles milk by breaking bonds that hold the casein protein together. Since the purified enzyme is immediately available (the cheesemakers don't have to wait for bacteria to grow and produce it), rennin cheeses are made faster than starter cheeses.

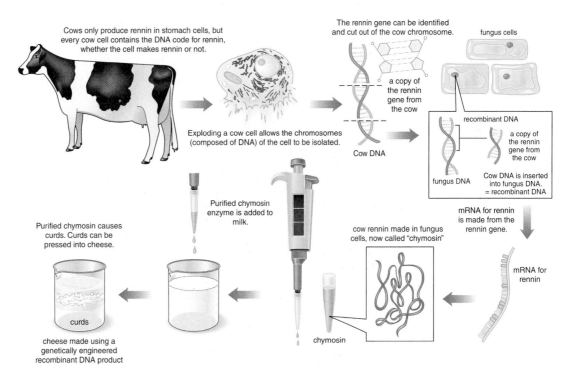

Cows only produce rennin in stomach cells, but every cow cell contains the DNA code for rennin, whether the cell makes rennin or not.

The rennin gene can be identified and cut out of the cow chromosome.

fungus cells

a copy of the rennin gene from the cow

Exploding a cow cell allows the chromosomes (composed of DNA) of the cell to be isolated.

Cow DNA

recombinant DNA

a copy of the rennin gene from the cow

fungus DNA   Cow DNA is inserted into fungus DNA. = recombinant DNA

mRNA for rennin is made from the rennin gene.

Purified chymosin enzyme is added to milk.

cow rennin made in fungus cells, now called "chymosin"

mRNA for rennin

Purified chymosin causes curds. Curds can be pressed into cheese.

curds

chymosin

cheese made using a genetically engineered recombinant DNA product

Figure 1.10. **Milk Curdling with the Protease, Chymosin**   The genetically engineered enzyme chymosin can be produced in fungi faster and more economically than in calves. Chymosin is a form of cow rennin that has been produced in fungi.

Purpose

Using a controlled experiment and collecting numerical data, determine which curdling agent tested produces cheese at the fastest rate.

Hypothesis

Since chymosin is a product of scientific manipulation to create a better curdling enzyme, it might be expected to produce the largest volume of cheese in the shortest amount of time.

Materials

Tubes, 15 mL, sterile	Pipet pumps, blue and green	Graduated cylinder, 25 mL
Whole milk	Buttermilk	Plastic funnels, short-stemmed
Micropipet, P-1000	Rennin, bovine	Filter paper, 12.5 cm
Micropipet tips for P-1000	Chymosin, recombinant rennin	Permanent lab marker pens
Pipets, 1 mL, 2 mL and 10 mL	Test tube racks for 15 mL tubes	

Procedure

37°C

1. Using a 10-mL pipet and pipet pump, transfer *exactly* 7 mL of whole milk into a labeled, 15-mL conical tube.
2. Using a preset P-1000 micropipet or a 1-mL pipet and pump, add 0.25 mL (250 µL) of one of the four curdling agents to the 7 mL of milk. Use buttermilk, rennin, chymosin, or deionized water (negative control) as assigned by your supervisor. 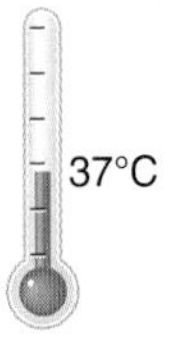
3. Cap the tube and mix by gently inverting three times. Record this "initial time" in the data section of your lab record.
4. Place the milk-containing portion of the tube deep in your armpit, like a thermometer, and incubate it there for at least 15 minutes.
5. Using a stopwatch, check for curdling every 5 minutes, recording the time to curdle in minutes. To check for curdling, gently tilt the tube, being careful to not break up any curds. Curds are large lumps of solidified milk. After 15 minutes, place the tube upright at room temperature and check for curdling every 15 minutes for 2 hours. If curdling has not occurred within 2 hours, continue checking once every 4 hours. With the greatest accuracy possible, record the time, in minutes, until the milk curdles to the greatest extent.
6. If curdling has not occurred by the end of the laboratory period, bring the tube home (keep at room temperature) and back to class in 24 hours. Keep the tube upright so any curds fall to the bottom of the tube.
7. On your return to the lab, measure the volume of curds (solids) and whey (liquid) in the tube. You may be able to read the volume of each directly from the tube, although it may be difficult. Better yet, filter the curds as described below, using a "whey-o-meter" (see Figure 1.11).
8. On your return to the lab, create a filter paper cone by folding medium flow filter paper as directed by your supervisor and then filter the whey and curds mixture through a filter paper funnel into a 10-mL graduated cylinder (a "whey-o-meter"). Allow the whey to filter through the paper filter for a total of 30 minutes. Determine the volume of whey collected in the graduated cylinder, using a pipet, if necessary, to measure small amounts. By subtraction, determine the volume of curds. Can you suggest another method to determine the amount of curds produced in each treatment?

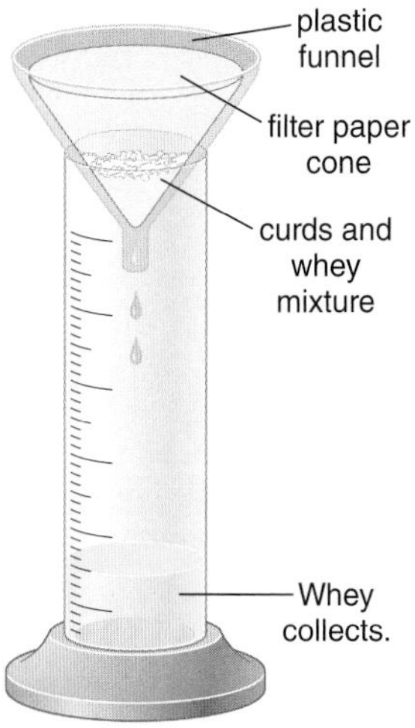

Figure 1.11. Whey-o-meter
A whey-o-meter measures the amount of whey in a curdled milk sample. By subtracting the whey volume from the total volume of reagents used, you can estimate the volume of curds.

(figure labels: plastic funnel; filter paper cone; curds and whey mixture; Whey collects.)

Table 1.2. The Effects of Cheese-Curdling Agents on Curdling Time and Volume

Curdling Agent	Estimated Time to Curdling (min)	Volume of Whey (mL)	Volume of Curds (mL)	Technician/ Comments
buttermilk				
rennin				
chymosin				
deionized water (control)				

9. In your notebook, in a data table similar to Table 1.2, record the data for your sample plus one each of the other variable groups. This will give you data for one experimental trial of each curdling agent. Record the name of the person from whom you obtained data.

How well do these single trials of the experiment support the original hypothesis? Explain.

Using Microsoft® Excel®, the lab supervisor or a student colleague will enter each individual's data into a class data table showing multiple replications of the experiment. Averages for each variable group should also be recorded in this data table. Averaged data are the best answer to an experimental question. Can you explain why?

Data Analysis

Using Microsoft® Excel® or a piece of graph paper, produce two graphs: one showing the average time to curdling for each enzyme treatment and one showing the average volume of curds produced by each enzyme treatment. Use the Microsoft® Excel® tutorial, "How to create a chart," if necessary.

Create a data table to report the average rate of cheese curdling by each curdling agent. Produce the curdling rate data by dividing the average curd volume for each treatment by the average time to curdle for each treatment.

Conclusion

Imagine you are an employee at a cheese company and you must summarize the results of your experiments and give your supervisor the "best" answers to the scientific questions asked. Write a conclusion that thoroughly reports and analyzes the experimental data. Following the "REE, PE, PA" method of writing the conclusion ensures a thorough discussion of the experimental results. REE stands for "results" with "evidence" and "explanation," PE stands for "possible errors," and PA represents "practical applications."

In the first paragraph of your conclusion, describe the results of the experiment (answer to the purpose question), including evidence and explanations for your findings. Discuss how well the results support the hypothesis. (This is "REE.")

In the second paragraph, identify sources of errors in the procedure that may lead to variations in results or invalid data. Identify the error and explain what might happen as a result of the error. (This is "PE.")

In the third paragraph, make a recommendation to the company supervisor. Identify which curdling agent should be used for production or the target of continued testing. Include a discussion of any adjustments in the procedures that you think may improve cheese production. Include a proposal for the next set of experiments. (This is "PA.")

Witnessing

In the biotechnology industry, the work of others is reviewed and "OK'd" by peers. This is called "witnessing." When you witness data and review a concluding statement, check for the following:

- accuracy of statements (and that they make sense)
- completeness (REE, PE, PA)
- evidence (numerical data with units of measurement)
- grammar and spelling errors

Make corrections and suggestions right on the page in ink.

- For corrections, draw a single line through the error, correct it, and initial it.
- Write your suggestion for the correction in the margin and draw an arrow to where it should be placed. Then initial and date your entry.

Witness a colleague's conclusion. When you complete the witnessing, write, "Witnessed by" at the end of the conclusion, and then write your full name and the date.

Thinking Like a Biotechnician

The curdling agent experiment has many factors or variables that can impact the results. To have confidence in the results, you will need a thorough examination of all factors to be controlled.

1. In your notebook, make a chart similar to Table 1.3 that has at least eight rows and four columns. You will use the table to analyze the variables in this experiment that need to be controlled if a technician were to have confidence in the results.
2. In this experiment, each curdling agent is tested multiple times and an average result is determined. Look at the class data. Does it appear that the number of replications for each curdling agent experiment was sufficient? Yes or no? Explain your answer.
3. Do you think that the whey-o-meter instrument was adequate for an accurate determination of whey volume and, indirectly, the curd volume? Why or why not? If yes, explain why. If no, propose a better system to determine the volume of curds or the volume of whey.

Table 1.3. **Analysis of Variable(s) in Curdling Experiment**

Variable or Factor That Could Affect Results	Why Control Is Needed	Suggested Ways to Control the Variable or Factor	Relative Importance 1 = very important 10 = not very important
temperature	Hands have different temperatures.	Place all tubes in a 37°C water bath.	8
	Samples are held for different time periods.	Have timer set to ring every 5 minutes.	Not as important to see difference in buttermilk or negative control.
	Higher temperatures may give fast reactions.	Lift and invert one timethen return to bath.	Very important to see any difference between chymosin and rennin.

2 Basic Biology for the Biotechnician

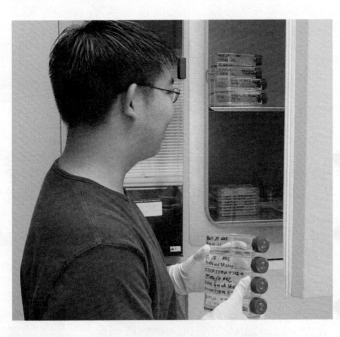

A research associate (RA) transfers freshly prepared cultures of genetically engineered mammalian cells to a carbon dioxide (CO2) incubator.
Photo by author.

If you work in biotechnology, you will be using, studying, or modifying molecules, cells, or organisms. Each is complex and sensitive to even minor changes in the environment. Molecules and most cells are too small to be visualized without the aid of instruments, and technicians must learn to how to handle and study them.

In the following activities, you will learn some of the techniques used to study cells and the molecules they produce. Specifically, you will learn the following:

- how scientific models can help explain scientific phenomenon
- how to use indicator solutions and standards to test for the presence of biologically important molecules, such as carbohydrates, proteins, and nucleic acids
- how to grow and monitor cell cultures
- how to use a microscope to measure and study cell structures and cell processes
- how the structure of molecules affects their characteristics
- to test the effect of alcohol concentration on membrane integrity

The laboratory methods practiced in this chapter will be applied in later chapters to the manufacture and testing of a protein product made through recombinant DNA (rDNA) technology.

Laboratory 2a
An Egg as a Scientific Model

Background

Scientific models are used to help better understand scientific structures or phenomenon. Like a toy car model or a globe of the world, a scientific model may be almost an exact replica of the "real thing" or it may be similar in some ways and not others.

Scientific models may be drawings, three-dimensional structures, equations, graphs, or descriptions. A good scientific model describes something in such a way that a better understanding results. Ball and stick models of molecules, a mobile of the solar system, an equation that describes how light travels are all examples of scientific models.

A bird's egg is a pretty good model of a cell. It's yolk sits in the center of liquidy egg white like a nucleus in cytoplasm. It has a membrane that behaves like a plasma membrane, and a shell surrounding the inside of the egg, both of which are permeable. The egg's molecular makeup is similar to what is seen in a typical, single animal cell.

However, a bird's egg is a bit more complicated than a typical animal cell. To create the egg that we eat, a bird ovulates a single egg cell at a time. The egg cell is what we call the yolk. As it travels, the egg cell matures and adds some layers of cells (membranes) in preparation for fertilization. Prior to laying the egg, the bird's body adds a shell to protect the egg in case it has been fertilized. The eggs most often purchased at a store are unfertilized.

In addition, bird eggs are much larger than a typical cell. Most cells and their structures are too small to be seen without the aid of a microscope. However, bird eggs are large enough to study macroscopically (without magnification) and that makes the bird egg a good model.

Although microscopic measurement is presented in an upcoming activity, you can gain an appreciation of how small some cells are by considering their relative sizes. The average cell is approximately 50 micrometers (μm) in diameter, or about one-tenth the diameter of a human hair. Most organelles are even smaller (less than 1 μm) and, certainly, their molecules are extremely small, less than 0.01 μm in diameter. Molecules are too small to be seen even with standard electron microscopes and have only recently been "seen" with a new microscope called the scanning tunneling microscope.

phenol red

pink

CO_2

yellow

beaker of water
at a neutral or
alkaline pH

acidic pH

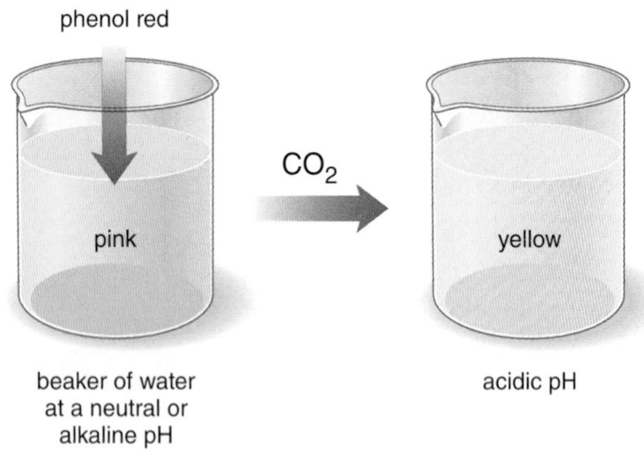

Figure 2.1. Phenol Red Indicator.

Since cells are composed of a variety of molecules, a first step in understanding an organism and its components is to analyze its molecular composition. The basic composition of a cell can be determined through separating its structures (fractionation) and testing for the presence of molecules using indicators, which are chemicals that change color when another molecule is present. Phenol red is a common indicator that can be used to indicate the presence of the molecule, carbon dioxide (CO_2), in a solution (see Figure 2.1). When CO_2 is added to a solution, phenol red changes from a red to a yellow color. The color change is due to a drop in the pH (acid/base level).

Some other indicators that are useful in a biotechnology laboratory include Benedict's solution (indicates monosaccharides), iodine (indicates starch), and Biuret reagent (indicates protein). Indicators are mixed with the molecules they are known to indicate. These are positive, standard tests, so that a positive test is recognizable. Unknown samples are then tested with an indicator. Color changes in the tested unknown samples are compared to the positive control (standards) tests and to negative control (lacking the indicator's target molecule) tests. Through the use of indicators, and positive and negative controls, researchers can detect and sometimes quantify molecules.

Purpose

What parts of an egg model the structure and function of a typical animal cell?
What parts of an egg "cell" test positive for proteins, carbohydrates, and fats?

Environmental Health
and Safety Officer

Materials

Eggs	Tubes, glass, 13 × 100 mm	Sodium hydroxide, 10%
Beaker, 250 mL	Peg racks for 13 × 100-mm tubes	Copper sulfate pentahydrate, 5%
White vinegar	Glucose (dextrose), 2%	Oil
Plastic wrap	Benedict's solution	Brown paper bag
Slotted spoon	Hot plate stirrer	Sudan IV solution
Sodium chloride, 5%	Test tube holder	Scalpel handles, #4
Distilled water	Starch, soluble, 2%	Scalpel blades, #22, for #4
Beaker, 100 mL	Lugol's Iodine solution	handles
Pipets, 5 mL	Vortex mixer	Trays, plastic
Pipet pump, green	Gelatin, 1%	

Procedure

Part I: Studying a Model of The Plasma Membrane

1. Place an uncooked egg into a beaker of white vinegar. Label and cover it with plastic wrap. Leave it for 24 hours then pour off the used vinegar and cover the egg with fresh vinegar and leave for an additional 24 hours. While the shell dissolves, proceed to Part II.
2. After 24 to 48 hours, the shell should have dissolved in the vinegar (acetic acid). Gently pick up the egg with a slotted spoon and rinse it in water to remove the vinegar. A chemical reaction has happened here. What chemicals were involved as reactants and products?
3. Feel the outer membranes of the cell. The outer membrane, which is different from the membrane around the yolk, provides a good model of the a cell's plasma membrane. Cell membranes are thin and flexible. They are permeable to some substances and prevent the movement of others. To test that water can enter and leave the cell easily, place the egg in a beaker of 5% NaCl solution for 24 hours. Describe the appearance of the egg after 24 hours. What may have caused the change in appearance? Is there evidence that the membrane is semi-permeable?
4. Gently rinse off the egg again with water. Then place the egg in a beaker of distilled water for 24 hours. Describe the appearance of the egg after 24 hours. What caused the change in appearance? Is there evidence that the membrane is semi-permeable?
5. To retrieve the yolk (in our model the nucleus of a cell, but actually the entire unfertilized egg cell of a bird), gently slice open the egg's membranes, and let the egg white drip through the slots of the spoon into a 100-mL beaker. Try to get all of the egg white into the beaker without piercing the yolk (egg cell with a clear, flimsy cell membrane around it).
6. Place the egg yolk into another beaker, and set aside the egg membranes. In Part III, the yolk, the egg white, and the membranes will be tested for the presence and relative concentration of the carbohydrate, protein and fat.

Part II: Testing Standard Solutions

Standards are samples that give expected results when they are tested. Following the steps below, test four standard solutions of known composition (positive controls) with their respective indicator solution. The standards show what a positive or a negative test should look like for monosaccharides, starch, proteins, or lipids. Record all data in a data table similar to Table 2.1.

Table 2.1. **Results of Standard Molecule Testing Using Different Indicators**

Standard (Molecule Tested)	Indicator Used	Description Positive Control (Standard) Test Results	Description Negative Control Test Results
glucose	Benedict's solution		
starch	Lugol's iodine		
protein	Biuret reagent		
fat	none—paper bag test or Sudan IV		

Monosaccharide Indicator Standard Test

100°C

1. Test for glucose: In a test tube, mix 2 mL of a 2% glucose (a monosaccharide) solution with 2 mL of Benedict's solution. Heat for 2 minutes in a boiling hot water bath (100 mL of water in a 250-mL beaker at 100°C). Record all color changes and the length of time for each color to appear (refer to Table 2.1).
2. Test for water (negative control): In a test tube, mix 2 mL of deionized water with 2 mL of Benedict's solution. Heat for 2 minutes in a boiling hot water bath (100 mL of water in a 250-mL beaker at 100°C). Record all color changes and the amount of time for each color to appear (refer to Table 2.1).

Starch Indicator Standard Test

1. Test for starch: In a test tube, mix 2 mL of well-mixed 2% starch suspension with 0.1 mL of Lugol's iodine. Gently swirl to mix. **DO NOT HEAT.** Record the color change.
2. Test for water (negative control): In a test tube, mix 2 mL of deionized water with 0.1 mL of Lugol's iodine. Gently swirl to mix. **DO NOT HEAT.** Record the color change.

Protein Indicator Standard Test

Environmental Health and Safety Officer

Caution: Sodium hydroxide (NaOH) is a strong base, is caustic, and can burn. Wear goggles and gloves. Wipe spills immediately. Flush exposed surfaces with tap water.

1. Test for protein: Place 2 mL of 1% gelatin (protein) solution in a test tube. Wearing goggles and gloves, add 0.5 mL of 10% NaOH and 0.25 mL of 5% copper sulfate pentahydrate ($CuSO_4 \bullet 5H_2O$) and gently mix. The NaOH and $CuSO_4 \bullet 5H_2O$ mixture is called Biuret reagent. Mix well. Record color change after 30 seconds.
2. Test for water (negative control): Place 2 mL of deionized water in a test tube. Wearing goggles and gloves, add 0.5 mL of 10% NaOH, and 0.25 mL of 5% $CuSO_4 \bullet 5H_2O$, and gently mix well. Record color change after 30 seconds.

Lipid Indicator Standard Test*

1. Test for lipid(s): Place a drop of oil (100% fat) on a piece of brown paper bag. Let it "dry" for 10 minutes. Hold up the paper to light. Record how much light passes through the spot (the percentage of translucence).
2. Test for water: Place a drop of water on a piece of brown paper bag. Let it "dry" for 10 minutes. Hold up the paper to light. Record how much light passes through the spot (the percentage of translucence).

Part III: Molecular Composition of Egg Model Components

Test each of the egg components for the presence of monosaccharides, starch, protein, and lipid.

1. Conduct each indicator test, as described in Part II, but *substitute* each egg component to be tested for the sugar, starch, protein, or fat in the test. All volumes and test conditions are the same as in Part II; only the item tested (the unknowns) is changed. **Make sure that you do not add any of the standard solutions.**
2. Record the results of testing the egg membranes, the yolk, and egg white for all four molecules on another data table (see Table 2.2).
3. Give a numerical value to each test result using the system described in the key, which is based on a comparison with the standard tests. Also, include a brief description of color changes.

---

*An alternative to the translucence test is to use a lipid indicator, Sudan IV. Add 60 µL of Sudan IV solution to 2 mL of sample. Gently mix. Red is a negative lipid test and orange is a positive lipid test.

Table 2.2. The Presence and Relative Amount of Organic Molecules Found in Egg
Key: 3 = very strong/positive test; 2 = strong/positive test; 1 = weak/positive test; 0 = no color change in indicator/negative.

Egg Component Tested	Indicator Reaction				
	Benedict's Solution	Iodine	Biuret Reagent	Paper Bag or Sudan IV Test	Comments
egg membranes					
yolk					
egg white					

Data Analysis

Write a conclusion that reports the results of the experiment (check the purpose questions) and the chemical nature of the egg. Describe the observations you made that model of the cell components. How well does the bird egg model typical cell structure and function? Identify sources of errors in how you carried out the procedures that may lead to false positive or false negative results. Suggest possible variations or extensions of these laboratory procedures. Propose other applications of molecular indicator testing in future experiments or in industry.

Thinking Like a Biotechnician

1. Describe how you would test kidney bean seeds for the presence of glucose, starch, and protein. Include all reagents, volumes, and testing conditions. Describe the results that you would expect to occur.
2. Which type of molecule(s) tested strongly in all of the egg component samples? How do you explain those results?
3. If a pea green color resulted for a sample tested with Benedict's solution, what would you conclude about the sugar content? Propose a quantitative method by which the amount of sugar could be determined.
4. An enzyme is thought to have starch-digesting activity. What indicator might you use to show that starch is being broken down to glucose by an enzyme? How would you measure the reaction? What data would you collect?
5. Why is it necessary to have a negative control group for each test (testing water with each indicator)? What does the negative control result tell you?
6. In what ways are these procedures a "controlled" experiment? List the parameters that must be kept constant to obtain meaningful variations in results.
7. Propose some other use by scientists or consumers for any one of these indicator tests.

Laboratory 2b
The Characteristics of Model Organisms

Millions of species of plants, animals, and microorganisms inhabit the earth. Obviously, scientists cannot study all of them in any great detail. However, a significant amount of evidence from biochemical and physiological studies suggests that the basic operations of all cells and many related organisms are the same. Therefore, after scientists learn a bit about a certain organism's characteristics, they often pick the same organism to study further. This allows the science community to build a large body of information about an organism's growth and behavior. The organism becomes what is called a "model organism," one that is grown and studied as representative of closely related species. Model organisms have the following characteristics:

- relatively easy to grow and maintain in a restricted space (eg, a lab, a field)
- relatively easy to provide necessary nutrients for growth
- relatively short generation time (birth " reproduction " birth)
- relatively well understood growth and development
- closely resembles others organisms or systems (eg, monkeys to humans)

In the animal kingdom, rats and mice are model organisms. Most studies of animal physiology, nutrition, genetics, and cancer are conducted in these mammals. Not only is much known about mice and rats, but they also have other characteristics, such as a large number of offspring per litter, that make them ideal lab animals to study.

In the bacterial world, *Escherichia coli (E. coli)* is the model organism. It has been used for genetic studies for more than 50 years. More is known about *E. coli* than any other organism in the world, including its growth requirements, physiology, and genetic code. It is easy to grow in the lab on a solid media (agar) or in a liquid (broth) culture. Most biotechnology companies that grow bacteria use *E. coli* bacteria.

A few fungal species act as model organisms, including *Aspergillus*, a type of bread mold, and both baker's and brewer's yeast. *Aspergillus* is a multicellular fungus with a well-understood life cycle (see Figure 2.2). Its fuzzy body is easy to grow on agar in the lab, and its prominent reproductive spores make studying reproduction easy. Yeast (*Saccharomyces cerevisiae*) is a unicellular fungus. Like *E. coli*, yeast is easy to grow on solid or liquid media. Because of their size, yeast cells are easy to observe using a microscope.

To grow and study an organism in a laboratory, one should know the environmental preferences of the species. Maintaining an organism at less than optimal light intensity, temperature, or oxygen level, for example, may put the organism under stress, possibly affecting its growth or other processes.

Purpose

What are the temperature preferences shown by three model organisms (*E. coli, Aspergillus niger,* and baker's yeast) grown in the biotechnology lab?

Figure 2.2. Aspergillus, a type of bread mold, is growing on potato dextrose agar.
Photo by author.

Materials

Laminar flow hood
Lysol® disinfectant
Petri dishes, 60 × 15 mm, sterile
LB agar base (prepare per recipe on bottle, pour into Petri dishes, one-half full)
LB broth base (prepare per recipe on bottle)
E. coli DH5alpha, overnight culture (one colony per 10 mL of sterile LB broth, grown at 37°C for 24 hours, shaking)
Tubes, 50 mL, sterile
Tube racks for 50-mL tubes
Loop, inoculating, sterile
Bleach solution, 10%
Plastic beaker, 1L
Incubator ovens
Potato dextrose agar, prepared, 125 mL
Culture tube and caps, 38 × 200 mm
Aspergillus sp, plate culture
Scalpel handles, #4
Scalpel blades, #22, for #4 handles
Yeast, baker's
Glucose
Flask, Erlenmeyer, 250 mL
Yeast malt agar, prepared, 125 mL

General Safety Precautions

Environmental Health and Safety Officer

- Do sterile work in a laminar flow hood, if available. Run for 10 minutes prior to use.
- Do *Aspergillus* work in a clean, disinfected chemical fume hood with the fan off and protective shield down. Do not inhale *Aspergillus* spores. When the work is done, turn on the fume hood fan for several minutes to remove airborne spores.
- Use all standard precautions with the Bunsen burner, including tying back hair and using goggles, etc.
- Dispose of any bacteria- or fungus-contaminated products in autoclave bags or soak them in a 10% bleach solution for 30 minutes.

Procedure

Part I: Growing *E. coli* Cells

Pre-Lab

- If a laminar flow hood is available, use it for the sterile work. Run it for 10 minutes before using.
- Disinfect all surfaces prior to transferring bacteria.
- Wash hands before and after handling bacteria.

1. Label the bottom of an LB agar Petri plate. Labels should be small, but readable, and placed at the outer edge of the bottom plate (see Figure 2.3). Include your initials, the date, the media type (LB), and the sample identification (*E. coli*).

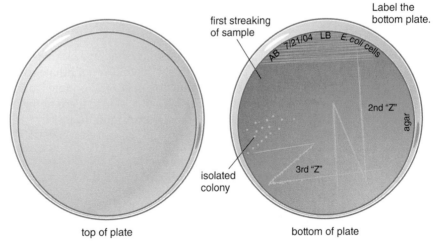

top of plate

bottom of plate

Figure 2.3. **Triple Z Streaking Method.**

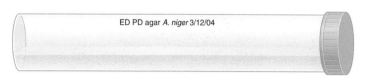

Figure 2.4. **Aspergillus Tube Culture.**

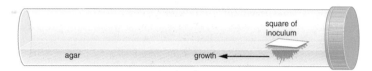

Figure 2.6. **Aspergillus Growth Tube.**

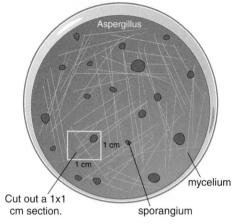

Figure 2.5. **Aspergillus Plate Culture.**

2. Using a sterile, plastic 1-µL inoculating loop, collect a loopful of *E. coli* broth culture.

3. Streak the bacterial broth culture onto a sterile LB agar Petri plate (see Figure 2.3).
    a. Streak the broth back and forth across the agar on the top one-eighth of the plate. Discard the plastic inoculating loop into a 10% bleach solution. Consider this first set of streaking to be the "1st Z."
    b. Rotate the plate 90°. Streak a new sterile inoculating loop at a right angle through previous streak. You should go through the first streak only once to pick up the fewest bacteria cells possible. Make a "Z"-shaped streak. This is the "2nd Z." Discard the plastic inoculating loop into a 10% bleach solution.
    c. Rotate the plate another 90°. Streak another sterilized loop at a right angle through the first "Z" streak. You should go through that streak only once to pick up the fewest bacteria cells possible. Make a "Z." This is the third "Z." Discard the plastic inoculating loop into a 10% bleach solution.
    d. Replace the lid onto the Petri plate. Place your inoculated LB plate **upside down** in one of the incubation ovens designated by the instructor.
    e. Be careful to keep the top of the Petri plate over the bottom to minimize contamination.

4. Each person will streak and monitor one plate. Several plates will be incubated in each of the following conditions:

    4°C in the dark   room temperature in the dark   30°C in the dark
    37°C in the dark   42°C in the dark

Part II: Growing *Aspergillus*

Environmental Health
and Safety Officer

- For steps 2–3, do the *Aspergillus* sampling in a clean, disinfected chemical fume hood with the fan off and protective shield down. Do not inhale *Aspergillus* spores. When the work is done, turn on the fume hood fan for several minutes to remove airborne spores. Once the sample is sealed in a racing tube, it is safe to place in the oven.
- Disinfect all surfaces prior to the transfer of fungi.
- Wash hands before and after handling fungi.

1. Label the *Aspergillus* racing tube containing potato dextrose agar with a small piece of labeling tape containing your initials, the media, the sample identification, and the date (see Figure 2.4).
2. Using a sterile scalpel, cut a wedge of *Aspergillus* fungus mycelium (fuzzy body), 1 cm by 1 cm, out of the stock plate (see Figure 2.5).
3. Transfer the fungus, using the sterile scalpel as a spatula, fungus side down, to the potato dextrose agar just inside the lip of the tube. Press it down lightly to make sure it sticks (see Figure 2.6).

4. Each person inoculates and monitors one tube with *Aspergillus.* Several tubes will be incubated in each of the following conditions:

4°C in the dark   room temperature in the dark   30°C in the dark
37°C in the dark   42°C in the dark

Part III: Growing Yeast Cells

- Do sterile work in a laminar flow hood, if available. Run for 10 minutes prior to use.
- 12 hours prior to use, prepare a yeast broth culture for the class using a package of yeast, 0.5 g of glucose, and 100 mL of dH$_2$O. Incubate for 12 hours at 37°C (see Figure 2.7).

1. Using a sterile, plastic 1-µL inoculating loop, collect a loopful of yeast broth culture.

2. Streak the yeast broth culture onto a sterile yeast malt agar Petri plate, using the "triple Z" technique described above.

3. Each person inoculates and monitors one plate of yeast. Several plates of yeast will be incubated in each the following conditions:

4°C in the dark   room temperature in the dark   30°C in the dark
37°C in the dark   42°C in the dark

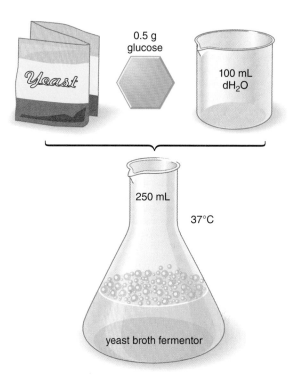

Figure 2.7. **Yeast Culture.**

Part IV: Data Collection and Analysis

1. Observe each sample after 24 hours.
2. Record the amount and type of growth on each plate, or in each tube, in a data table similar to Table 2.3. Devise a method to quantify the amount of growth seen on the plates or in the tubes, and write a description of your method in your notebook.
3. Collect data from your own cultures as well as from two other technicians in your group. Average each set of data.

Data Analysis

Write a conclusion that reports the results of the temperature of incubation experiment and the variations in the growth of each organism. Identify sources of error in the techniques that may lead to erroneous results. Suggest possible variations or extensions of these laboratory procedures. For each organism, identify one other environmental factor that might be tested. Discuss the reasons that testing growth rate and environmental preferences may be important to genetic engineers and biotechnologists.

Table 2.3.   The Amount of Growth Observed in Three Model Organisms in Different Temperatures

Temperature (Degrees Centigrade, °C)		Amount of Growth		
		E. coli	*Aspergillus*	Yeast
room temperature	Trial 1			
	Trial 2			
4	Trial 3			
	Average			
30	Trial 1			
	Trial 2			
	Trial 3			
	Average			
37	Trial 1			
	Trial 2			
	Trial 3			
	Average			
42	Trial 1			
	Trial 2			
	Trial 3			
	Average			

Thinking Like a Biotechnician

1. In this experiment, you averaged the results of three technicians' individual experiments. Based on your analysis of the growth data, discuss the advantages and disadvantages of using multiple replications from different technicians.

2. In this experiment, potential biohazards were used (*E. coli* – although you used a safe laboratory strain, *Aspergillus*, and yeast). Describe the measures that should be taken by a lab technician or lab manager to protect workers and the public from biohazard contamination.

3. In addition to temperature, many other variables will affect *E. coli*'s growth and reproduction. Consider three other variables that could be varied and tested to determine their effect on *E. coli* growth. For each variable you suggest, describe the way an experiment would be conducted to test response to the variable. Include the measuring instruments to be used and the type of data to be collected. Report the variables to be tested, experiment plan, and data collection on a chart.

4. *Aspergillus sp*, like many fungi, is light sensitive. Design an experiment to test the effect of different light levels on *Aspergillus* growth. Propose step-by-step instructions on how to conduct the experiment. Include materials and quantities for each, and data that should will be collected.

5. In this activity, *E. coli* was grown on a solid culture medium (agar). To grow large amounts of *E. coli* broth culture (liquid), large fermentation tanks are used. Search the Internet to find a picture of a fermentation tank that is used to grow large amounts of bacteria. Print an image of the tank, and label it with the reference (Web site URL). Propose a different environmental condition that should be varied and tested when growing *E. coli* in broth instead of on agar.

6. Suppose a biotechnology company is growing cells to make a protein product to sell. Describe the possible impact on a company of growing cells in less-than-optimum conditions.

Laboratory 2c
Using a Compound Light Microscope to Study Cells

Background

All living things are made up of one or more cells. Most cells are very small, averaging between 10 and 30 μm in diameter. A micrometer is 0.001 millimeter (mm), and there are 1000 μm in a millimeter. To picture cell size, imagine the sharpest pencil point and consider that it would make a mark about 100 μm in diameter.

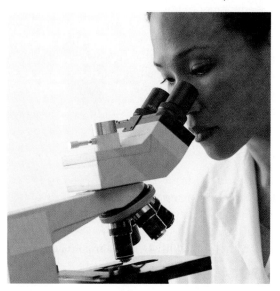

Figure 2.8. **A light or compound microscope uses light, and two or more lenses to enlarge and focus an image. The lens at the top is called the eyepiece, or the ocular lens. The ocular lens usually magnifies by 10 times (10X). By rotating an objective lens of 4X, 10X, 40X, or 100X into position, you can achieve magnifications of 40X, 100X, 400X, and 1000X, respectively. To see a significant amount of detail in prokaryotic cells, you need a magnification of 1000X.** © Corbis.

Scientists and technicians learn how a cell functions by studying its structure and biochemistry. Cells are most commonly observed with a light microscope that allows a look inside of all but the tiniest cells (see Figure 2.8). To see even smaller cell structures, one must use an electron microscope.

Some cells appear to have a simple organization. Prokaryotic cells, such as bacteria and blue-green algae, lack a nucleus or membrane-bound organelles. Prokaryotic cells are about 1 μm in size. Cells can be complicated in their organization, containing many specialized organelles; these types of cells are called eukaryotic. A cell's structure is related to its environment and function(s). This is why a nerve cell from the brain looks so different from a red blood cell (RBC).

All cells have certain structures in common: a cell membrane, cytoplasm, and one or more chromosomes. The presence and number of other organelles depend on the type of cell. Cells can be superficially grouped together as bacteria-like, plant-like, or animal-like, depending on the type of structures present, such as cell walls or chloroplasts.

Since most organelles are very small, many will not be visible through a light microscope. When observing cells, one should consider which organelles might be seen. A magnification of 450 times (450X) will resolve (distinguish clearly) to about 2 μm. Review the list below and separate the organelles/structures into two groups: 1) those large enough to be seen in cells using compound microscopes (with a maximum magnification of 1000X), and 2) those that are only visible through an electron microscope. Use images on the Internet to make your predictions.

Some Cellular Structures

mitochondria	nuclei	lysosomes
Golgi bodies	chromosomes	cell walls
ribosomes	vacuoles	endoplasmic reticula
chloroplasts		

It is very important to learn how to handle and use a microscope properly to make accurate observations, avoid damage to lenses, and reduce frustration. For the microscope in your laboratory, identify the following parts:

> eyepiece/ocular lens
> objectives/objective lens: low power, medium power, high power, oil immersion
> focus adjustment knobs: coarse adjustment, fine adjustment
> light diaphragm
> light source
> stage
> neck (arm)
> base

When using a microscope, take care to follow the rules below:

Rules for Microscope Use

1. Carry the microscope by holding it by both the neck and the base. Place the microscope on a flat surface away from the edge. Place the arm of the scope opposite the user (see Figure 2.8).
2. Do not touch the lenses with anything except lens paper.
3. To focus the microscope on an image, place a slide on the stage with the object centered over the light path. Start with the low power objective (4X) in position and the coarse adjustment knob turned so that the objective lens is close to the stage. Slowly turn the coarse adjustment knob to bring the objective up until the image is in focus. Center the image and focus with the fine adjustment knob. If desired, bring the medium-power objective (10X) into position, and use the fine adjustment knob to focus. Center the image and, if desired, bring the high-power objective (40X) into position, and use the fine adjustment knob to focus. Do not use the coarse adjustment while using the 40X objective. To get the best contrast between structures, adjust light to the lowest level that gives the sharpest focus. Before removing the slide, reset the low-power objective over the slide.

Part I: Observing Prepared Slides

Purpose

What details can be seen in prepared slides of silk, blood, and bacteria?

Materials

Prepared slides (silk, blood, bacteria)   Microscope, compound, with 4X, 10X, and 40X objectives

Procedure

1. Using low power, focus the silk thread slide so that all three threads of silk are centered and in sharp focus. Move the medium power objective into place and center the specimen and then focus the image using the fine adjustment knob.
2. Observe, draw, and label the threads so that their color, depth, and size are clear and accurate in the microscopic field of vision.
3. Center the human blood slide over the light. Focus on a red blood cell (RBC), first on low power, then on medium power, and then on high power. RBCs look like doughnuts. Observe, draw, and label the RBCs, the white blood cells (larger and may be stained a contrasting color), and the platelets (smaller discs), so that the color, depth, size, and number of each are accurate in the field of vision. Is a nucleus visible in any of these cells?
4. Focus the bacteria slide (*E. coli* or *Bacillus (B.) subtilis*) on high power, after focusing with the low- and medium-power objectives. The bacteria are very, very tiny and will appear as tiny specks of dust on low and medium power. Observe, draw, and label the bacteria so that their color, shape, and size are clear and accurate in the microscopic field of vision. The shapes of bacteria include rods, spheres, and/or spirals. Your diagram should show enough detail to identify the bacteria as one or more of these shapes.

Part II: Preparing and Observing Wet Mount Slides

Purpose

What structures are visible in various cells using a light microscope?

Environmental Health and Safety Officer

Materials

Microscope, compound, with
  4X, 10X, and 40X objectives
Microscope slides
Microscope slide coverslips,
  glass
Transfer pipets, 3 mL
Toothpicks

Methylene blue stain, 1%
Elodea densa
Onion
Lugol's iodine solution
Mixed algae culture
Prepared slides, onion root tip
Tomato

Paramecium caudatum culture
Protozoan culture
  (cereal media)
Aspergillus sp or other bread
  mold, plate culture

Procedure

Use clean, dry slides and coverslips. To the center of the slide, add a small drop of water. Add a small amount of sample. Gently place a coverslip on the slide, so that one edge touches the edge of the liquid on the slide. Next, gently lower the coverslip to press out any air bubbles. The coverslip should appear perfectly flat on the slide.

1. Make a stained, wet mount of human cheek cells adding the smallest drop of methylene blue. Gently scrape the inside of your cheek for cells. Observe, draw, and label on 400X.
2. Make a wet mount of a *tiny* piece of *Elodea* leaf. Look on the edge of the leaf for individual cells showing moving cytoplasm. Observe, draw, and label on 100X.
3. Make a stained, wet mount of onion epidermis (skin from the leaf in the bulb) adding iodine as the stain. Observe, draw, and label on 100X.
4. Make a wet mount of a *tiny* bit of green algae. Observe, draw, and label on 400X.
5. Observe a prepared slide of dividing cells (*Allium* root tip). Make sure you are observing cells about 40 cells back from the growing tip. Observe, draw, and label on 400X.
6. Make a wet mount of a *tiny* bit of tomato pulp. Observe, draw, and label on 100X.
7. Make a wet mount of a *tiny* drop of the protozoa culture. **Do not add a coverslip.** Observe, draw, and label on either 100X or 400X, depending on the size of the protozoa.
8. Make a wet mount of a *tiny* bit of bread mold. Observe, draw, and label on 400X.
9. Make sure that all drawings are accurate in size, color, and detail within the field of vision. Label all visible organelles. Record the sample name and magnification of observation by each drawing.
10. Prepare a data table to record the structures seen in each of the cell samples. Label cell structures (from page 22) along the top, and label the rows with the sample names. Put a check in a square when you observe a structure in a cell.

Data Analysis

In a conclusion statement, discuss the similarities and differences you saw in the cell structures from the plant or plant-like samples. Discuss the similarities and differences in these cell structures compared with those taken from animal or animal-like samples. Include observations on size, shape, and structure. Describe any difficulties you encountered when trying to focus on cells or cell structures. What might have caused these difficulties?

Thinking Like a Biotechnician

1. What cell structures did you observe in all of the cell samples?
2. What structures were only visible in the *Elodea* cells? What is their function? Why do the other cells not have these structures? What might happen if stain is used (accidentally) on *Elodea*?
3. What is the purpose of using stain to observe cheek cells and onion cells, but not on *Elodea* or the protozoa? What are the advantages and disadvantages to using a stain?
4. Which cells were from multicellular organisms, and which cells were single-celled organisms? What evidence of this do you have from your observations?
5. If you are having trouble getting something into focus on high power, list three things you should do to correct the problem.
6. Identify any samples that were difficult to observe. Describe reasons for the difficulties. Propose changes in the procedures that might result in better wet mounts or observations.

Laboratory 2d
Making Microscopic Measurements

Background

When making observations with a compound microscope, you should record the size of each specimen. If you know the size of the field of vision at a specific magnification, you can estimate the size of a specimen.

In many microscopes used at companies and universities, a ruler called a micrometer is actually built into the objectives. However, many microscopes do not have micrometers, including those used in most introductory biotechnology courses. Instead, you can estimate the size of each field of vision by measuring the low-power field of vision directly with a piece of graph paper.

To measure the diameter of the low-power field, use a wet mount of 1-mm grid graph paper and count the number of millimeters across the center of the field. The value is converted from mm to µm since microscopic measurements are most commonly reported in micrometers. A micrometer (µm) is equal to 1/1000th (0.001) of a millimeter (mm). In other words, there are 1000 µm in a mm. Micrometers are often called microns, and the terms are used interchangeably in a biotechnology lab.

On most microscopes, the medium- and high-power fields are too small to be measured directly. However, the sizes of the medium- and high-power fields can be determined indirectly if you realize that the field is smaller by the same value that the magnification has been increased (see Figure 2.9). For example, if the size of the low-power (40X) field on a microscope is 5 mm or 5000 µm, then the size of the medium (100X) field would be 2-1/2 times smaller, or 2000 µm. Similarly, the high-power (400X) field would be 10 times smaller, or 500 µm.

Once the field size has been determined, cell sizes can be estimated by what percentage of the field they occupy. For example, a human stomach cell is fairly rectangular, and its length fills about one-third of the field (see Figure 2.10). So, since the cell's length takes up approximately one-third of the medium-power field, it is approximately 2000/3 µm long, or 666.7 µm.

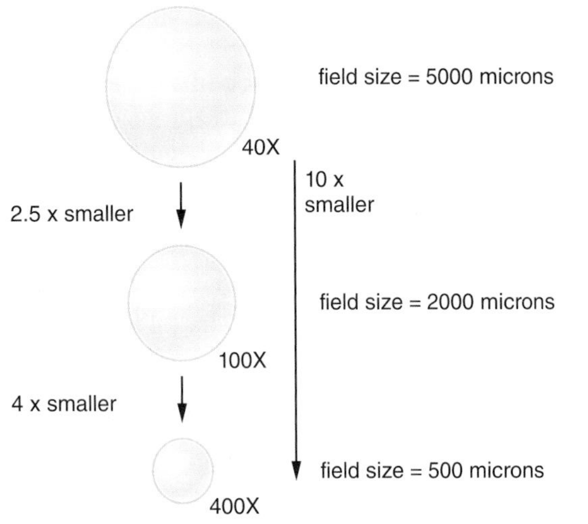

field size = 5000 microns

40X

2.5 x smaller

10 x smaller

field size = 2000 microns

100X

4 x smaller

field size = 500 microns

400X

Figure 2.9. Sizes of the Fields of Vision on a Microscope.

Purpose

What are the diameters of the fields of vision on our microscopes at different magnifications? What are the dimensions, in µm and mm, of some familiar materials?

Materials

Microscope, compound
Microscope slides
Microscope slide coverslips, glass
Graph paper, 1-mm grid, download at
   www.mathsphere.co.uk/downloads/graph-paper/
   graph-paper-blue.pdf
Transfer pipets, 3 mL
Human hair
Banana
Lugol's iodine solution

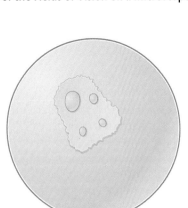

Figure 2.10. A human stomach cell at 100X occupies about one-third of the field of vision.

Procedure

1. Make a wet mount of a 10 mm² piece of 1-mm grid graph paper. Count how many 1-mm squares go across the diameter of the low-power field. Convert the diameter measurement from mm to μm. Record the size of this field in both mm and μm in a data table of your own design.
2. Next, do the division, as described above, to determine the sizes of the medium- and high-power fields. Report the values in both mm and μm in the data table.
3. Make a wet mount of a short piece of human hair. Observe, draw, and label on 400X. Determine the width of the hair in mm and μm. Create a second data table to record measurements of this and other samples.
4. Prepare a wet mount of a very small amount of banana cells. Lightly stain with iodine. Observe, draw, and label the specimen on 100X. Determine the width and length of the banana cells in mm and μm. Record these measurements in the data table.
5. Go back and measure any other cells you have observed in previous lab activities. Record their length and width measurements in the data table.

Data Analysis

1. Create and label a line scale (similar to a timeline) that shows measurements between 500 μm (0.5 mm) and 1 μm (0.001 mm) with every centimeter (cm) representing 50 μm. Put a label on the line for each measurement you have made. Include all the cells you have measured: *Elodea*, human hair, banana, tomato, etc.
2. What patterns do you observe in the size or shapes of the samples you have measured? Explain.

Thinking Like a Biotechnician

1. A technician determines the length of a banana cell at both 100X and 400X. He or she determines the length at 100X is 75 μm, but the length at 400X is 100 μm. Which measurements are more likely to be accurate and why?
2. You may have noticed that the contrast (sharpness) of the image decreases as you increase the magnification of a sample. List a few steps you can take to improve the resolution (ability to distinguish points) of the images at higher magnification.
3. A 100X objective can be used on a compound microscope, bringing the total possible magnification to 1000X. This lens is called an oil immersion lens since a drop of oil is needed between the objective lens and the coverslip to help gather more light. (The oil corrects for the refractive index of air.) Predict what organelles might be visible if the oil immersion lens is used to view eukaryotic cells. Also, list those organelles you think are so small that even 1000X magnification is not high enough to visualize them.
4. To visualize very tiny organelles, one needs a scanning electron microscope. Go to the Internet and find an electron micrograph (picture from an electron microscope) that shows one or more Golgi bodies. Record the magnification of the micrograph. Record the Web site reference.

Laboratory 2e

The Effect of Alcohol Solutions on Cell Membranes

This lab was developed by Simon Holdaway, The Loomis Chaffee School, Windsor, CT and modified by Ellyn Daugherty.

Background

A membrane called the plasma membrane or cell membrane surrounds all cells. To study molecules and organelles from cells, researchers must dissolve or remove the membrane to release the cell contents.

Cell membranes are composed of membrane proteins embedded in a double layer of phospholipid molecules, the majority of which are non-polar and have little or no charge. The nonpolar phospholipid molecules do not dissolve in water (they are hydrophobic) since water is polar (with charged sides to the molecule). To dissolve the hydrophobic lipid molecules and disrupt the cell membrane, biotechnologists must use other solvents that will dissolve the membrane and explode the cell. These nonpolar solvents, including alcohols and detergents, are routinely used in the first steps of DNA and protein purification from cells.

To demonstrate how alcohol can be used to dissolve membranes and release cell contents, beet root samples may be used. Beets are a common plant grown for their edible taproot and they have distinctive deep red color caused by the molecule betanin. Betanin, sometimes called Beetroot Red, cannot cross intact cell membranes, and so in healthy, intact cells it remains trapped inside the cell. The betanin will only leak out into the surrounding fluid if there is membrane damage. Since betanin is a colored molecule, a visible spectrophotometer can be used to assess the amount of betanin released after treatment with various alcohols.

Purpose

What is the optimum type and concentration (%) of alcohol for maximum membrane disruption as indicated by betanin release?

Materials

Methanol
Ethanol
Isopropanol
12-well plate
P-1000 Micropipette + tips
Beets

Cork Borer Set
Petri Dish
Distilled water
Scalpel/Single-sided razor
   blade
Tweezers

5-ml pipets and pipet pumps
Spectrophotometer and
   cuvettes
Safety Goggles
Gloves

Procedure

1. Prepare the 12-well plate with the different % alcohol concentrations by pipetting the following amounts of distilled water into each well.

	10%	20%	40%	60%
Methanol	3600 μl	3200 μl	2400 μl	1600 μl
Ethanol	3600 μl	3200 μl	2400 μl	1600 μl
Isopropanol	3600 μl	3200 μl	2400 μl	1600 μl

2. Add the following amounts of the designated alcohol to each well. Pipet up and down one time to mix. The volume in each well should be the same, 4 mL. Be sure to change tips between alcohol samples.

	10%	20%	40%	60%
Methanol	400μl	800μl	1600μl	2400μl
Ethanol	400μl	800μl	1600μl	2400μl
Isopropanol	400μl	800μl	1600μl	2400μl

3. Prepare the beet samples by using a cork borer to section the beet and create a long cylinder of red beet. Each group will likely need two cylinders. Use a borer of slightly smaller diameter to push the beet out of the corer tube and into a petri dish filled with distilled water.
4. Cut the ends off the beet cylinders and discard. The ends will have the epidermal covering on the beet taproot and are unwanted in this experiment.
5. Using a scalpel or razor blade cut the beet cylinder into <u>equal</u> length sections. Each section needs to fit into the wells on the 12-well plate used in steps 1 & 2. Record the length of the beet cylinders that you used in mm. _____
6. Wash the sections in the distilled water to remove and trace amount of betanin on the outside of the cylinders.
7. As quickly as possible, transfer the beet cylinders to the individual wells of the 12-well plate. Start a timer. Be sure not to agitate the plate. Leave the samples undisturbed for 30 minutes.
8. Turn on the spectrophotometer and set the wavelength to 477nm.
8. Examine the beet samples at 5-minute intervals and note which alcohol at which concentrations seems to be the best at dissolving the cell membranes?
9. After the 30-minute incubation, using a 5-ml pipet, transfer similar volumes of the solution in each well to a clean spectrophotometer cuvette. This produces 12 samples. Label each sample at the top of the cuvette with the type and concentration of alcohol used.
10. A "blank" sample, containing no betanin, is needed to calibrate the spectrophotometer prior to its use. Prepare a "blank" tube by adding a similar volume of distilled water to a tube labeled "B".
11. After the supervisor explains how to use the spectrophotometer to measure a sample's light absorbance, measure the absorbance of each sample at 477nm (A_{477}). Record the absorbance values (in au.) in a data table.
12. Prepare a 3-line graph that shows the relationship between alcohol type and concentration with the amount of betanin released from the beet cell samples.
13. Determine which type and concentration of alcohol was most effective at disrupting the cell membrane.

Data Analysis and Conclusion

Using quantitative data (numerical values) discuss how effective each type of alcohol was at releasing betanin from the beet cells. If one treatment appeared to be more effective than the others, how much more effective was it? Did you and your partner have the same results as others groups? Why or why not? List technical errors in setting up the experiment that might lead to erroneous data. Discuss the value of learning how to burst open cells. How would this technique be valuable to biotechnologists?

Thinking Like A Biotechnician

1. Scientists often use 70% ethanol solutions to sterilize their workspaces before starting experiments. Use the Internet to perform a search and find out why alcohol percentages above 80% are actually less effective as sterilization agents.
2. Several detergents are used in cell lysis solutions to explode cells for DNA or protein extractions. Use the Internet to find out about one of the most common cell lysis detergents, sodium dodecyl sulfate (SDS). Find and record its molecular structure and how and when it is used in DNA or protein extractions.

Laboratory 2f

Variation in the Structure and Properties of Carbohydrates

Background

Every molecule has a distinctive size, shape, and arrangement of atoms. A hydrogen peroxide molecule (H_2O_2), for example, has the same atoms as a water molecule (H_2O), with the exception of one additional oxygen atom. That extra oxygen atom has huge repercussions when it comes to chemical activity and characteristics. Although both are clear liquids, H_2O_2 is an oxidizing agent and will kill cells, while water is nontoxic and is required for life.

The dramatic effects of the composition and arrangement of atoms in a molecule can be seen when one studies carbohydrates. All carbohydrates have the same basic composition of elements, a combination of one carbon atom for every two hydrogen atoms and one oxygen atom (a 1:2:1 ratio), written $C_nH_{2n}O_n$. However, tiny differences in the number and arrangement of these atoms can affect a carbohydrate's taste, texture, and biological activity.

Three factors determine the nature of a particular monosaccharide:
1. The length of the carbon skeleton (ie, four, five, or six carbons), as shown in Figure 2.11.
2. Where its carbonyl (the double-bonded oxygen atom) group is located. If the oxygen is attached at the end of the carbon chain, the sugar is called an aldehyde; 6-carbon aldehydes, such as glucose, make a six-sided ring (attached C1 to C5 through a bond with oxygen). If the oxygen is attached at the middle of the carbon chain, as in fructose, the sugar is called a ketone (C2-C5), as shown in Figure 2.12.
3. The orientation of its atoms around asymmetrical carbons. For example, glucose and galactose are identical, except for the direction of atoms at the No. 4 C (see Figure 2.13).

The number and the type of monosaccharide units also influence disaccharide and polysaccharide characteristics.

Purpose

What are the differences in the structures of some common carbohydrates?
What are the differences in texture and taste of different carbohydrates?
How does their structure affect their characteristics?

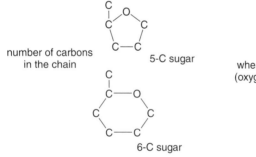

Figure 2.11. **Carbon Skeleton Length.**

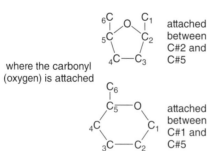

Figure 2.12. **Oxygen Atom Position.**

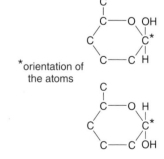

Figure 2.13. **Orientation of Atoms.**

Materials

Sucrose
Glucose (dextrose)
Fructose
Galactose
Maltose

Lactose
Starch, soluble
Cellulose
Petri dishes, 60 × 15 mm, sterile

Plastic spoons
Paper cups
Tap water

Procedure

Part I: Gathering Structural Information

1. Use the Internet to find the structure and function of each of the molecules being tested (listed in the "Materials" section). If a structure is labeled "D" or "L," use the D form. If a structure is labeled "right-handed" or "left-handed," use the right-handed form.
2. Draw a structural diagram of each molecule, showing the specific arrangement of atoms in the molecule. Next to each drawing, write a short description of the main functions of the molecule and its distinguishing structure. Also, include bibliographical reference information.

Part II: Comparing the Characteristics of Carbohydrates

- **Caution: If you are a diabetic, do not conduct the experiment.**
- Refrain from eating or chewing candy for at least 1 hour before this experiment.
- Rinse your mouth with tap water between taste tests.

Environmental Health and Safety Officer

1. Scoop a tiny bit of sucrose onto a plastic spoon. Use this sample for the test and then discard the spoon into the trash. Do not return any samples to the stock dishes.
2. Touch your finger to the sucrose. Touch the sucrose to your tongue and take at least 10 full seconds to mentally note its sweetness. Let this amount of sweetness be a standard of 100 on an arbitrary sweetness scale that ranges from 0 to 200. Based on their structure, predict the sweetness of the other carbohydrates. Which do you think will be the sweetest, and which do you think will be the least sweet?
3. Describe the texture of the sucrose.
4. For each of the other carbohydrates, use a new spoon and repeat steps 1 through 3. Rank the sweetness of each sample based on the sucrose standard of 100.
5. Record your data in a data table (see Table 2.4). You may have to use reference materials to determine the function of some of the carbohydrates.

Table 2.4. **Characteristics of Various Carbohydrates**

Carbohydrate Tested	Type of Carbohydrate	Degree of Sweetness	Color	Texture	Function(s)
sucrose	disaccharide	100	white	granular	energy, transport
glucose (dextrose)					

Data Analysis/Conclusion

1. Which carbohydrates were sweetest? Does the number of sugar rings affect how sweet the carbohydrate tastes?
2. Are there any other observed characteristics that appear affected by the number of sugar rings?
3. Did all testers give each sample the same rating? List three reasons why the rating of the same samples could be different for different tasters.
4. Look at the structural formulas for the monosaccharides. Are the structurally similar ones alike in other characteristics? Explain.

Thinking Like a Biotechnician

1. How might carbohydrate structural differences affect how they function in cells and organisms?
2. What causes humans to taste sweetness? Use the Internet to learn how the tongue tastes. Use this information to explain how the tasters could rank the sweetness of the same samples differently.

3 Basic Chemistry for the Biotechnician

A research associate uses a 25-mL pipet and an automated pipet pump to dispense solution into replicate reaction chambers. The solution has been prepared at a specific volume and concentration.
Photo courtesy of Cell Genesys, Inc.

Virtually every chemical reaction in a lab or manufacturing facility, as in cells, occurs in a watery environment or solution. A lab technician, therefore, must be able to quickly prepare any volume of solution at any concentration of molecules.

Solution preparation (solution prep) is the most basic laboratory skill required of every scientist or technician. Solution prep involves measuring liquid volumes with a variety of instruments, weighing chemicals with a balance or scale, and mixing them together in the correct proportions. Solution prep also includes pH measurement and adjustment since the structure and functions of most biological molecules in solution are affected by even slight changes in pH. In the following laboratory activities, you will learn how to use several instruments to measure ingredients and prepare solutions. The skills you will develop include the following:

- measuring liquid volumes using graduated cylinders, pipets, and micropipets
- measuring solids using tabletop and analytical balances
- performing calculations that determine the amount of solids or liquids needed in a solution
- preparing solutions of varying amounts (concentrations) of solute and solvent
- measuring and adjusting the pH of a solution
- buffer preparation to protect molecules from changes in pH
- preparing dilutions of concentrated solutions

When conducting research experiments or manufacturing products, scientists and technicians routinely make hundreds of solutions. Preparing solutions can be challenging at first because of the calculations required. However, with practice, you will master the calculations so that preparing solutions at various concentrations will become second nature to you. In later chapters, you will learn to prepare a variety of buffered solutions to use in the research and manufacturing of selected nucleic acids and proteins.

Laboratory 3a

Measuring Small Volumes in a Biotechnology Lab

Background

While graduated cylinders are typically used to measure volumes greater than 50 mL, serological pipets are used to measure volumes from 0.5 mL (500 µL) to 100 mL. The most commonly used pipets are 10-, 5-, 2-, and 1-mL pipets. Pipets are named by the maximum volume they measure. Therefore, a 5-mL pipet measures volumes up to 5 mL.

This activity introduces pipeting technique (see Figure 3.1). As with all fine motor skills, learning how to accurately use a pipet takes practice and determination, but it is essential that you are able to measure volumes with accuracy. The standard practice is to allow for *no more than 10% deviation from the intended value*. In many applications, much less deviation is acceptable. You must also be precise in measurement; that is, you must be able to replicate your measurements repeatedly.

To measure and deliver samples, technicians most commonly use a plastic pipet pump. A blue pump is

Figure 3.1. **A pipet is used to measure milliliter (mL) volumes. Pipet at eye level for more accuracy.**
Photo by author.

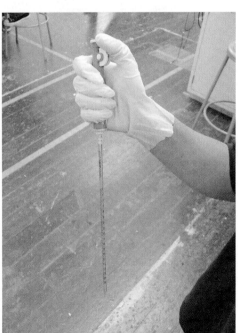

Figure 3.2. **Use blue pipet pumps with 1- and 2-mL pipets. Use green pumps with 5- and 10-mL pipets.**
Photo by author.

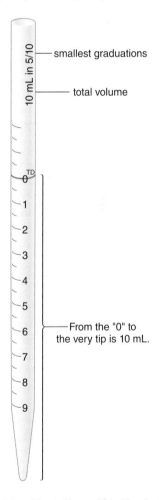

Figure 3.3. **10 mL Pipet** This 10-mL pipet measures 1 to 10 mL in 0.5-mL increments. Use a green pipet pump with a 10-mL pipet.

appropriate for a 1- or 2-mL pipet (see Figure 3.2), and a green pump is appropriate for a 5- or 10-mL pipet (see Figure 3.3). To ensure accurate measuring, operate the pipet pump slowly, and watch carefully as volumes are taken up and dispensed by the pipet. **Mouth pipeting is never allowed.** Other pipet aids may be available, including pipet bulbs or electronic pumps.

Follow these guidelines for correct pipeting technique:

Pipeting Technique Using a Pipet Pump

1. Use a blue pipet pump for 1- or 2-mL pipets. Use a green pipet pump for 5- or 10-mL pipets. Use a red pipet pump for 25- or 50-mL pipets. Make sure you can understand the values of the graduations on the pipet.
2. Insert the pipet into a pipet pump. Gently twist and push the top of the pipet (end with label) into the pump *just until it is held securely.* Do not push too far as this may damage the inside of the pump.
3. Put the pipet tip into the solution. Be careful the sample does not overflow the container due to displacement.
4. Keeping the tip under the surface and holding the container at eye level, roll the pump wheel up to pull solution into the pipet. Pull the solution up until the bottom of the meniscus (the concave surface of the liquid in the pipet) is at the volume value desired.
5. Move the pipet into the recipient container. Roll the pump wheel down (all the way) to dispense solution from the pipet. Touch the tip to the side of the container so that adhesion pulls off any liquid on the side of the pipet. Allow the solution to leave the pipet, but do not force out the last tiny bit. The pipets labeled "TD" measure "to delivery." If the last remaining drop is blown out, a mismeasurement will occur.
6. Remove the pipet from the container. Holding the pipet pump bottom, gently twist and pull the pipet out of the pump. Discard the pipet if it is disposable. Clean it if it is reusable.

Precautions for Using Pipets

- **Use a pipet pump to withdraw and dispense liquids** (see Figure 3.4). Do not pipet by mouth.
- **Hold the bottom of the pipet pump when inserting and removing the pipet.** The bottom part of the pipet pump sometimes sticks to the pipet, and can accidentally be pulled out and thrown away. The pipet pump is useless if this happens.
- **Always keep the pipet in an almost vertical position when there is fluid in the tip.** To avoid contamination, do not allow liquid to accidentally run back into the pipet pump.

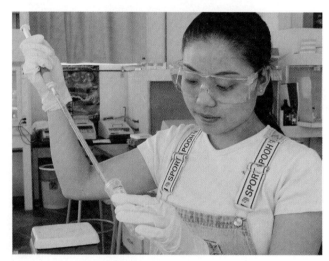

Figure 3.4. Always use a pipet pump or pipet aid with a pipet. Never pipet by mouth! Keep the pipet almost vertical when pipeting.
Photo by author.

- **Use your thumb to roll the pipeting gear up and down. Do not pull or push on top the of pipet pump.**
- **Do not pipet a liquid sample into another liquid, unless directed to do so.** Instead, pipet a sample onto the inside of the recipient vessel and allow it to flow down the vessel. This practice minimizes cross contamination of samples. Gently mix by finger flicking, vortexing, or inverting the container. Avoid bubbling.

Purpose

Which pipets are best used to measure specific volumes?
How precisely can you measure using each pipet (1, 2, 5, and 10 mL)?
How accurately can you prepare samples using each pipet (1, 2, 5, and 10 mL)?

Materials

Tubes, glass, 13 × 100 mm
  Plug caps for 13 × 100-mm tubes
Permanent lab marker pens
Food coloring, package of 4 colors
Solution 1 (1 mL red dye: 499 mL tap H_2O)
Solution 2 (1 mL blue dye: 499 mL tap H_2O)
Solution 3 (1 mL green dye: 499 mL tap H_2O)
Solution 4 (1 mL yellow dye: 499 mL tap H_2O)

Solution 5 (tap H_2O)
Pipets, 10-, 5-, 2-, 1-mL
Pipet pump, blue
Pipet pump, green
Tubes, 50 mL, conical
Tube racks for 50-mL tubes
Plastic beaker, 1L
Peg racks for 13 × 100-mm tubes

Procedure

1. Using a permanent marker, label four empty 13 × 100-mm tubes with A, B, C, and D, your initials, and the date.
2. Carefully, study each pipet available for use. What is the maximum amount each pipet can measure? What is the value of the smallest graduation on each pipet? For each pipet, randomly put your thumbnail somewhere on the graduations. If you drew up liquid to that height, what volume would be measured? Record all of this information. Check with your lab colleagues to ensure that you are reading the pipet correctly.
   Also, check to see if there is a "TD" label on the pipet. If there is, that means that the pipet is accurate "to delivery" and that the tiny drop left in the bottom of the pipet after dispensing should not be forced out.
3. Using the smallest pipet possible, measure the following dye solutions into each tube according to the matrix shown in Table 3.1. Unless told otherwise, add the smallest volume first. Add the next volume to the inside of the tube, allowing it to flow down to the bottom. Finger flick the tube to mix the volumes.
4. Compare the A through D tubes with the "key" tubes provided by the instructor. These are the standards for comparison. For each sample tube, check the level of the final volume, the final color (indicative of accurate measurement and thorough mixing), and proper labeling.

Table 3.1.   **Practicing with Pipets Matrix**

Tubes	Solution 1 (mL)	Solution 2 (mL)	Solution 3 (mL)	Solution 4 (mL)	Solution 5 (mL)
A	6.3	0.5	0.25	- - -	- - -
B	2.4	1.08	- - -	0.19	0.73
C	4.0	1.5	0.5	- - -	- - -
D	3.5	2.0	- - -	0.25	0.2

5. If the volume of any tube is not within one meniscus of the "key" tubes, it should be remade. Keep track of your attempts to prepare the sample tubes. Make a data table to record your evaluation of your tube preparation with all the observations from Procedure steps 3 through 4.
6. Make a table to collect data on how many students in the class had their first Tube 1 sam ples fall within the one meniscus range of acceptable variation.
7. Using a spectrophotometer (already set to read the light absorbance by molecules at a wavelength of 400 nm), read the absorbance of your four samples in absorbance units (au). Compare the absorbance values with the absorbance of the instructor's "key" tubes. Does the absorbance of your samples fall within 10% of the key tubes' absorbance values? What does the data mean?

Reflection/Analysis

For volumes between 0.1 mL and 10 mL, explain which pipet and pump are appropriate to use for measuring and dispensing. Make three suggestions that other technicians can use to improve their pipeting accuracy. Based on the Tube 1 class data, describe how much precision the students in the class demonstrated in preparing these samples.

Thinking Like a Biotechnician

1. A 250-µL sample is needed from a sterile vessel that is too thin to use with anything but a sterile pipet. Which pipet and pipet pump could be used to withdraw the mL equivalent of 250 µL from the vessel?
2. A 1.75 mL sample is needed for an experiment. Both a 2- and a 5-mL pipet will measure this amount. Which pipet is best to use and why?
3. Practice pipeting dye-solution samples to create the mixtures specified in Table 3.2.
   a. Measure all solutions into 13 × 100-mm tubes. Label each tube with the tube letter, your initials, and the date.
   b. Although you may help each other, pipeting the samples as independently as possible is better practice.

Table 3.2.   **Pipeting Practice Matrix**

Tube Letter	Red Dye Volume (mL)	Blue Dye Volume (mL)	Green Dye Volume (mL)	Total Volume (mL)
A	1.1	1.7	0.33	
B	1.27	0.85	2.9	
C	0.7	2.8	1.8	
D	4.6	1.9	0.66	

- Use the smallest instrument possible for each measurement.
- More than one pipet may be necessary to measure these amounts.
- Evaluation criteria: labels, final volume, and final color/mixing.

Laboratory 3b

Measuring Very Small Volumes in a Biotechnology Lab

Background

Very tiny amounts of chemicals and biological reagents are used in many biotechnology experiments. To measure these minute volumes, technicians use micropipets that measure microliter (µL) amounts. There are 1000 µL in 1 mL and 1 µL = 0.001 mL or 1/1000th of a mL.

This activity introduces micropipeting technique. As with all fine motor skills, learning how to use a micropipet takes practice and determination. You must be able to measure these very tiny volumes with accuracy. Operate the micropipet slowly and carefully.

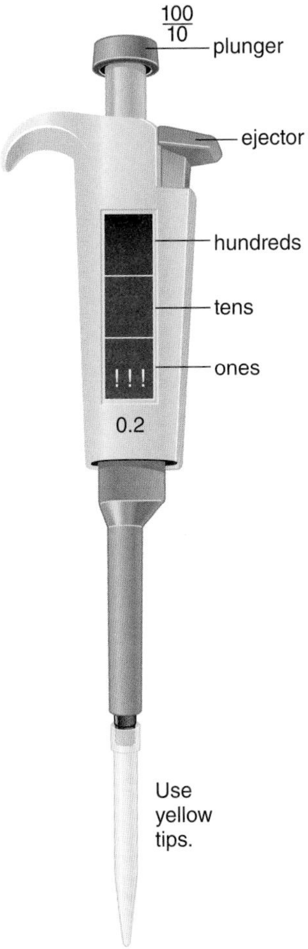

Picking and Setting the Micropipet

1. Check that you have the correct micropipet for the job. Most labs have three sizes of micropipets, often a P-10 (for 0.5 to 10 µL), a P-100 (for 10 to 100 µL), and a P-1000 (for 100 to 1000 µL) (see Figure 3.5).
   Note: Many laboratories use a P-20 (for 2 to 20 µL) instead of a P-10, or a P-200 (for 20 to 200 µL) instead of a P-100.
2. Dial the desired volume. Do you understand how to read the scale? If not, ask your instructor or review the background information in the text. **Hint:** By knowing the maximum volume of the micropipet, you can figure out what each of the digits on the readout means.
3. Gently, push the end of the micropipet into the proper-size tip. P-10 tips are usually white or in a white or gray box. Yellow tips are usually for the P-20, P-100, and P-200 micropipets. P-1000 tips are usually blue or white. The tips are disposable and usually intended for one use.

How to Take Up a Sample with a Micropipet

4. Before picking up the micropipet, open the cap or lid of the tube from which you are taking fluid. (Or, have your lab partner do this.)
5. Hold the micropipet in one hand, at a 45° angle from vertical. In this way, contaminants from your hands or the micropipet will not fall into the tube. Hold the test tube in your other hand. Both should be almost at eye level.
6. **Depress** the plunger of the micropipet to the **first** stop, and **hold** it in this position.
7. Place the tip into the solution to be pipeted.
8. Draw fluid into the tip by *slowly* releasing the plunger.

How to Expel a Sample from the Micropipet

9. With your other hand, open the cap or lid of the tube you are filling.
10. Hold the micropipet in one hand, at about a 45° angle from vertical. Hold the tube in your other hand. Both should be at about eye level.
11. Gently touch the micropipet tip to the inside wall of the reaction tube into which you want to expel the sample. This creates a tiny surface-tension effect that helps draw the fluid out of the tip.
12. Slowly, depress the plunger of the micropipet to the first stop. Then, continue to the second stop to expel the last bit of fluid, and hold the plunger in this position (see Figure 3.6).
13. Slowly, remove the pipet from the tube, keeping the plunger depressed to avoid drawing any liquid back into the tip.
14. Always change tips for each new reagent you pipet. To eject a tip, depress the ejector button on the top of the micropipet.

Figure 3.5. **P-100 Micropipet.** Different models of micropipets are operated slightly differently. Make sure you know how to operate and read the micropipet before using it.

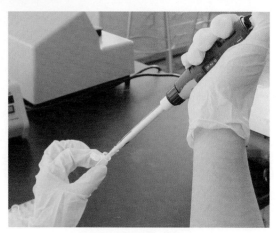

Figure 3.6. To ensure that the entire sample is released, push the plunger all the way down to the second and final stop as you withdraw the tip from the collection tube.
Photo by author.

Precautions for Using Micropipets

- Set pipet volume *only* within the range specified for that micropipet. Do not attempt to set a volume beyond the pipet's minimum or maximum values.
- When using a micropipet, first apply a tip. Failure to do this will cause liquid to enter into the nose cone. Since a micropipet works by air displacement, its internal mechanism must remain dry.
- Always keep a micropipet in a vertical position when there is fluid in the tip. Do not allow liquid to accidentally run back into the nose cone.
- Use your thumb to control the speed at which the plunger rises after taking up or ejecting fluid. Releasing the plunger too abruptly will cause leakage or bubbles that will trap air and make the measurement inaccurate.

Purpose

Which micropipets are best used to measure specific volumes? How precisely can you measure using each micropipet? How accurately can you prepare samples using each micropipet?

Materials

Tube rack for 1.7 mL tubes
Reaction tubes, 1.7 mL
Permanent lab marker pens
Food coloring, package of 4 colors
Red dye
  (1 mL food coloring: 499 mL tap H_2O)
Blue dye
  (1 mL food coloring: 499 mL tap H_2O)

Green dye
  (1 mL food coloring: 499 mL tap H_2O)
Yellow dye
  (1 mL food coloring: 499 mL tap H_2O)
tap H_2O
Micropipet, P-10
Micropipet, P-100
Micropipet, P-1000
Micropipet tips for P-10

Procedure

Practicing with Micropipets

1. Use a permanent marker to label five empty reaction tubes with A, B, C, D, or E and your initials.
2. Using the indicated micropipet, measure the dye solutions into each tube according to the matrix shown in Table 3.3. Unless told otherwise, add the smallest volume first. Add each volume to the inside of the tube without letting the drops touch. Each drop will stick because of adhesion. When all the volumes have been added, bring the drops to the bottom of the tube with a quick wrist flick.

Table 3.3. **Practicing with Micropipets Matrix**

Reaction Tubes	Micropipets to Use	Red Dye (µL)	Blue Dye (µL)	Green Dye (µL)	Yellow Dye (µL)	Tap Water (µL)	Total Volume (µL)
A	P-100 or P-200	22.3	31.6	-	44.4	-	
B	P-10 or P-20	3.0	5.5	2.7	-	-	
C	P-1000	253	-	-	-	557	
D	Student choice	-	125.8	3.6	74.9	-	
E	Student choice	11.1	122.2	-	3.5	333.3	

3. Find a partner and spin the tubes in a microcentrifuge for 1 to 2 seconds to pool the solutions. Make sure each tube is opposite a tube of equal volume. See the centrifuge instructions at the end of the procedures.
4. After centrifuging, compare your tubes with the standard "key" tubes and other classmates' tubes. Check the tube volume, color/mixing, and labeling.

5. As an additional check of accuracy, set the micropipet to the total volume (μL) that should be in the tubes and carefully withdraw all of the fluid from a tube. The contents should just fill the tip, with no air space at the bottom of the tip and no leftover fluid in the tube. Repeat with each tube.

6. Is there any liquid left in each microtest tube? If so, determine its volume. Can you think of a way to measure the leftover amount? Hint: 1 gram of water weighs 1 mL.
What *percent error* did you have in your micropipeting of these small volumes? Use the equation below to determine the percent error in pipeting these samples:

$$\frac{\text{amount left in test tube}}{\text{total amount pipeted}} \times 100 = \% \text{ error in measurement}$$

Centrifuge Instructions (see Figure 3.7)

- Tightly close the caps on all of the tubes to be placed in the microcentrifuge (also called microfuge).
- The microfuge (sample holder) rotor must always be balanced. You cannot, for example, spin *one* tube in a microfuge. **Spinning in an unbalanced arrangement like this would damage the motor and ruin the centrifuge.**
- The volume and mass of sample in the tubes should be the same. Otherwise, the rotor will spin unevenly (like wet towels spinning out of balance in a washing machine). You can always prepare a "blank" tube with the same volume of liquid to balance a single tube.

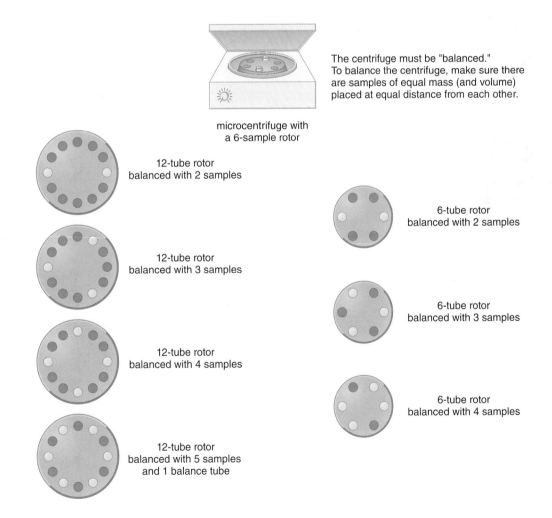

The centrifuge must be "balanced."
To balance the centrifuge, make sure there are samples of equal mass (and volume) placed at equal distance from each other.

microcentrifuge with a 6-sample rotor

12-tube rotor balanced with 2 samples

12-tube rotor balanced with 3 samples

12-tube rotor balanced with 4 samples

12-tube rotor balanced with 5 samples and 1 balance tube

6-tube rotor balanced with 2 samples

6-tube rotor balanced with 3 samples

6-tube rotor balanced with 4 samples

Figure 3.7. **Centrifuge Basics.**

- After you have replaced the metal top (if your type of microfuge has a rotor top) and secured the lid of the microfuge, give the tubes a 1- to 2-second pulse. This will mix and pool all the reagents into a droplet in the bottom of each tube.

Reflection/Analysis

1. For volumes between 1 and 1000 μL, explain which micropipet is appropriate to use for measuring and dispensing. Make three suggestions that other technicians can use to improve their micropipeting accuracy.
2. Check your micropipeting skill by completing the Micropipeting Secret Code Activity below.

Micropipeting Secret Code

A. Obtain a 96-well plate.
B. Locate columns 1 through 12 and rows A through H. Notice how wells in the plate can be assigned a well number such as A4, D9, or C11 (like an Excel® spreadsheet).
C. Pipet the volumes listed in the Micropipeting Secret Code Matrix (Table 3.4) into the appropriate well. Notice how several wells have more than one dye to be added. If possible, add the smallest volume for a well first and the largest volume for a well last. When complete, a 350-μL, color-coded "secret" message should appear.

Table 3.4. **Micropipeting Secret Code Matrix**

Cell	Yellow	Red	Blue	Green		Cell	Yellow	Red	Blue	Green
D4	0	0	350 μL	0		C7	50 μL	50 μL	50 μL	200 μL
E4	0	0	350 μL	0		D7	50 μL	50 μL	50 μL	200 μL
F4	0	0	350 μL	0		F7	50 μL	50 μL	50 μL	200 μL
C8	0.2 mL	0	50 μL	100 μL		C6	0.1 mL	50 μL	50 μL	150 μL
F8	0.2 mL	0	50 μL	100 μL		E6	0.1 mL	50 μL	50 μL	150 μL
A12	325 μL	25 μL	0	0		F6	0.1 mL	50 μL	50 μL	150 μL
G12	325 μL	25 μL	0	0		C5	25 μL	100 μL	225 μL	0
B11	225 μL	100 μL	0	25 μL		F5	25 μL	100 μL	225 μL	0
C11	225 μL	100 μL	0	25 μL		C3	0	0	300 μL	50 μL
D11	225 μL	100 μL	0	25 μL		F3	0	0	300 μL	50 μL
E11	225 μL	100 μL	0	25 μL		C2	0	75 μL	250 μL	25 μL
F11	225 μL	100 μL	0	25 μL		F2	0	75 μL	250 μL	25 μL
C10	75 μL	0.25 mL	0	25 μL		D1	0	100 μL	250 μL	0
E10	75 μL	0.25 mL	0	25 μL		E1	0	100 μL	250 μL	0
D9	0	350 μL	0	0		F1	0	100 μL	250 μL	0

Thinking Like a Biotechnician

1. For most experiments, several reagents must be added to the same tube. Propose a method to keep track of the samples that have been added to a reaction tube.
2. Demonstrate the effect of micropipeting incorrectly by doing the following:
   a. Set a P-20 or P-10 to 2 μL.
   b. Purposely, misuse the P-20 or P-10 pipet, and depress the plunger to the second stop.
   c. Suck up this apparent 2-μL volume and release onto a piece of wax paper.
   d. Now, correctly collect a 2-μL volume using the P-20 or P-10.
   e. Release it onto the wax paper next to the other drop. Are the drops noticeably different in size?
   f. How much more is there in the "misused" volume? (Use the pipet to suck up the misused volume in 2-μL increments.)
   g. If a balance or scale is available, and you have been trained to use it, make these mea-surements on it. Determine the percentage error that would occur if you were to accidentally misuse the pipet in this fashion.
3. Into 1.7 mL tubes, prepare the samples in Table 3.5.

Table 3.5.   **Micropipeting Practice Matrix**

Tube No.	Red Dye Volume (µL)	Blue Dye Volume (µL)	Green Dye Volume (µL)	Total Volume (mL)
1	27.2	313.0	59.3	
2	555.0	222.0	7.8	
3	133.3	19.8	235.0	
4	9.4	4.1	2.25	

- Use the smallest instrument possible for all measurements.
- Change tips for each measurement.
- Total volumes may be checked by using a P-1000.
- Evaluation criteria: labels, final volume, and final color/mixing.

4. A balance may be used to determine if a micropipet is measuring within an acceptable range. Since 1 mL of water weighs 1.0 g, you can estimate the expected mass for any volume of water. For example, 1.5 mL of water should weigh 1.5 g, 0.25 mL of water should weigh 0.25 g, and 150 µL (= 0.15 mL) of water should weigh 0.15 g. Water dispensed by a micropipet can be weighed on a balance.

   Determine if the micropipets listed below are measuring within the accepted margin of error of the expected measured volumes. Make all mass measurements on a piece of tared wax or weigh paper. For any error that is outside of the acceptable range, re-measure. Comment on your results and record the data in your notebook. If there are variations from what is expected, are these due to instrument or technician error?

Micropipet	Volume (µL)	Acceptable Amount of Error (%) and Comments on Results
P-1000	1000	1%
P-1000	257.0	1%
P-100 or P-200	100.0	3%
P-100 or P-200	53.0	3%
P-100 or P-200	20.0	3%
P-10 or P-20	7.5	5%
P-10 or P-20	2.0	5%

Laboratory 3c
Measuring Mass

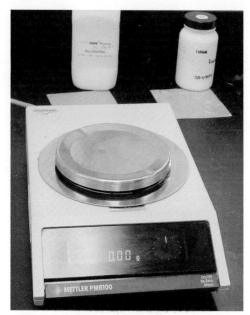

Figure 3.8. **This electronic tabletop balance reads to 0.01 g.**
Photo by author.

Figure 3.9. **This electronic tabletop balance reads to 0.0001 g.**
Photo by author.

Background

Using DNA, enzymes, and other reagents in the laboratory requires weighing small amounts, or masses, of these chemicals. Measurements must be made using precision instruments. In a biotechnology laboratory, mass measurements are performed on electronic balances or scales. There are several different kinds of balances with different features, depending on the manufacturer and the cost. Most balances measure in grams (g). Values can be converted to mg or µg.

Basically, electronic balances come in two forms: 1) tabletop/portable (see Figure 3.8) ranging from $300 to $1500 each, and 2) analytical balances, beginning in price at about $1500 each (see Figure 3.9).

The tabletop (top-loading) balances vary in the precision they measure, and each balance has a maximum mass that may be measured. Some measure to within 1 g, some measure to within 0.1 g, and some measure to 0.01 g. The last decimal place is an approximation.

Each balance is used in a similar fashion. The weighing protocol that follows ensures that the balance is used properly and is not damaged.

Weighing Protocol

Note: Wear goggles and gloves when using chemicals.
1. Set the balance on a clean, dry, flat surface.
2. If there is a leveling apparatus, level the balance.
3. Check that the power cord is plugged in properly. Press the "ON" button. The balance will undergo a series of self-checks.
4. Check to make sure that the balance is displaying a "g," to show that it will be measuring in grams. If it is not displaying the "g," press the "MODE" button until it does.
5. Make sure that the weigh pan is clean.
6. Press the "TARE" or "zero" button to zero the balance.
7. Add a weigh boat or a piece of weigh paper. **Never place chemicals directly on the weighing pan. Weigh boats and weigh paper are single-use-only items.**
8. Press the "TARE" button again to zero the balance.
9. Using a clean scoop, add the chemical to be weighed to the weigh boat until the desired mass is obtained. Keep the stock bottle directly over the weigh boat to minimize spills.
10. Remove the weigh boat/paper. Close bottles and return them to the chemical stock area. Clean any spilled chemicals.

In this activity, you will prepare and test glucose solutions using glucose test strips, such as those from Diastix® (Bayer Diagnostics). The test strips, which detect the presence of glucose in urine and other solutions, measure in mg/dL. One dL, or deciliter, is equal to 0.1 L, or 100 mL. Using the B⇆S Rule (see Lab 3e), one can convert between dL and mL (dl⇆mL).

Purpose

To measure small amounts of glucose on an appropriate balance.
To make glucose solutions with a given mass of glucose in a specified volume.
To verify mass and volume measurements.

Materials

Balance, analytical
Balance, tabletop milligram
Weigh paper, 7.6 × 7.6 cm
Weigh boat, 3.5" × 3.5"

Glucose (dextrose)
Lab scoops
Tubes, 15 mL, conical
Tube racks for 15 mL tubes

Permanent lab marker pens
Pipets, 10 mL
Pipet pump, green
Glucose test strips

Procedure

1. Measure the required mass of glucose to prepare the solutions listed in Table 3.7. Use an electronic balance for the first two solutions and the analytical balance for the third.
2. Prepare each solution in a 15-mL conical tube mixing the glucose with enough deionizded water to give a final volume of 10 mL. Mix well to dissolve. Label each tube with the name and concentration in mg/dL of the sample, your initials, and the date.
3. Using glucose test strips, test each solution. Follow the directions on the package, allowing the solution to react for the total time stated.
4. Determine the concentration of the prepared samples by matching the color of the test strips to the standard concentration key on the test strip package (see Figure 3.10). Record the test strip data for each sample in a data table similar to Table 3.7.
5. Determine how closely the measured concentration is to the expected concentration. What do the data say about your mass measuring technique?

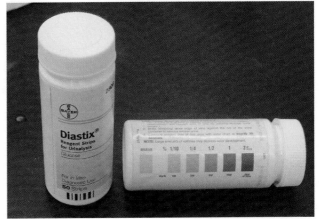

Figure 3.10.   The indicator squares on the glucose test strips are matched to the key on the back of the bottle. Glucose concentrations are reported in % and mg/dL.
Photo by author.

Table 3.6.   Glucose Mass Testing

Solution to be Prepared (mg/dL)	Equivalent Concentration (g/mL)	Final Volume (mL)	Mass of Glucose (g)	Test Strip Result (mg/dL)	Glucose Concentration Value (g/mL)	Comments
250.0	0.0025	10	0.025			
100.0	0.001	10	0.01			
50.0	0.0005	10	0.005			
0	0	10	0			

Data Analysis/Conclusion

Does it appear that your measurements and the solutions were made correctly? Give evidence for your statements. Identify two technical errors that could be made that would result in inaccurate concentration readings.

Thinking Like a Biotechnician

1. In this activity, why is it important to have a "0 mg/dL" glucose sample?
2. In your opinion, how precise are the test strips in measuring glucose concentration? Give evidence.
3. Suggest how the glucose test strips might be used for some other application.
4. Complete the Metric Instrument and Conversion Review Sheet that follows.

Metric Instrument and Conversion Review Sheet

Convert each unit and select the appropriate instrument for its measurement.

Instrument Choices

graduated cylinder
10-mL pipet
5-mL pipet
2-mL pipet

1-mL pipet
tabletop balance
P-1000
P-200

P-100
P-20
P-10
analytical balance

1. *example*	8. *example*	15. *example*
75.34 mg =0.07534 g <u>analytical balance</u>	7.34 mL =0.00734 L <u>10-mL pipet</u>	7.534 g =7534 mg <u>tabletop balance</u>
2. 4.3 mL = _____ µL	9. 0.34 g = _____ mg	16. 5.034 L = _____ mL
3. 0.111 mL = _____ µL	10. 34.0 g = _____ kg	17. n34 mg = _____ µg
4. 440.3 mL = _____ L	11. 0.004 L = _____ mL	18. 15.4 mg = _____ g
5. 66 mg = _____ µg	12. 80.34 µL = _____ mL	19. 1308 g = _____ kg
6. 3.33 g = _____ µg	13. 4.67 µL = _____ mL	20. 99.1 g = _____ mg
7. 330.2 mL = _____ L	14. 0.022 g = _____ mg	21. 0.23 mL = _____ µL

Laboratory 3d
Making Solutions of Differing Mass/ Volume Concentrations

Background

Solutions are prepared with a certain mass of solute in a certain volume of solvent, similar to the glucose solutions made in the previous activity. Any metric mass in any metric volume is possible, but the most common units of mass/volume concentrations are as follows:

g/mL	grams per milliliter	µg/µL	micrograms per microliter
g/L	grams per liter	ng/L	nanograms per liter
mg/mL	milligrams per milliliter	ng/µL	nanograms per microliter
µg/mL	micrograms per milliliter		

Although concentrations can be reported in any mass/volume units, these 7 mass/volume units are the most common in biotechnology applications. The prefix "nano-" means one-billionth. A nanogram is equal to 0.001 µg, and there are 1000 ng in 1 µg.

To determine how to prepare a certain volume of a solution at a certain mass/volume concentration, use the equation that follows. Make sure units that are used can be cancelled and convert any units, if necessary.

Mass/Volume Concentration Equation

concentration desired × total volume desired = mass of solute in the total volume desired.
(for example, g/mL)   (for example, mL)   (for example, g)

Suppose that a technician needs 50 mL of 15mg/mL pepsin solution for an experiment. Pepsin is a protein-digesting enzyme that is produced and functions in the stomach. Using the concentration in mass/volume equation,
50 mL × 15 mg/mL = 750 mg = 0.75 g pepsin

Notice how the mL units cancel out during multiplication so as to leave the answer in mg to be weighed out. Since the balances measure in grams, the mg must be converted to g. To make this solution, 0.75 g of pepsin is measured and put into a graduated 50-mL tube. Solvent (deionized water or buffer) is added to reach a total volume of 50 mL (see Figure 3.11).

Reminder: The math is easiest if the units of measurement are the same. Use the B⇆S Rule to convert between units. When converting from a bigger to a smaller unit, move the decimal point to the right the number of zeroes in the conversion factor. Move the decimal point to the left the number of places in the conversion factor if converting from a smaller to a larger unit. Here are the units of metric measurement:

L ⇆ mL ⇆ µL
km ⇆ m ⇆ cm ⇆ mm ⇆ µm
kg ⇆ mg ⇆ µg ⇆ ng

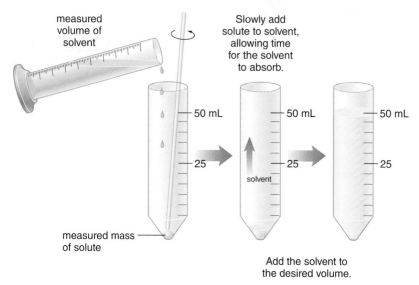

measured
volume of
solvent

Slowly add
solute to solvent,
allowing time
for the solvent
to absorb.

50 mL

50 mL

50 mL

25

25

25

solvent

measured mass
of solute

Add the solvent to
the desired volume.

Figure 3.11.   **How To Prepare a Mass/Volume Solution.**

Purpose

To make copper sulfate pentahydrale ($CuSO_4 \cdot 5H_2O$) solutions of differing mass/
volume concentrations.

Materials

Environmental Health
and Safety Officer

Caution: Wear goggles and gloves when measuring chemicals.

Balance, analytical
Balance, tabletop milligram
Weigh paper, 7.6 × 7.6 cm
Weigh boat, 3.5" × 3.5"
Lab scoops

Copper sulfate pentahydrate
  ($CuSO_4 \cdot 5H_2O$)
Tubes, 15 mL, conical
Tube racks for 15 mL tubes
Deionized water
Permanent lab marker pens

Tubes, glass, 13 × 100 mm
Peg racks for 13 × 100-mm tubes
Pipets, 5 mL
Pipet pump, green
VIS spectrophotometer, such as
  Spectronic D+

Procedure

• Label all tubes with the sample name and concentration, your initials, and the date.
• Review the use of the balance and weigh boats before beginning.

1. Prepare the solutions listed in Table 3.7 in labeled 15-mL conical tubes using deionized
   water as the solvent. Use the Mass/Volume Concentration Equation to determine the mass of
   $CuSO_4 \cdot 5H_2O$ to use in each solution to give the correct concentration at the desired volume.
   In your notebook, record the mass/volume equation calculation (with units) for each solution
   preparation. Also draw a labeled diagram of how each solution is prepared.

Table 3.7.   **$CuSO_4 \cdot 5H_2O$ Mass/Volume Solution Preparation**

Tube No.	$CuSO_4$ Solution To Be Made
1	5.0 mL of 300 mg/mL
2	4.5 mL of 150 mg/mL
3	4.0 mL of 75 mg/mL
4	3.5 mL of 37.5 mg/mL
5	3.0 mL of 18.75 mg/mL

2. In your notebook, create and fill a chart similar to Table 3.8 that summarizes the critical
   measurements in your mass/volume solution preparation and the type of solution preparation
   vessel you used.

Table 3.8.   Summary Mass/Volume Solution Preparation Chart

Tube No.	Total Volume (mL)	Concentration (mg/mL)	Mass of Solute Used (g)	Tube, Bottle, or Beaker Used
1				
2				
3				
4				
5				

3. Prepare the solutions in labeled 15-mL capped, conical tubes, using deionized water as the solvent.

4. Is the difference in concentration of the tubes obvious in one tube versus another? Explain. If any volumes or colors are obviously wrong, dump them out and remake them. Compare your tubes' colors and volumes to the standard "key" solutions prepared by the instructor and to solutions prepared by other technicians in the lab.

5. A spectrophotometer shines light on a sample and "detects" the amount of light absorbed by the molecules in the solution. If you are using the spectrophotometer correctly, and there are more molecules in one solution versus another, more absorbance of light occurs (the absorbance unit [au] goes up).

   Use a spectrophotometer to check your solution preparation. The directions below are for a Spec 20D+ spectrophotmeter. If you are using a different brand, follow the directions in the User's Manual to operate the spectrophotometer and measure absorbance. This activity is just a brief introduction to spectrophotometry. Spectrophotometers and their use in biotechnology are discussed in detail in Chapter 7.

Using the Spectrophotometer to Check Copper Sulfate Pentahydrate Samples

   a. Turn on the spectrophotometer (Spec 20D). It needs 15 minutes to warm up.
   b. Set the wavelength to 590 nm.
   c. Transfer 3 mL of each sample, numbers 1 through 5, to 13×100-mm glass tubes. Label the tubes, along the top, with numbers and initials.
   d. Prepare a blank by placing 3 mL of water into a 13×100-mm tube. A blank has everything in the sample except the molecule of interest (in this case, copper sulfate pentahydrate).
   e. Calibrate the spectrophotometer.
   • Set the transmittance to 0 (by turning the left knob). The sample holder should be empty and closed.
   • Place the blank into the sample holder. Set the transmittance to 100% (right knob). That means 100% of the light is going through whatever is in the sample holder. Now the spectrophotometer is ignoring the glass tube and solvent.
   f. Set the mode to absorbance and read the absorbance of all five sample tubes. Absorbance is measured in au. Since the spectrophotometer is ignoring the glass and solvent, an absorbance reading above 0.02 au is due to the amount of copper sulfate pentahydrate in the sample.
   g. Record the absorbance data for each concentration of $CuSO_4 \bullet 5H_2O$ in a data table. Do the absorbance data make sense for the solution concentrations you prepared? Compare your data to those of other technicians in the lab. Are the data values similar? Why or why not?
   h. Using Microsoft® Excel®, prepare a line graph comparing the absorbance of each concentration of sample.
   i. Look at the data on the graph. Do they create a straight line (or almost a straight line)? Why is a straight line expected? If most of the data points appear to be in a straight line, but a single data point is not on the line, what can be said about the data or sample? Have the supervisor approve your tubes and graph before you proceed to step 5.

6. Now, add enough deionized water to each of the five tubes to bring the total volume of each to 10 mL. What has happened to the concentration of $CuSO_4 \cdot 5H_2O$ in the five tubes? Consider how much mass of $CuSO_4 \cdot 5H_2O$ is dissolved in how much total volume. Create a data table similar to Table 3.9 to show calculations and report data. Report the final concentration in both g/mL and mg/mL.

7. Using the graph, make predictions of what you think the absorbance of each new sample will be. Check your absorbance predictions on the spectrophotometer. Record the absorbance of these samples in the data table.

Table 3.9. **New Concentrations of the $CuSO_4 \cdot 5H_2O$ Solution Tubes**

Tube No.	Total Volume (mL)	Mass of $CuSO_4 \cdot 5H_2O$ (g) in Each Tube	Concentration (g/mL)	Concentration (mg/mL)	Absorbance (au)
1	10 mL				
2	10 mL				
3	10 mL				
4	10 mL				
5	10 mL				

Data Analysis/Conclusion

Observe the tubes prepared in step 6. Do these tubes appear to be the correct concentration for their observed color? Explain. Besides spectrophotometry, suggest a method of checking to see if the concentrations of these tubes are actually accurate. Also, identify the errors that a technician might make that could result in erroneous concentrations. Describe some ways that a technician could minimize his or her solution preparation error.

Thinking Like a Biotechnician

1. Most solutions used in a biotechnology facility are colorless. How can the concentration of a colorless solution be checked?
2. A technician needs to read the absorbance of several samples on a spectrophotometer. But, after calibrating the spectrophotometer for reading the samples, he or she finds that all of the values are over the upper limit of 2.0 au. Why are all of the absorbance readings so high? What might the technician do to be able to use the spectrophotometer to check the samples?
3. Complete the Making Solutions Review Sheet No. 1.

Making Solutions Review Sheet No. 1

Convert the values as indicated. Specify the appropriate instrument with which the final measurements should be made. For items 10 through 17, show the calculation (equation and units) for the preparation of each solution. Then, draw a diagram of how to make the solution in an appropriate container.

Instrument Choices

graduated cylinder	10-mL pipet	P-200
2-mL pipet	5-mL pipet	P-100
P-1000	1-mL pipet	P-10
P-20	tabletop balance	analytical balance

1. 3.4 mL = _____ μL _____	4. 8000 μg = _____ mg _____	7. 10.5 μL = _____ mL _____
2. 43.9 mL = _____ L _____	5. 5.39 g = _____ mg _____	8. 7.503 mL = _____ μL _____
3. 0.17 mL = _____ μL _____	6. 30.6 mg = _____ g _____	9. 330 mL = _____ L _____

Solution To Be Prepared	Diagram of How To Prepare It
10. 25 mL of 0.05 g/mL NaCl solution	11.
12. 10 mL of 50 mg/mL $CuSO_4 \cdot 5H_2O$ solution	13.
14. 2 L of 0.05 g/mL dextrose solution	15.
16. 100 mL of 0.005 g/mL NaOH solution	17.

Laboratory 3e
Making Solutions of Differing % Mass/ Volume Concentrations

Background

A lab technician must be able to make any solution at any concentration or volume. Most commonly, solutions are made with concentrations reported in one of these three measurements:

Measurement	Example
mass/volume	4 mg/mL salmon sperm DNA solution
% (in mass/volume or volume/volume)	2% sucrose solution
molarity (moles/liter)	0.5 M TRIS solution

Technicians must be able to recognize which chemicals should be measured out, in what amounts, and what math must be done to calculate these amounts. To consistently prepare solutions at the correct volume and concentration takes practice.

Preparation of % mass/volume solutions is presented in this activity. You will prepare several % mass/volume solutions and check their preparation using spectrophotometry. Keep in mind that a 1% solution contains 1 g of solute in a total volume of 100 mL.

Since you will be required to make a variety of % mass/volume solutions at several different concentrations and volumes, use the % Mass/Volume Concentration Equation shown below to calculate the mass of each solute needed for a solution at some volume. Notice that as with preparing mass/volume solutions in the previous activity, the math is relatively simple. Multiply concentration desired (in decimals) with the volume needed (in mL).

% Mass/Volume Concentration Equation

Step No. 1

$$\text{Convert the \% to a decimal} \quad \frac{\%}{\text{percent value}} = \text{decimal value of the g/mL}$$

Step No. 2

$$\overline{\text{decimal (g/mL) of the \% concentration}} \times \overline{\text{volume (mL)}} = \text{grams of solute to measure. Add solvent to solute until the desired volume is reached.}$$

Purpose

To make copper sulfate pentahydrale ($CuSO_4 \bullet 5H_2O$) solutions of differing % mass/ volume concentrations.

Materials

Caution: Wear goggles and gloves when measuring chemicals.

Balance, analytical	Tube racks for 15 mL tubes
Balance, tabletop milligram	Permanent lab marker pens
Weigh paper, 7.6 × 7.6 cm	Tubes, glass, 13 × 100 mm
Weigh boat, 3.5" × 3.5"	Plug caps for 13 × 100-mm tubes
Lab scoops	Peg racks for 13 × 100-mm tubes
Copper sulfate pentahydrate ($CuSO_4 \bullet 5H_2O$)	Glass rods, 200-mm
Tubes, 15 mL, conical	VIS spectrophotometer, such as Spectronic D+

Environmental Health
and Safety Officer

Procedure

Use 15-mL conical tubes or 13×100-mm tubes as directed for the solution preparation and measurement in this activity. Use the % Mass/Volume Concentration Equation to determine the mass of solute to use in each solution to give the correct concentration at the desired volume. In your notebook, record the % mass/volume equation calculation (with units) for each solution preparation. Also draw a labeled diagram of how each solution is prepared.

Part I: Prepare 5 mL of 10% CuSO₄ Pentahydrate Stock Solution

1. Calculate the amount of $CuSO_4$ pentahydrate needed to make 5 mL of 10% $CuSO_4 \bullet 5H_2O$. Show your calculations and create solution preparation drawings in your notebook.
2. Confirm your math by checking with other lab groups.
3. Use a tabletop electronic balance to weigh out the $CuSO_4$ pentahydrate.
4. Pour the $CuSO_4$ pentahydrate into a 15-mL conical tube.
5. Slowly, add dH_2O to bring the mixture to a total volume of 5 mL. Make sure the chemical dissolves into the water. Check to make sure the final volume is correct.
6. Cap the tube. Label it with the sample name and concentration, your initials, and the date.
7. Store at room temperature for up to 2 weeks. Some of this stock solution will be used in Part III and some of it will be used in Lab 3k.

Part II: Prepare 5 mL each of 5%, 2.5%, 1.25%, and 0.625% CuSO₄ Pentahydrate Solutions

1. Calculate the amount of $CuSO_4$ pentahydrate needed to make each solution. Show the calculations and drawings of the solution preparations in your notebook.
2. Confirm your math by checking with other lab groups.
3. Use either a lab top electronic or an analytical balance (where appropriate) to weigh out the $CuSO_4$ pentahydrate samples.
4. Pour each $CuSO_4$ pentahydrate sample into the appropriately labeled 13×100-mm tubes. **Note:** It is essential that all mass and volume measurements be as accurate as possible since you are looking for a proportional decrease in concentration (see step 5).
5. Slowly, add dH_2O to bring the mixture to a total volume of 5 mL in each tube. Place 5 mL of water in an empty tube and mark the bottom of the meniscus. Use this tube as a gauge when filling the other tubes. (See Figure 3.12). Place a plug-cap on each tube and invert each gently until all the solute goes into solution. Label each tube near the top with the % mass/volume value.
6. Dispense 5 mL of the 10% $CuSO_4$ pentahydrate solution into a 13×100-mm tube, Label this tube.
7. In your notebook, create and fill a chart similar to Table 3.10 that summarizes the solution preparation. Include a 0% (water only-negative control) tube.

Table 3.10. **Preparation of % Mass/Volume CuSO₄ Pentahydrate Solutions**

Tube Label	Mass of Solute Used (g)	Total Volume (mL)	Relative Color of the Solution	Comments
10%				
5%				
2.5%				
1.25%				
0.625%				
0%				

Part III: Determine the Absorbance of % Mass/Volume CuSO₄ Pentahydrate Solutions

1. Following the spectrophotometer protocol presented in Lab 3d, determine the absorbance of each solution. Create a data table that shows the absorbance of each concentration of $CuSO_4$ pentahydrate solution. Record the absorbance data in the data table.
2. Graph the absorbance data. Does it form a straight line? What does the data tell you about the $CuSO_4$ pentahydrate solutions' % mass/volume concentration and preparation?

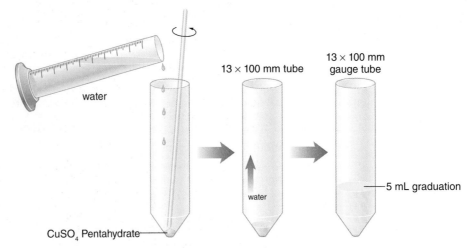

Add water slowly to the 5 mL mark on the gauge tube.

Figure 3.12. **Preparing 5-mL Volume of CuSO$_4$ Pentahydrate Solution**

Analysis/Conclusion

Do the solutions appear to be prepared correctly. Give absorbance data that supports your statement. Do the colors indicate the expected difference in concentration? How so or not? Describe any errors in technique that could result in misleading data. What might be done to decrease the chances of erroneous data or interpretation? Explain how the results of solution absorbance tests could be applied to testing of other solutions of unknown concentration.

Thinking Like a Biotechnician

1. The solutions prepared in this activity are reported as % mass/volume concentration. How would the following % mass/volume concentrations be reported in g/mL units?
   10% NaOH = _____ g/mL NaOH
   5% CuSO$_4$•5H$_2$O = _____ g/mL CuSO$_4$•5H$_2$O
   1.25% gelatin = _____ g/mL gelatin
2. The Spec 20D+ requires that a solution have color to be analyzed. Some protein solutions, such as rennin in solution, are colorless. How might colorless solutions be made colorful so they could be analyzed in a Spec 20D+?
3. Complete the Making Solutions Review Sheet No. 2 that follows.

Making Solutions Review Sheet No. 2

Convert the values as indicated. Specify the appropriate instrument with which the final measurements should be made. For items 10 through 17, show the calculation (equation and units) for the preparation of each solution. Then draw a diagram of how to make the solution.

Instrument Choices

graduated cylinder
2-mL pipet
P-1000P-200
P-20P-10
10-mL pipet
1-mL pipet
P-100
analytical balance
5-mL pipet
tabletop balance

Environmental Health and Safety Officer

1.	4.	7.
0.079 L = _____ mL	922 mg = _____ g	0.085 mL = _____ µL
2.	5.	8.
10.7 µL = _____ mL	841 µg = _____ mg	1.223 mL = _____ µL
3.	6.	9.
0.3 mL = _____ µL	3.64 g = _____ mg	0.19 g = _____ µg

Solution To Be Prepared	Diagram of How To Prepare It
10. 40 mL of 6.5 mg/mL $CuSO_4$ pentahydrate solution	11.
12. 200 mL of 8% NaCl solution	13.
14. 0.75 L of 5% dextrose solution	15.
16. 10 mL of 1.25% NaOH solution	17.
18. 150 mL of 0.5% NaCl solution	19.

Laboratory 3f
Making Solutions of Differing Molarity Concentrations

The concentration of many solutions is reported as moles/liter (mol/L or M; the M is spoken "molar") or some fraction of those units. This concentration measurement is called *molarity*. Molarity is sometimes a challenging concept to understand. However, with your recently acquired solution preparation skills, you will see that making molar solutions requires only one extra calculation.

To understand how to make a solution of a given molarity, you must know what a "mole" is. A mole of a compound is equal to 6.02×10^{23} molecules, but that is not really a very useful number. So, in biotech, it is easier to use this definition: **The unit "1 mole" is the mass, in grams, equal to the molecular weight (MW),** also called "formula weight" (FW), of a substance (see Figure 3.13). The FW can be determined by using a Periodic Table or by adding the atomic weights of the atoms in a molecule. An easy way, though, is to just read the label of a chemical reagent bottle, which lists the "MW" or "FW" formula. The weight of NaCl is 58.5 atomic mass units (amu) since the Na atom weighs 23 amu, and a Cl atom weighs 35.5 amu.

Molarity concentrations are reported as the number of moles per liter (mol/L or M). If the concentration is very low, then the concentration could be reported in millimoles/liter (mmol/L or mM). If you wanted a 1M NaCl solution, you would measure out 1 mole of NaCl (58.5 g) and dissolve it in water to a total volume of 1 L. This gives you 1 mole of NaCl per liter of solution, 1 M NaCl.

A liter of solution is a large volume for most research and development purposes. In research and development labs, mL or µL quantities are usually used. To determine how to mix up a smaller volume of a solution of some molarity, follow the example below.

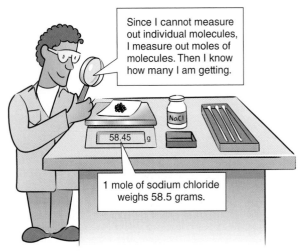

Since I cannot measure out individual molecules, I measure out moles of molecules. Then I know how many I am getting.

58.45 g

1 mole of sodium chloride weighs 58.5 grams.

Figure 3.13. **Measuring Moles.** A mole is a convenient method of measuring a large number of molecules (6.02×10^{23}) at one time. A mole of salt (NaCl) is 58.5 g since the molecular weight of NaCl is 58.5 amu.

Multiply the volume desired (L) by the concentration (molarity) desired (mol/L), as you did in the mass/volume calculations. Then, multiply the result by the compound's molecular weight (g/mol) to account for measuring in moles, as in the following equation:

Molarity Concentration Equation

$$\text{volume wanted (L)} \times \text{molarity desired (mol/L)} \times \text{molecular weight of the solute (g/mol)} = \text{grams of solute to be dissolved in solvent to the final desired volume}$$

Convert smaller or larger units to these as necessary. The "L" units cancel out and the "mol" units cancel out, leaving the mass in grams of the solute needed to make the solution.

Remember that the math is easiest if the units of measure can be cancelled during multiplication. Use the B⇆S Rule to convert between these metric units of measure:

$$L \leftrightarrows mL \leftrightarrows \mu L$$
$$Km \leftrightarrows m \leftrightarrows cm \leftrightarrows mm \leftrightarrows \mu m$$
$$Kg \leftrightarrows g \leftrightarrows mg \leftrightarrows \mu g$$
$$M \leftrightarrows mM \leftrightarrows \mu M$$

Purpose

To make copper sulfate pentahydrate solutions of different volumes and molar concentrations.

Materials

Environmental Health
and Safety Officer

Caution: Wear goggles and gloves when measuring chemicals.

Balance, analytical
Balance, tabletop milligram
Weigh paper, 7.6 × 7.6 cm
Weigh boat, 3.5" × 3.5"
Lab scoops

Copper sulfate pentahydrate
  ($CuSO_4 \bullet 5H_2O$)
Tubes, 15 mL, conical
Tube racks for 15-mL tubes
Deionized water
Permanent lab marker pens

Tubes, glass, 13 × 100 mm
Peg racks for 13 × 100-mm tubes
Pipets, 5 mL
Pipet pump, green
VIS spectrophotometer, such as
  Spectronic D+

Procedure

- Label all tubes with the concentration of the sample, your initials, and the date.
- Review the use of the balance and weigh boats before beginning.

1. In labeled 15-mL conical tubes, prepare the solutions listed in Table 3.11 using deionized water as the solvent. Use the Molarity Concentration Equation to determine the mass of $CuSO_4 \bullet 5H_2O$ to use in each solution to give the correct concentration at the desired volume. In your notebook, record the molarity equation calculation (with units) for each solution preparation. Also draw a labeled diagram of how each solution is prepared.

Table 3.11. **Molar Solutions To Be Made**

Tube No.	Solution To Be Prepared
1	5 mL of 1.0 M $CuSO_4 \bullet 5H_2O$
2	5 mL of 0.5 M $CuSO_4 \bullet 5H_2O$
3	5 mL of 0.1 M $CuSO_4 \bullet 5H_2O$
4	5 mL of 0.05 M $CuSO_4 \bullet 5H_2O$
5	5 mL of 0.01 M $CuSO_4 \bullet 5H_2O$

2. In your notebook, create and fill a chart similar to Table 3.12 that summarizes the critical measurements in your molar solution preparation and the type of solution preparation vessel you used.

Table 3.12. **Summary Molar Solution Preparation Chart**

Tube No.	Total Volume (mL)	Concentration (M)	Mass of Solute Used (g)	Tube, Bottle, or Beaker Used
1				
2				
3				
4				
5				

3. Following the protocol presented in Lab 3d, use the spectrophotometer to check the copper sulfate pentahydrate solutions' molar concentration and preparation. Graph the absorbance data. Does it form a straight line? What does the data tell you about the concentration and the solution preparation?

Data Analysis and Conclusion

Are the differences in concentration of your five tubes obvious in one tube versus another? Describe any differences and explain why the differences are observed. If any volumes or colors are obviously wrong, dispose and remake them. Compare the colors and volumes of your samples to others in the class. Describe the impact if the final volume is incorrect. What will happen to the concentration of copper sulfate pentahydrate in the samples? Does the absorbance data support good solution preparation?

Thinking Like a Biotechnician

1. Each of the tubes in this activity was made "from scratch" by measuring out a specific mass of dry chemical and mixing it with a specified volume of solvent. Suggest a method to make a 0.5M solution from the 1M solution. Also, suggest a way to make a 0.1M solution from the 0.5M solution.

2. Calculate the mass/volume concentration in each tube and the % mass/volume concentration in each tube and record these data in a table similar to Table 3.13. Be sure to make the "calculations" column wide enough to show the equations you used.

Table 3.13.   Concentration Equivalents of 5 mL CuSO$_4$ • 5H$_2$O Solutions

CuSO$_4$ • 5H$_2$0 Concentration (M)	Concentration (g/mL)	Concentration (%)	Calculations
1.0			
0.5			
0.1			
0.05			
0.01			

3. For each of the solutions below, show the calculation (equation and units) for their preparation, and then draw a diagram showing how to make the solution.

   550 mL of 9.5 mg/mL NaOH solution

   150 mL of 2% CuSO$_4$•5H$_2$O solution

   3.0 L of 0.025% dextrose solution

   125 mL of 10 M NaOH solution

   75 mL of 0.1 M NaCl solution

   25 mL of 10 mM NaCl solution

Laboratory 3g
Measuring the pH of Solutions

Background

The pH of a solution is a measurement of the concentration of hydrogen ions (H^+). The concentration of H^+ ions is reported in moles/liter (M). A solution that has a neutral pH contains $1 \times 10^{-7}\ M$ hydrogen ions in solution. It also has $1 \times 10^{-7}\ M$ hydroxide ions (OH^-) in solution. A neutral solution has a pH of 7.0.

Acidic solutions have H^+ concentrations greater than $1 \times 10^{-7}\ M$ hydrogen ions in solution. The pH value for an acid is less than 7.0. Basic (alkaline) solutions have H^+ concentrations less than $1 \times 10^{-7}\ M$ hydrogen ions in solution. The pH value for an alkaline solution is greater than 7.0.

Measuring the pH involves using pH paper/indicator strips and/or pH meters. These meters are also used to monitor changes in pH (see Figure 3.14).

Acids and bases can cause serious burns. Use caution when handling them; wear goggles and gloves. Store acids and bases in cabinets designed specifically for them. Use a chemical fume hood, with the fan on, when measuring strong acids or strong bases (see Figure 3.15).

Purpose

What is the pH of some common solutions used in the biotechnology laboratory and at home?

Materials

Caution: Wear goggles and gloves when using chemicals. Use a wet paper towel for small spills.

Environmental Health and Safety Officer

pH paper, wide-range, pH 0–14	PBS, 1X
pH paper, narrow-range, pH 0–6	Alka-Seltzer® in water, decarbonated
pH paper, narrow-range, pH 5–10	White grape juice
pH meter and electrode	Lemon-lime soda, decarbonated
pH calibrating buffer (pH 7)	Milk
TE buffer (Lab 4a)	Orange juice
TAE buffer, 1X (Lab 4j)	Coffee
PAGE electrophoresis buffer (Lab 5f)	Tea
TBE buffer, 1X	Apple juice

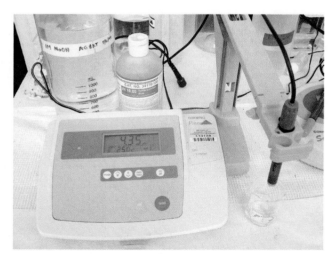

Figure 3.14. A pH meter must be calibrated. Calibrating buffers can be purchased. They are often color-coded: pH 7 = yellow, pH 4 = pink, and pH 10 = blue.
Photo by author.

Figure 3.15. Acid-Base Cabinet and Fume Hood.
Photo by author.

Procedure

1. Determine the pH of each solution using wide- and narrow-range pH paper/indicator strips (see Figure 3.16).
2. When you are fairly certain of the pH of each solution, calibrate a pH meter to pH 7 and use it to confirm the pH of each solution.

pH Meter Calibration

Although every brand of pH meter is different, the basic methods of calibrating and using a pH meter are the same.

a. Turn on the pH meter. Rinse the electrode with distilled water. Set the temperature knob to room temperature.
b. Place the electrode in the pH 7.0 buffer standard. While swirling the solution, adjust the calibration knob until the display reads "7."
c. Rinse the electrode with distilled water. Place the electrode into the solution to be tested. Swirl the solution until the pH display stops changing. Read the pH value.
d. If the solution is a strong acid or base, use a pH 4.0 or pH 10.0 buffer, respectively, to calibrate the meter. Depending on the pH meter, the alternate calibration buffer may be used in a single step or might be used after calibration has been done with pH 7 buffer, then using the "slope" button for the pH 4 or pH 10 buffer.

3. Report the pH determined by each method in a data table in your notebook.

Data Analysis

Draw a pH line from 0 to 14 to report the relative strength of each acid or alkaline solution. Each solution tested should be added to the pH line. Use the pH determined by the method in which you have the most confidence, either pH paper/indicator strips or a pH meter. Label it as you would a timeline.

Use the Internet to look up the pH of some other common solutions such as tomato juice, lemon juice, cola, ammonia, milk of magnesia, etc. Add these to the pH line.

Thinking Like a Biotechnician

1. Certain substances, including bleach, alcohols, and oils, do not have a "pH" value; they give false readings, or no readings, with the indicator strips or pH meter. What characteristic must a solution have to give it a pH reading?
2. A fermentation tank full of bacterial cell culture needs to be monitored for changes in pH. If the pH becomes too high or too low, the cells could die. Propose a method to monitor and maintain the pH of the culture.

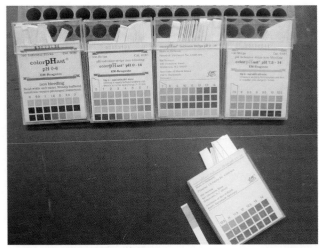

Figure 3.16. Dip the pH indicator strips into the solution and immediately remove. Compare the color on the pH strip to the colored key on the packet.
Photo by author.

Laboratory 3h
The Effect of pH Change on Protein Structure

Background

Milk is a watery mixture of many different molecules, including proteins, carbohydrates, and lipids. Casein is the group of proteins in the highest concentration in milk. Casein proteins and fat globules are responsible for most of the white color of milk. Like all proteins, casein is particularly sensitive to changes in temperature and pH.

The range of pH values is from 0 to 14; values below 7 are considered acidic and those above 7 are considered basic. A pH value of 7 is considered neutral. An acid has more H^+ ions (protons) than OH^- ions (hydroxyl ions). The stronger an acid is, the more H^+ ions there are in solution. Acids get 10 times stronger with each pH unit approaching 0. Thus, tomato juice with a pH of 4 has 10 times more H^+ ions than coffee with a pH of 5.0.

A base has more OH^- ions than H^+ ions. The stronger the base is, the more OH^- ions there are in solution. Bases get 10 times stronger with each pH value approaching 14. Thus, Borax® (U.S. Borax, Inc.) solution, a type of detergent with a pH close to 9.5, has almost 100 times more OH^- ions than blood with a pH close to 7.5.

The extra + or – charges in an acidic or basic solution can affect the structure and function of proteins (see Figure 3.17). The excess charges can interact with the charged areas on a protein and cause it to unwind (denature). In the case of casein, curdling is one indication of a significant change in protein shape. A change in shape can cause a change in protein function. Thus, it is important for a protein to be maintained at an "optimal" pH if it is to function properly.

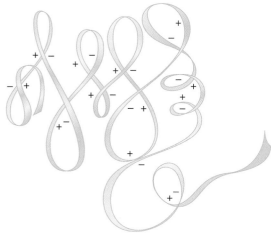

Figure 3.17. **Protein Shape.** A protein has an optimum shape determined by the interactions between different parts of the polypeptide chain. To maintain its function, it must maintain its shape.

Purpose

How much acid or base is necessary to observe an obvious change in structure?

Materials

Environmental Health and Safety Officer

Tubes, glass, 13 × 100 mm	Micropipet, P-1000	Pipet pump, green
Plug caps for 13 × 100-mm tubes	Micropipet tips, blue,	Lemon juice
Peg racks for 13 × 100-mm tubes	100–1000 μl	Sodium hydroxide solution, 1%
Pipets, 5-mL	pH paper, wide-range 0–14	Milk

*Caution: When using acids and bases, wear goggles and gloves. Wipe spills with a damp paper towel. Flush skin with large amounts of water.

Procedure

Part I: The Effect of Acid on Protein Structure

1. Place 3 mL of milk in a 13 × 100-mm culture tube. Use pH paper to measure the pH of the milk. Use pH paper to measure the pH of the lemon juice. Record these values in a data table similar to Table 2.5.
2. Add 200 μL of lemon juice (an acid) to the milk. Cap and invert one time to mix. Observe and record any changes in the color or texture of the milk.
3. If no change is apparent, add another 200 μL of lemon juice. Cap and invert one time to mix.

4. Repeat step 3 until there is an obvious change in the consistency (curdling) of the milk.

5. Measure the pH of the solution (point of structural change).

6. Record the pH of the treated milk in the data table along with a description of its appearance (see Table 3.14).

Table 3.14. **How Acid or Base Can Affect Protein Structure**

Solution Added	pH of Milk before Adding Acid or Base	Volume of Acid or Base Added to Cause Curdling (µL)	pH of Milk after Adding Acid or Base	Physical Appearance of Solution	Comments
lemon juice (an acid) pH = _____					
1% NaOH (a base) pH = _____					

Part II: The Effect of Base on Protein Structure

Environmental Health and Safety Officer

1. Place 3 mL of milk in a 13 × 100-mm culture tube. Use pH paper to measure the pH of the milk. Use pH paper to measure the pH of the 1% NaOH (a base). Record these values in the data table.

2. Add 200 µL of 1% NaOH to the milk. Cap and invert one time to mix. Observe and record any changes in the color or texture of the milk.
   Caution: NaOH is a strong base; it is caustic and can burn. Wear goggles and gloves. Wipe spills immediately. Flush exposed surfaces with tap water.

3. If no change is apparent, add another 200 µL of 1% NaOH. Cap and invert one time to mix.

4. Repeat step 3 until there is an obvious change in the consistency (curdling) of the milk.

5. Measure the pH of the solution (point of significant structural change).

6. Record the pH of the treated milk in the data table along with a description of its appearance.

Thinking Like a Biotechnician

Data Analysis/Conclusion

Describe how, and at what point, the addition of acid or base changed the appearance of the milk. Explain how structural changes could affect the structure and function of a protein. Discuss why it is important for biotechnicians to know the pH of the protein solutions they use. Suggest an experiment to test how temperature affects protein structure.

1. A technician checks the pH of an *E. coli* broth culture that is producing the protein insulin. The technician finds that the pH has dropped to 5.7 from the desired pH of 6.5. How can the pH be adjusted back to 6.5?

2. Several proteins will only function within a very specific pH range. Go online and find the optimum pH for the following proteins: pepsin, amylase, and trypsin.

Laboratory 3i
Demonstration of Buffer Efficacy

Developed with the assistance of Avi Moussa, Biotechnology student.

Background

Buffers are designed to resist changes to pH within a certain pH range. Different buffers are more effective than others in their ability to maintain the pH of a solution.

Purpose

What is the buffering efficacy of some common buffers?

Materials

Balances, analytical and tabletop	Na_2HPO_4	Hydrochloric acid, $1M$
Weigh paper and weigh boats	Beakers, 100 mL	Sodium hydroxide, $1M$ or 10%
Lab scoops	Permanent lab marker pens	pH paper, wide and
TRIS	Graduated cylinders, 25 mL	narrow range
$NaH_2PO_4 \cdot H_2O$	pH meter and electrode	Micropipet, P-100
	pH calibrating buffer (pH 7)	Micropipet tips for P-100

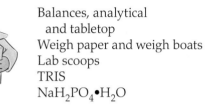

Environmental Health and Safety Officer

Safety Precautions

- Wear goggles and gloves when using chemicals.
- Use lab matting or a paper towel to cover the lab tabletop while conducting the experiment.
- Use a wet paper towel for small spills.
- If exposed to acid or base, rinse the affected area with large amounts of water.

Procedure

1. Calibrate the pH meter to 7.0.
2. Prepare 50 mL of a $0.1M$ TRIS buffer at pH 8.0, and 50 mL of a sodium phosphate buffer ($0.1M$ $NaH_2PO_4 \cdot H_2O$, $0.01M$ Na_2HPO_4) at pH 6.8. In your notebook, show all calculations, and draw a diagram of each buffer preparation.

Buffering Efficacy of Water

3. To a clean 50-mL beaker, add 25 mL of dH_2O.
4. Determine the pH of the dH_2O.
5. Add 20 µL of $1M$ HCl to the dH_2O.
6. Mix well. Determine the new pH of the water solution.
7. Repeat steps 5 and 6, four times, for a total of 100 µL of acid.
8. Repeat steps 2 through 7, using $1M$ NaOH instead of the acid.
9. In your notebook, record the pH of all the water mixtures in a data table.

Buffering Efficacy of a Sodium Monophosphate Buffer

10. To a clean 50-mL beaker, add 25 mL of the sodium phosphate buffer.
11. Confirm the pH of the sodium phosphate buffer.
12. Add 20 µL of $1M$ HCl to the sodium phosphate buffer.
13. Mix well. Determine the new pH of the sodium phosphate buffer.
14. Repeat steps 12 and 13, four times, for a total of 100 µL of acid.
15. Repeat steps 10 through 14, using $1M$ NaOH instead of the acid.
16. Add the pH data for all the buffer mixtures to the data table.

Buffering Efficacy of TRIS Buffer

17. To a clean 50-mL beaker, add 25 mL of the TRIS buffer.
18. Confirm the pH of the TRIS buffer.
19. Add 20 µL of $1M$ HCl to the TRIS buffer.

20. Mix well. Then determine the pH of the TRIS buffer.
21. Repeat steps 19 and 20, four times, for a total of 100 μL of acid.
22. Repeat steps 17 through 21, using 1M NaOH instead of the acid.
23. Add the pH data for all the buffer mixtures to the data table.

Data Analysis

Using Microsoft® Excel®, graph the data for all three solutions on a three-line, line graph. Put the amount of acid or base along the x-axis and the pH of the sample on the y-axis. Color-code and label each line on the graph.

Conclusion

Write a conclusion statement discussing the characteristics of each buffer and the evidence for each buffer's efficacy or lack of efficacy. Also, discuss the value of using buffers, instead of water, as the solvent for protein or nucleic acid solutions.

Thinking Like a Biotechnician

1. When preparing a buffer, why is water added in two stages? Why is water not added to the buffering agent up to the desired final volume, all in one step?
2. Look at other results for this experiment. Do the graphs of other groups look the same as yours? Consider two groups that have conducted the TRIS buffer efficacy test. Both groups' graphs are the same shape, but Group 1's entire graph is 1 pH unit lower than Group 2's graph. Explain how this could happen.
3. In March, a buffer is prepared and used. The unused portion is stored at 4°C. In August, a technician wants to use it. On inspection, the technician sees a tiny bit of fuzz in the buffer on the bottom of the bottle. Is the buffer usable? Why or why not? What do you think the fuzz is?

Laboratory 3j
Making Dilutions of Concentrated Solutions

Background

Making dilutions of concentrated solutions is a common practice in a biotechnology lab. A concentrated solution is generally called a "stock solution," and the diluted solution is called the "working solution." Preparing a concentrated stock solution saves a lot of time and is easier to store than large volumes of diluted working solutions. Making a working solution simply requires diluting some volume of stock solution to the concentration needed.

The working concentration of a solution is represented as 1X. A concentrated solution could be represented as 10X if it has 10 times the amount of solute per unit volume compared with the working solution. A 50X stock has 50 times the concentration of solute as a working solution. For example, an enzyme storage buffer may be made from the organic base TRIS (hydroxymethyl aminomethane). TRIS buffer is commonly used at a concentration of 0.01 M. This is the working concentration of the TRIS solution (1X). But because of shipping costs, a small amount of the enzyme buffer is shipped as a 10X solution with a concentration of 0.1 M TRIS. When the technician is ready to use the buffer, it is diluted with deionized water down to 1X (0.01 M TRIS).

Let's say a technician has a stock bottle of 1M TRIS solution but needs 150 mL of 0.1 M TRIS for an experiment. A dilution of the concentrated 1 M TRIS can be calculated using the simple ratio equation below:

To figure out how to dilute something from a concentrated solution, we use a simple ratio equation as shown in the following equation:

Dilution Equation

$$C_1 V_1 = C_2 V_2$$

Where C_1 = the concentration of the concentrated stock solution (the starting solution)
V_1 = the volume to use of the stock solution in the diluted sample
C_2 = the desired concentration of the diluted sample
V_2 = the desired volume of the diluted sample

So, if the technician needs 150 mL of 0.1 M TRIS,
C_1 = 1 M TRIS (the starting solution)
V_1 = volume of the starting stock solution to use for the dilution
C_2 = 0.1 M TRIS (the working solution)
V_2 = 150 mL

$$(1\ M)\ (V_1) = (0.1\ M)\ (150\ mL)$$

$$(V_1) = 15\ mL$$

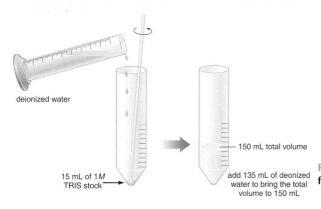

deionized water

15 mL of 1M TRIS stock

150 mL total volume

add 135 mL of deionized water to bring the total volume to 150 mL

Therefore, to make 150 mL of 1.0 M TRIS from the concentrated stock, measure out 15 mL of the concentrated 0.1 M TRIS stock, add 135 mL of deionized water to it, and mix well (see Figure 3.18).

Figure 3.18. **Preparing 150 mL of 0.1M TRIS from 1M Tris stock**

The $C_1 V_1 = C_2 V_2$ equation may be used with any concentration units (ie, mass/volume, %, or molar) as long as the units are the same on each side of the equation (for canceling purposes). When a number of dilutions must be made and each is proportionally the same dilution as the one before, the process is called a *serial dilution* (see Figure 3.19). Performing a serial dilution makes sense for experiments when many samples of varying concentrations are needed. A serial dilution is also useful for preparing very dilute solutions that are hard to make from scratch, because the solute masses can be too small to measure on a balance.

The serial dilution example in Figure 3.19 shows how equal parts of solvent and sample (1 part each) are mixed to give a dilution that is 1 part in a total of 2 parts (1:2 dilution, read 1 in 2 dilution). To make the first dilution in the series,

C_1 = 1 M NaCl (the starting or stock solution)
V_1 = volume of the stock solution to use for the first dilution
C_2 = 0.5 M NaCl (the working solution)
V_2 = 1000 mL

$$(1\ M)\ (V_1) = (0.5\ M)\ (1000\ \text{mL})$$
$$(V_1) = 500\ \text{mL of } 1\ M\ \text{NaCl}$$

500 mL of 1 M NaCl is mixed with 500 mL of deionized water to make 1000 mL of 0.5 M NaCl. Use the $C_1 V_1 = C_2 V_2$ equation to prove that the other dilutions are done correctly.

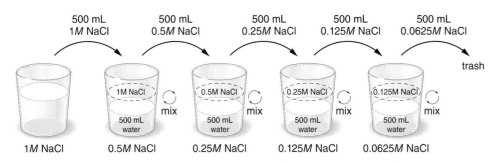

Figure 3.19. Serial Dilution. Each of these dilutions is one part (previous) sample and one part solvent. This is called a 1:2 dilution, or one part sample in two total parts. This could be read "1 to 2," which could erroneously result in a preparation with three parts. In biotechnology, by convention, a 1:2 dilution is actually "1 in 2" total parts.

Purpose

To make dilutions of concentrated solutions and report their concentration in different ways.

Materials

Caution: Wear goggles and gloves when measuring chemicals.

Balance, analytical	Tubes, 15 mL, conical	Peg racks for 13 × 100-mm tubes
Balance, tabletop milligram	Tube racks for 15 mL tubes	Pipets, 5 mL
Weigh paper, 7.6 × 7.6 cm	Tube, 50-mL, conical	Pipet pump, green
Weigh boat, 3.5" × 3.5"	Tube racks for 5-mL tubes	VIS spectrophotometer, such as
Lab scoops	Deionized water	Spectronic D+
Copper sulfate pentaydrate	Permanent lab marker pens	
($CuSO_4 \bullet 5H_2O$)	Tubes, glass, 13 × 100 mm	

Procedure

1. In a 50-mL conical tube, prepare 25 mL of 300 mg/mL $CuSO_4$ pentahydrate solution. Mix well. **Consider this a 300X stock solution.**
2. In labeled 15-mL conical tubes, prepare the diluted solutions listed in Table 3.15, using deionized water as the solvent. Use the Dilution Equation ($C_1V_1=C_2V_2$) to determine the volume of concentrated $CuSO_4 \bullet 5H_2O$ stock to use in each dilution to give the correct concentration at the desired volume. Micropipets may be required to make some measurements.

3. In your notebook, record the dilution equation calculation (with units) for each solution preparation and draw a labeled diagram of how each dilution is prepared. Record the volumes of concentrated stock needed for each dilution in a table similar to Table 3.15.

4. Following the spectrophotometer procedures in Lab 3d, determine the absorbance of each diluted solution. 3 mL of each sample will have to be transferred to 13 × 100-mm tubes for use in the spectrophotometer. In your notebook, record the measurements for the dilutions and the absorbance values in your Table 3.15. Graph the absorbance data. Does it form a straight line?

Table 3.15. The Absorbance of Dilutions of the 300X Stock $CuSO_4 \cdot 5H_2O$ Solution

Starting $CuSO_4 \cdot 5H_2O$ Stock Concentration (X)	Volume of Concentrated Stock Needed (mL)	Diluted Volume Desired (mL)	$CuSO_4 \cdot 5H_2O$ Dilution Concentration Needed (X)	Absorbance of Diluted Sample (au)
300		5	150	
300		5	30	
300		5	15	
300		5	3	
300		5	1	

5. Prepare a 1:2 dilution of the concentrated (300 mg/mL) stock $CuSO_4 \cdot 5H_2O$ to make a 150 mg/mL solution. Then prepare a 1:10 serial dilution (review Figure 3.19) of the 150 mg/mL $CuSO_4 \cdot 5H_2O$ solution to make three more diluted solutions.

6. In your notebook, record the dilution equation calculation (with units) for each solution preparation and draw a labeled diagram of how each dilution is prepared. Record the volumes of concentrated stock needed for each dilution in a table similar to Table 3.16.

7. In labeled 15-mL tubes, prepare the other diluted solutions using deionized water. Start by making 10 mL of 15 mg/mL solution from the 150 mg/mL solution, but then use the 15 mg/mL solution as the starting solution for the next dilution. By the end, most of the diluted solutions will have only 5 mL volumes because they have been used for a subsequent dilution. Micropipets may be required to make some measurements.

8. Following the spectrophotometer procedures in Lab 3d, determine the absorbance of each diluted solution. 3 mL of each sample will have to be transferred to 13 × 100-mm tubes for use in the spectrophotometer. In your notebook, record the measurements for the dilutions and the absorbance values in a data table similar to Table 3.16. Graph the absorbance data. Does it form a straight line?

Table 3.16. The Absorbance of Dilutions of the 300 mg/mL Stock $CuSO_4 \cdot 5H_2O$ Solution

Starting $CuSO_4 \cdot 5H_2O$ Concentration (mg/mL)	Volume of Starting Solution Needed (mL)	Diluted Volume Desired (mL)	$CuSO_4 \cdot 5H_2O$ Dilution Concentration Needed (mg/mL)	Absorbance of Diluted Sample (au)
300		10	150	
150		10	15	
15		10	1.5	
1.5		10	0.15	

Data Analysis/Conclusion

Look at the absorbance data from the first set of dilutions (Table 3.15 and the line graph). Which of the solutions appear to have been prepared correctly? Compare your line graph and absorbance data with your classmates' graphs and data. Do any of the samples need to be discarded and remade?

Look at the absorbance data from the serial dilution (Table 3.16 and the line graph). Which of the solutions appear to have been prepared correctly? Compare your line graph and absorbance data to others' in the class. Do any of the samples need to be discarded and remade?

Thinking Like a Biotechnician

1. Describe the value of having a concentrated stock solution, such as a 300X solution versus a 1X.

2. Let's say you need 10 mL of 5 mM CaCl$_2$ solution. Is it easier and/or more accurate to make it from scratch, weighing out the solute, or to make it from a 1 M CaCl$_2$ solution? Explain your answer using the preparation equations to support your answer.
3. Complete the Making Solutions Review Sheet No. 4 that follows.

Making Solutions and Dilutions Review Sheet No. 3

Show the calculation (equation and units) for the preparation of each solution. Then, draw a diagram of how to make the solution. Allow extra space in the column for the drawings.

Solution To Be Prepared	Diagram of How To Prepare It
50 mL of 15 mg/mL NaOH solution from 100 mg/mL NaOH	
10 mL of 0.5 M CuSO$_4$•5H$_2$O solution from 10 M CuSO$_4$•5H$_2$O	
2 L of 5 mg/mL gelatin solution from 1 g/mL gelatin	
950 mL of 1X CuSO$_4$•5H$_2$O solution from 25X CuSO$_4$•5H$_2$O	
5 L of 0.2 M dextrose solution from 5 M dextrose solution	
100 mL of 2.5X NaOH from 50X NaOH	
50 mL of 5 mM NaCl from 1 M NaCl	

4 DNA Isolation and Analysis

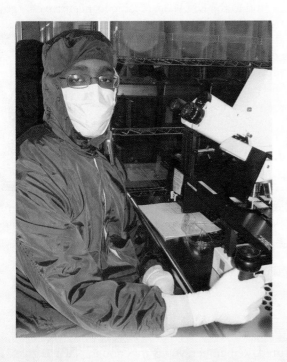

As a Manufacturing Technician at Fluidigm, Corp. Suman Dasgupta uses photolithography to manufacture the "molds," or silicon wafers, that are an integral part of Fluidigm's microfluid array chips. The arrays are used to study DNA, RNA, gene products, gene expression, and genetic diversity and have applications in personalized medicine and in wildlife conservation. Suman is "gowned up" to protect the array chips from contamination. Learn more about Fluidigm's new technologies at www.fluidigm.com. Photo by author.

It has been said of the biotechnology industry that, "DNA is the flash, and proteins are the cash."

This is because isolating and modifying deoxyribonucleic acid (DNA) molecules use some of the newest scientific technologies. By utilizing the new techniques, companies are able to manufacture and market hundreds of new protein products.

In the following lab activities, you will learn some of the techniques used to grow specific cell lines. Working with bacterial cell cultures, you will learn how to isolate and analyze DNA from the cells. Some of the new lab techniques in this chapter include the following:

- sterile technique
- growing cells, also called "cell culture"
- cell culture media preparation (media prep)
- Gram stain analysis
- bursting cells open, or "cell lysis"
- separation, or precipitation, of genomic DNA
- DNA analysis by horizontal gel electrophoresis

These are introductory DNA laboratory procedures. In later chapters, you will learn how to introduce foreign DNA into cells to modify their characteristics. This is called genetic engineering, the technology that revolutionized science in the 1970s. Another revolutionary technology that will be discussed later is the polymerase chain reaction (PCR), a method to make billions of copies of short sections or DNA for research and diagnostics.

Laboratory 4a
Making Solutions for DNA Isolation

Background

For genetic engineering, PCR, or other work with DNA, a pure DNA sample is required. DNA must be purified from cells, removing all other cellular constituents and contaminant molecules. Many purification protocols include a step to remove protein contaminants using a salt solution.

One of the final steps in DNA isolation is to precipitate DNA, or take the DNA out of solution. In most cases, DNA precipitation is done using alcohol. In several upcoming laboratory activities, DNA strands will be precipitated from solution. In Laboratory 4b, genomic salmon testes DNA will be precipitated onto a glass rod. To increase the number of DNA strands that will spool around the glass rod, 5 M sodium chloride (NaCl) is added to the solution prior to alcohol precipitation. The Na+ ions in a NaCl solution bind to the DNA, decreasing its negative charge, allowing DNA molecules to come closer together and spool more easily.

Isolated DNA can be stored for long periods in sterile TE buffer (containing TRIS and EDTA). The TE buffer contains TRIS to maintain the pH of the DNA sample and EDTA to denature any DNases, which might contaminate the sample. In this activity, you will prepare 5 M NaCl solution and TE buffer.

Purpose

To make 10 mL of 5 M NaCl solution.
To make 100 mL of TE buffer (10 mM TRIS, 1 mM EDTA, pH 8.0)

Materials

Balance, analytical	Sodium chloride	Media bottle and cap, 125 mL
Balance, tabletop milligram	Tubes, 15 mL, conical	pH paper, wide/narrow-range
Weigh paper, 7.6 × 7.6 cm	Tube racks for 15-mL tubes	Hydrochloric acid
Weigh boat, 3.5" × 3.5"	TRIS	Sodium hydroxide
Lab scoops	EDTA, disodium salt	Glass rods

Environmental Health and Safety Officer

4°C

Procedure

Part I: Preparation of 5 M of NaCl

1. Determine the mass of NaCl to be measured. Remember, you want enough NaCl to give a concentration of 5 M, *but* you only want to make 10 mL of this solution. In your notebook show the calculations and draw a diagram of how the solution will be prepared.
2. Weigh the amount of NaCl needed and place it in a 15-mL conical tube. Slowly add dH$_2$O, while stirring, until a final volume of 10 mL is reached.
3. Cap the tube and invert it for several minutes until the salt dissolves completely into solution. Check to make sure that the volume is still 10 mL. If it is not, add a tiny amount of dH$_2$O until the final volume is 10 mL. Label the tube with the sample name, concentration, date, and technician's initials. Store at 4°C until ready to use.

Part II: Preparation of TE Buffer

Note: The calculations for each solute (TRIS and EDTA) are done separately based on a final volume of 100 mL.

1. Determine the mass of TRIS to be measured (from the bottles in the chemical storeroom) to give the correct concentration and volume in the final TE buffer. Show the calculations in your notebook.
2. Determine the mass of EDTA to be measured (from the bottles in the chemical storeroom) to give the correct concentration and volume in the final TE buffer. In your notebook show the calculations and draw a diagram of how the TE buffer solution will be prepared.

3. Measure out the TRIS and EDTA, and add them to a 250-mL beaker.
4. Add 80 mL of deionized water and mix until the chemicals dissolve. Use pH paper to determine the pH. The desired pH is 8.0. If the pH is between 7.5 and 8.5, record the pH on the label and do no further pH adjustment. If the pH is not within this range, slowly mix in small volumes of 1 M of HCl to lower the pH or 10% NaOH to raise the pH until it is in range.
5. Add more deionized water until a total volume of 100 mL is reached. If a filter unit is available, filter-sterilize the mixture (see Figure 4.1). If an autoclave sterilizer is available, "jiggly-capped" bottles may be sterilized for 15–20 minutes at 15–20 psi.
6. If no filter unit or sterilizer is available, pour the buffer into a 125-mL bottle. Cap it. Label it with the sample name, concentration, date, and your initials. Store at 4°C until ready to use up to 2 months.

4°C

Thinking Like a Biotechnician

1. A 5 M NaCl solution is used in several laboratory activities. Show the calculations and a drawing to explain how to prepare 1 liter (L) of 5 M NaCl solution.
2. EDTA solution is usually prepared as a concentrated solution and added in small volumes to existing solutions. What volume of 0.5 M EDTA should be added to a solution to make it 1 L at a concentration of 1 mM EDTA?
3. TE buffer is used in relatively large amounts in DNA laboratories. It is usually prepared at 10X. What masses of TRIS and EDTA would be needed to make 10 mL of 10X TE buffer?
4. The TE buffer protocol suggests sterilizing the filter. Why sterilize the TE buffer? Propose another method to sterilize the TE buffer besides filter sterilization.

Figure 4.1. **The top chambers of these filtering flasks have a piece of 0.22-μm filter paper lining the bottom. The 0.22-μm pore size of the filter is small enough that bacteria and fungal cells and their spores cannot pass through. When a vacuum pump is hooked up to the filtering flask, a solution will be pulled through and is sterilized since these microorganisms have been removed.**
© Huntstock/Getty Images.

Laboratory 4b
Precipitating DNA out of Solution: DNA Spooling

Background

DNA is arguably the most important molecule in living things. The long, thin fibers in the molecule store *all* of the information needed to produce *all* of the molecules in an organism, either directly or indirectly. The structure of a DNA molecule is related to its function, as it is with all molecules.

To conduct genetic engineering, scientists need DNA in pure form. DNA must be purified out of cells or viruses, isolating it away from other molecular contaminants, such as proteins, carbohydrates, and lipids. Based on its molecular characteristics, DNA can be drawn out of cellular or aqueous solution. These characteristics include the long double-helix shape and the charged phosphate groups on the outer sugar-phosphate backbone. The phosphate groups are repelled by nonpolar solutions, such as alcohol.

In this experiment, DNA molecules are precipitated from solution and spooled onto a glass rod (see Figure 4.2). The starting DNA stock solution contains DNA that has already been isolated from the nuclei of salmon sperm cells by technicians at the manufacturer. They have collected sperm samples, exploded the sperm cells, separated the contaminant proteins from the DNA, pulled the DNA out of the remaining aqueous solution using ethanol and then dried the pure DNA strands to form the crystalline DNA purchased by your supervisor. Your supervisor has put the pure DNA into TE buffer and let it go back into solution. Your task is to pull the pure salmon testes DNA strands back out of solution for later use as a positive control for other DNA extractions.

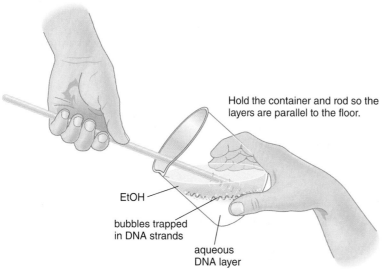

Hold the container and rod so the layers are parallel to the floor.

EtOH

bubbles trapped in DNA strands

aqueous DNA layer

Figure 4.2. **Spooling.** Keep the glass rod almost parallel to the floor when spooling so that it is easier to scoop and twirl DNA molecules around the rod. Don't let the DNA strands fall off the glass rod.

Purpose

Can DNA be spooled out of solution? What does it look like? What yield of DNA can be recovered during the isolation?

Materials

Environmental Health and Safety Officer

Beakers, 50 mL	5*M* NaCl	Plastic beaker, 1L Tri pour®
DNA, salmon testes, 4 mg/mL	Ethanol (EtOH), 95%	**Caution: Alcohol is**
Pipet, 2 mL	Glass rods	**flammable. Keep away from**
Pipet pump, blue	Tubes, 15 mL conical	**flame or ignition sources.**
Micropipet, P-1000	Tube racks for 15-mL tubes	
Micropipet tips for P-1000	Permanent lab marker pens	

Figure 4.3. Any samples containing DNA, RNA, or protein should be kept cold to decrease the amount of sample degradation.
Photo by author.

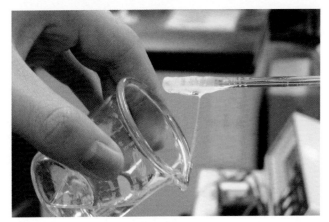

Figure 4.4. DNA is clear in solution. As it gets tightly wound on the rod, solvent is pushed out and it starts to look white.
Photo by author.

Procedure

In your notebook, make a data table to record all the data from the observations of DNA at different points in the extraction.

1. Using the TE buffer as the solvent and the $C_1 V_1 = C_2 V_2$ equation, determine how to make 2 mL of 2 mg/mL from a 4-mg/mL salmon sperm DNA solution. In your notebook, record the calculations and a drawing of how to make this dilution.

2. Prepare the diluted salmon sperm DNA solution in a prechilled, clean, 50-mL beaker. You will be using this 2-mg/mL DNA solution in the next step.

3. Describe the appearance, color, viscosity, etc, of the 2-mg/mL salmon sperm DNA. Add these data to the data table.

4. Using a micropipet, add 500 μL of 5 M NaCl solution to the salmon sperm DNA. Mix by swirling.

5. Keep everything as cold as possible (see Figure 4.3). *Slowly* trickle 4 mL of EtOH down the side of the beaker containing the DNA and NaCl. **Do not mix the alcohol and DNA layers.**

6. Observe the interface between the two solutions. You should see a layer of alcohol on the top of the layer containing the DNA and NaCl. Do not mix the two layers. Describe what the layers look like. Add these data to the data table.

Note: Before spooling, add 2 mL of TE buffer to a 15-mL conical tube for use in Step 11.

7. Place the glass rod at the interface of the two-layered solution. During spooling, you will force EtOH from the top layer down into the bottom DNA layer and pull the DNA out as it moves away from the EtOH (see Figure 4.4).

8. Holding the beaker tilted to the right 45°, wind (spool) the DNA that comes out of solution onto the rod/pipet. These are not single DNA molecules, but thousands of molecules. If you have a partner, be sure to take turns spooling, or each lab partner can spool his or her own samples. Watch the interface as you rotate the rod.

9. For one of the partner's spooled samples, examine and touch the DNA on the rod. Record the appearance of the DNA, including color, texture, and other characteristics. Add these data to the data table. Touching the samples exposes it to DNase enzyme, which chops DNA. Record whether or not your sample was touched.

10. Shake the ethanol off the spooled DNA. Touch it to a paper towel. Get rid of as much ethanol as possible without losing the DNA sample.

11. Scrape the spooled DNA into 2 mL of TE buffer in a labeled, capped, conical, 15-mL tube. It is best to prepare the tube to receive the DNA before spooling begins. Record the appearance of DNA in buffer in the data table.

12. Store at 4°C (refrigerate) for at least 1 week. During that time, the DNA should go back into solution. In the data table, record the appearance of the DNA in buffer after 1 week. At this time, the DNA is ready to use for indicator testing or gel electrophoresis.

4°C

Discuss how easily the DNA could be pulled out of solution in long, spoolable strands. Did you and your partner have the same results as others? Why or why not? Discuss the value of learning how to separate pure DNA molecules from a known liquid solution. How would this technique be valuable to biotechnologists? Consider where DNA is found naturally.

Thinking Like a Biotechnician

1. In this activity, you precipitated DNA, ordered from a biological supply house, out of a relatively pure solution. Which molecules did the supply company have to remove from the original cell source to purify this DNA?
2. If 100% of the DNA was recovered during spooling and transferred to the 2 mL of TE buffer in step 11, what would the approximate final concentration of DNA be in the tube?
3. Why is the final sample refrigerated?

Laboratory 4c
Yeast DNA Extraction

Protocol optimized by Prithanjan Bhattacharya and Kyle Siaotong, Biotechnology students, 2010

Background

Yeast is the common name of a group of unicellular fungi. A variety of different types of yeasts are used in brewing and baking. Baker's yeast (Saccharomyces cerevisiae) is used at home and in industry as a leavening agent for bread. Yeast cells are also grown in liquid culture and used as production molecules for some biotechnology products. As a production organism, yeast is well studied and its DNA has been sequenced.

Yeast DNA can be extracted from yeast cells fairly easily. For the extraction, the yeast cells must be rehydrated and incubated at 37°C in a broth solution of glucose and dH_2O. In this environment, a large density of cells will be available for DNA extraction.

Purpose

Can DNA be extracted from yeast cells grown in broth culture?

Materials

Balance, analytical	Sodium chloride	Lab tissues
Balance, tabletop milligram	Triton X-100	Hairdryer
Weigh paper, 7.6 × 7.6 cm	SDS, 10%	Heat block
Weigh boat, 3.5" × 3.5"	Tubes, 15 mL, capped	Fleischmann's RapidRise®
Lab scoops	Tube racks for 15-mL tubes	yeast or other baker's yeast
Glucose	TRIS (TRIS base)	Tabletop centrifuge for 15-mL
dH_2O	Glass stirring rod	conical tubes
Media bottles, 125 mL	pH meter or pH paper	Protease (papain or Adolph's®
Shaking incubator, 37°C	2-mL centrifuge tubes	meat tenderizer)
TRIS-HCl	High-speed microcentrifuge	Micropipets and tips, P-1000
EDTA, disodium salt	95% ethanol (EtOH)	and P-100

Procedure

Modified from procedures originally published by Hoffman and Winston, Gene, 1987.

Environmental Health and Safety Officer

Pre-Lab: Preparation of Yeast Broth Culture and Solutions (for a class of 16 lab groups)

1. At least 36 hours prior to DNA extraction, prepare five yeast broth cultures, each with 8 g baker's yeast, 0.2 g glucose, and 37°C dH_2O added up to the 40-mL graduation. Transfer the mixtures to 125-mL media bottles. Incubate for 36 hours at 37°C in a shaking incubator (250 rpm), until the broth is very cloudy and bubbly. Store at 4°C until ready to use.
2. Prepare 50 mL of Cell Lysis Solution that contains:
   5 mL $1M$ NaCl
   5 mL 100mM Tris-HCl (pH 8.0)
   5 mL 10mM EDTA (pH 8.0)
   1 mL 2% Triton X-100
   50 µL of 10% SDS
   Add dH_2O until a total of 50 mL is reached.
   Gently mix without allowing it to get foamy. Store at room temperature.
3. Prepare 5 mL of 5% protease solution (5% papain or Adolph's® meat tenderizer). Store at 4°C.
4. Prepare 50 mL of TE buffer (10 mM Tris, 1 mM EDTA, pH 8.0). Store at 4°C.
5. Prepare 5 mL of $4M$ ammonium acetate solution. Store at room temperature.

6. Transfer 10 mL of the 36-hour yeast broth culture into a 15-mL conical tube, and collect the yeast cells by centrifugation at 3000 rpm (high) for 10 minutes.
7. Discard the supernatant and resuspend the pellet of yeast cells in 0.5 mL of dH_2O.
8. Add 1 mL of the Cell Lysis Solution and crush the cell mixture for 1 minute using a glass stirring rod.
9. Add 200 μL of 5% protease and vortex the tube for 3 minutes.
10. Transfer the mixture to a 2-mL tube.
11. Centrifuge for 5 minutes at 6000 rpm in a high-speed microcentrifuge. Transfer up to 1 mL of the supernatant to a new 2-mL tube.
12. Add 1 mL of ice-cold 95% EtOH and invert tube to mix.
13. Centrifuge the tube at 14,000 rpm for 5 minutes. Make sure the cap's hinge is facing out. That way, when the clear pellet of DNA sticks to the bottom of the tube, you will know where it is even if you cannot see it.
14. Discard the supernatant (EtOH) and blot the rim of the tube on a lab tissue to remove any excess EtOH.
15. Resuspend the DNA pellet in 0.4 mL of TE buffer. Pipet up and down 3 times to wash the DNA off the bottom of the tube.
16. Place the tube in a heat block at 37°C for 10 minutes.
17. Add 1000 μL of $4M$ ammonium acetate and centrifuge the sample at 6000 rpm for 2 minutes.
18. Transfer the supernatant (about 750 μL, without precipitant) into new 2-mL tube.
19. Add 1 mL of ice-cold 95% EtOH, invert tube to mix, and centrifuge at 14,000 rpm for 2 minutes.
20. Discard the supernatant (EtOH) and blot the rim of the tube on a lab tissue to remove any excess EtOH. Then, to dry the DNA pellet, use a hairdryer to direct a stream of warm air across, but not into, the top of the tube until you cannot smell any EtOH.
21. Repeat steps 19 and 20. The DNA should be a clear smear on the bottom of the tube.
22. Resuspend in 100 μL TE buffer. Store at 4°C for at least 2 days until ready to use.

Data Analysis/Conclusion

To analyze the amount of DNA retrieved, use either the EtBr Dot Test (Lab 4d), gel electrophoresis (Lab 4j), or UV spectrophotometry (Lab 11i).

Thinking Like a Biotechnician

1. TritonX-100 and SDS are detergents. Why do you think detergents are ingredients in the Cell Lysis Solution?
2. Why is it important that the centrifugation of the yeast broth culture results in a big pellet of cells and very clear supernatant?

Laboratory 4d

EtBr Dot Test: A Quick Test for DNA in Samples

Note: Some states prohibit the use of ethidium bromide in college teaching or high school laboratories. As an alternative to the EtBr Dot Test, use an DNA indicator kit from G-Biosciences called NUCLEIC dotMETRIC™ which is available for purchase at www.gbiosciences.com/ResearchProducts/BTSNMSupport_Materials.aspx.

Background

To test for the presence of DNA in a solution, a quick ethidium bromide (EtBr) test can be conducted in a matter of moments. An EtBr test indicates the presence of DNA by glowing a "hot" pink-orange color under ultraviolet (UV) light.

When EtBr is mixed with DNA in solution, the EtBr intercalates (fits between) between the nitrogenous bases of the DNA molecule. This causes the bases to move farther apart and interact with light in a different manner. Shining a UV light on a mixture of EtBr and DNA will reveal a glowing pink-orange color. The degree of "glowing" indicates the presence and amount of DNA (see Figure 4.5). Since EtBr can change the shape of DNA molecules, it is a hazard to human cells. It is a known mutagen (can cause changes in the DNA code) and is a suspected carcinogen (cancer-causing agent). Safety precautions, including wearing goggles and gloves, must be taken when using EtBr or when working in an area where EtBr is used.

Purpose

What are positive and negative tests using EtBr as an indicator?
Do the DNA samples test positive for DNA using the EtBr dot test?

Materials

Gel photo imaging system
Paper, thermal
Printer, thermal
DNA, salmon testes, 2 mg/mL
DNA samples
Gloves, large
Glasses, safety, plastic
Ethidium bromide, 0.5 µg/mL
Micropipet, P-10
Micropipet tips for P-10
Deionized water

Safety Precautions

- EtBr is a hazardous chemical.
- EtBr is to be prepared and used only by the supervisor.
- Wear goggles and gloves while in an area where EtBr is used.

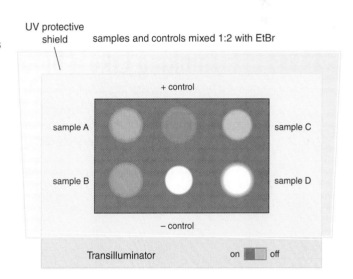

results:
A = 3
B = 4
C = 2
D = 0

Relative Amount of DNA
Glowing as Compared to Controls

Key 5 → 0

5 = as much as + control
3 = half as much as + control
0 = no glowing with EtBr, no DNA

Figure 4.5. EtBr Dot Test. When EtBr is mixed with DNA, the mixture glows under UV light. When the sample is compared with the positive and negative standards, one can determine the presence of DNA.

Procedure

EtBr Dot Test for DNA

    a. Clean and dry the glass surface of a transilluminator light box.

    b. Add 10 μL of sample to be tested to the transilluminator glass surface.

    c. Add 10 μL of EtBr solution to the sample. Pipet the mixture up and down once to mix.

    d. Other samples may be tested at other spots on the illuminator glass surface. Make sure the "dot" of sample is kept apart from other samples.

    e. Close the lid and turn on the UV lamp.

    f. Observe the amount of color and glowing of each sample compared with the positive (2 mg/mL of salmon sperm stock solution) and negative (deionized water) standards, each mixed with 10 μL of EtBr.

1. Using the EtBr dot-test procedures, test each (unknown) sample thought to contain DNA. Also, test deionized water as a negative control, and test 2 mg/mL of salmon sperm DNA solution as a positive control.

2. Photograph and evaluate the results. Use a 5 → 0 scale to assign a numerical rating to the relative amount of DNA in the sample compared with the controls (see Figure 4.5). Record the results in a data table in your notebook.

Data Analysis/Conclusion

Estimate the concentration of the unknown samples. Do this by converting the numerical rating they were given to an estimated concentration (mg/mL) compared with the positive- and negative-control concentrations. Discuss the results of the testing. Are the concentrations of the samples close to the concentrations you expected? If so, why? If not, why not? Suggest applications of the EtBr test in future experiments.

Thinking Like a Biotechnician

1. Why are the positive and negative controls necessary in the EtBr dot test?
2. EtBr is a dangerous chemical. Go online and find a Materials Safety Data Sheet (MSDS) for EtBr. Copy and paste the sections that describe the following:
   - potential health effects (acute and chronic)
   - first-aid measures
3. Suggest a method to better estimate the concentration of DNA in the unknown samples.

Laboratory 4e
Making Media for Bacteria Cell Culture (Media Prep)

Background

In the next several activities, bacteria cells are grown and used as a source of DNA. Bacteria are grown on or in their food source, called media. If the medium is a solid, it is called agar; if it is liquid, it is called broth.

The decision to use one type of medium or another depends on the kind of bacteria to be grown and the intended use. If single, isolated colonies are needed, cells must be grown on agar, usually in Petri plates. Depositing single, isolated cells on the agar surface results in individual colonies of cells. Each isolated cell grows and divides hundreds of times resulting in a colony of identical cells. All the cells in a colony are clones of each other. A plate culture is ideal for separating bacteria into individual colonies and isolated, pure, uncontaminated cultures.

Once isolated colonies are grown, a single colony can be transferred to broth culture with the goal of maximizing cell growth and reproduction. In a broth culture, cells have better access to nutrients. They grow, produce molecules, and divide into new cells at a maximum rate. Broth cultures, sometimes as large as tens of thousands of liters, are used in manufacturing to obtain a maximum number of cells to make a maximum amount of protein product.

E. coli bacteria will grow in many kinds of media, but they grow particularly well in Luria Bertani (LB) agar and broth. LB agar is an "all purpose" agar that supports the growth of many types of bacteria and fungi. Other nutrients may be added to the agar for different tests.

Media base (dry mixture of media components) is available for purchase from supply houses. The recipe for making a 1-L batch of agar or broth is printed on most stock media-base containers. Using a simple ratio equation, $Mass_1/Volume_1 = Mass_2/Volume_2$, you can determine the proper amounts of media for the volume of media needed:

Media Prep Equation

$$\frac{Mass_1}{Volume_1} = \frac{Mass_2}{Volume_2}$$

M_1 = the mass of media base to use in the original recipe's volume (in grams)
V_1 = the volume of solvent (dH_2O) in the original recipe's volume (usually 1000 mL or 1 L)
M_2 = the mass of media base needed for the desired volume (in grams)
V_2 = the desired final volume of media (in mL or L)

For example, suppose the recipe on a media bottle says to use 22 g of media base in 1 L of dH_2O. For an experiment, only 300 mL of prepared media are needed. What amount of media base is needed to make the 300-mL volume?

Convert 1 L to 1000 mL.

$$22g/1000 \text{ mL} = M_2/300 \text{ mL}$$

$$M_2 = \frac{22 \text{ g} \times 300}{1000}$$

$$M_2 = 6.6 \text{ g of media dissolved in } dH_2O \text{ to a total volume of 300 mL}$$

Prepare and autoclave all media in containers that are at least 2 times the volume of the prepared media volume. This allows room for boiling.

Purpose

To prepare LB agar and LB broth for growing *E. coli* cultures.

Environmental Health and Safety Officer

Materials

Balance, tabletop milligram
Weigh boat, 3.5" × 3.5"
Lab scoops
LB agar base
Beakers, 400 mL
Glass rods

Magnetic stir bars
Hot plate stirrer, 7" × 7"
Hot hands protector
Media bottle, 250 mL
Permanent lab marker pens
LB broth base

Beaker, 250 mL
Media bottle, 125 mL
Sterilizer/autoclave
Autoclave tape

Procedure

Note: Recipes can be adjusted for any desired volume of media.

Part I: Preparation of 125 mL of LB agar

- 125 mL of agar is the maximum that can be prepared in the 250-mL media bottles.
- Use $Mass_1/Volume_1 = Mass_2/Volume_2$ to determine the proper amounts of media base to use.

1. Wash a 250-mL media bottle and black cap. Label it with sample name, date, and your initials. (This is for sterilizing the media.)
2. Wash a 400-mL glass beaker. (This is for mixing the media.)
3. Measure out the amount of LB agar base required for the volume of agar desired. Use the $Mass_1/Volume_1 = Mass_2/Volume_2$ equation to calculate the mass needed for the desired volume. Record that mass (M_2) in your notebook along with the calculations. Pour the LB agar base into the clean 400-mL beaker.
4. *Very slowly*, add 90 mL of distilled water, stirring as it is added. The water should, at first, make a thick paste. As you add more water and stir the agar mixture, the LB agar base will eventually become suspended.
   Note: Some agar recipes require the addition of NaOH. If necessary, determine the amount of 1 *M* of NaOH to add to the suspended agar.
5. Add more water until a total volume of 125 mL of suspended agar is achieved.
6. Gently add a magnetic stirrer to the beaker by sliding it down the side of the beaker. Move the beaker of agar suspension onto a stirring, hot plate.
7. Heat on medium high, gently stirring the entire time, until **just** before it boils. **Do not let it boil.** The agar suspension should become clear.
8. Using hot hand protectors (like the Bel-Art Hot Hand® Protector), carefully remove the beaker from the hot plate and pour the hot agar suspension into the labeled, clean, 250-mL media bottle. **Very loosely cap the bottle with the black cap. The cap should jiggle but still stay on the bottle. This releases pressure without contamination. Add a small piece of autoclave tape to the bottle.**

Environmental Health and Safety Officer

Figure 4.6. **A pressure cooker can be used to sterilize media if an autoclave is not available. When using a pressure cooker or autoclave sterilizer, make sure the caps on the bottles are loose enough to release pressure (so they do not explode), but tight enough to stay on.**
Photo by author.

9. Place the media bottle into a pressure cooker or autoclave, along with the rest of the media to be sterilized (see Figure 4.6). Bolt down the pressure cooker's top or autoclave's door as directed by the supervisor, or according to the manufacturer's directions.
10. Heat until the pressure gauge reads 15 pounds of pressure per square inch (psi).
    Caution: Follow all pressure cooker or autoclave instructions.
11. Keep the bottles at 15 to 20 psi for 15 to 20 minutes. Cool the agar to 65°C (just barely cool enough to hold bottles). Continue to step 12 if there is time to pour plates. If there is not enough time to pour plates, let the agar cool and solidify. It can be reheated in a microwave at 50% power for about 4 minutes to completely liquefy. Cool to 65°C before pouring.
12. Pour the liquid agar into Petri plates one-half full, in a laminar flow hood or disinfected lab tabletop, as directed by your instructor.

Data Analysis/Conclusion

Evaluate your ability to prepare 125 mL of LB agar. Consider the final volume, color, mix, solidity, and labeling of the sample. Describe which of these tasks you performed well, and which you could improve on and how.

Procedure

Part II: Preparation of 50 mL of LB Broth

- 50 mL of broth is an appropriate volume for a 125-mL media bottle.
- Use the $Mass_1/Volume_1 = Mass_2/Volume_2$ to determine the proper amounts of media base to use.

1. Wash a 125-mL media bottle and black cap. Label it. (This is for sterilizing the media.)
2. Wash a 250-mL glass beaker. (This is for mixing the media.)
3. Measure out the amount of LB broth base required for the volume of broth desired. Record that mass (M_2) in your notebook along with your calculations. Place the LB broth base into the clean 250-mL beaker.
4. Very slowly add 35 mL of distilled water, stirring as it is added. The water should, at first, make a thick paste. As you add more water and stir the broth mixture, the LB broth base will eventually become dissolved. LB broth base goes into solution much more easily than agar base.
    Note: Some broth recipes require the addition of NaOH. If necessary, determine the amount of 1 M of NaOH to add to the liquid broth.
5. Add more water, stirring, until a total volume of 50 mL of suspended broth is achieved.
6. If the broth base is not completely dissolved, move the beaker of broth suspension onto a stirring, hot plate. Gently add a magnetic stirrer to the beaker by sliding it down the side of the beaker. Heat on medium high until the broth base has dissolved, gently stirring the entire time. **Do not let it boil.** Using bottle holders, remove the beaker from the hot plate.
7. Pour the hot broth suspension into the labeled, clean, 125-mL media bottle. **Very loosely cap the bottle with the black cap. Add a small piece of autoclave tape to the bottle.**
8. Place the media bottle into a pressure cooker or autoclave, along with the rest of the class's bottles. Bolt down the pressure cooker's top or the autoclave's door as directed by the instructor or the manufacturer's directions.
9. Heat until the pressure gauge reads 15 psi.
    Caution: Follow all pressure cooker or autoclave instructions.
10. Keep the bottles at 15 psi for 15 to 20 minutes. Cool the broth to room temperature before using.

Data Analysis/Conclusion

Evaluate your ability to prepare 50 mL of LB broth. Consider the final volume, color, mix, and labeling of sample. Describe which of these you performed well, and which you could improve on and how.

Environmental Health and Safety Officer

Thinking Like a Biotechnician

1. After making several batches of sterile LB broth, you see pieces of dust in the broth. Is the broth suitable to use? How could the dust have entered the bottles?
2. Why is it not advisable to heat or sterilize media longer than necessary?
3. Additional compounds can be added to agar before sterilization (or sometimes after). An example of this is "milk agar," in which 2% nonfat powdered milk is added to the agar base. Lactose-digesting bacteria like to grow on milk agar. How many grams of nonfat powdered milk should be added to the 125 mL of LB agar to end up with 2% milk LB agar? Show your calculations.
4. Growing mammalian, fungal, and bacterial cells in or on sterile, prepared media is critical for their study. Each type has specific requirements for growth. Access the following Web site to find information that allows you to compare and contrast the ingredients required by *E. coli* bacteria cells versus human cells in culture: biotech.emcp.net/BiologyPages.

   Record your analysis in your notebook. How many more ingredients are necessary for human cell culture? Explain why mammalian cells, such as human cells, have so many more required ingredients in their growth media.

Laboratory 4f
Sterile Technique and Pouring Plates

Background

Sterile technique is used in virtually all biotechnology research applications. When cells, tissues, organs, or organisms are grown in the laboratory, they are maintained in sterile environments. Specimens are grown on sterile solid (agar) or liquid (broth) media. Whichever media is used, it must be sterilized under heat and pressure for at least 15 to 20 min. at 121°C and 15 to 20 psi before it is used. Sterile technique is used through media prep and cell culture. Media is prepared and then sterilized in an autoclave. The high temperature and pressure cause the cells and spores of the microorganisms to explode. Media can be prepared, poured into Pyrex® (by Corning, Inc.) dishes or bottles, and then sterilized. Alternatively, media can be prepared and sterilized and then poured into sterile containers. Sterile Petri plates may be purchased in sleeves of 20 to 25.

Sterile technique includes all of the things done to one's person or equipment to decrease the possibility of transferring unwanted microorganisms to cultures, such as the following:

- use of disinfectants, including 10% bleach, 95% or 70% alcohol, Amphyl® disinfectant, or Lysol® disinfectant (both manufactured by Reckitt Benckiser, Inc.), on surfaces, equipment, or hands.
- use of flame (Bunsen burner) to flame-sterilize bottles, tubes, inoculating loops, etc.
- decrease of air currents into the inoculation area through the use of laminar flow hoods (or biosafety cabinets), removing baggy clothing, and tying back long hair. In some facility, employees "gown up" with special protective clothing to protect the product from contamination.

Figure 4.7. **Pouring agar plates and transferring the medium in a laminar flow hood is the best practice when sterile technique is important. The safest way to light a Bunsen burner is with an igniter/striker.** Photo by author.

Purpose

To pour a sleeve of Petri plates, under sterile conditions.

Materials

Environmental Health and Safety Officer

Laminar flow hood or biosafety cabinet	Permanent lab marker pens
Lysol® disinfectant	LB agar base or premade LB agar
Glasses, safety	Microwave oven
Bunsen burner	
Lab gas lighter	
Petri dishes, 100 × 15-mm, sterile	

Procedure

Before beginning, do the following:

a. Disinfect working surfaces, hands, and instruments with 10% bleach, 70% ethanol, or a commercial disinfectant.

b. Pouring plates should be done either in a laminar flow hood or on a countertop in an area with few or no air currents (see Figure 4.7).

c. Label Petri plates along the edge of the bottom of the plate with your initials, the date, period, and medium (see Figure 4.11).

d. If the medium is solidified, loosen the cap and heat in a microwave at 50% power until completely liquid (see Figure 4.8). Allow cooling to 65°C (just cool enough to hold bottle comfortably) before pouring.

Figure 4.8. **Make sure the cap is loosened, but still attached, when heating a bottle of medium in the microwave oven. If the cap is on too tightly, pressure will build in the bottle and it will explode. The medium should fill no more than one-half of the bottle to allow for boiling.** Photo by author.

To pour plates:

1. Turn on the laminar flow hood. Wipe the outside of the bottle of medium and the inside of the laminar flow hood with disinfectant.
2. Stack labeled Petri plates in threes beside the edge of the tabletop or hood top.
3. Remove the medium bottle cap and "flame" the bottle top (pass bottle top through the hot part of the flame three times).
4. Open the bottom Petri plate of the first stack. Pour agar over one-half the height of the Petri plate. Tilt the plate slightly to cover the bottom with agar.
5. Repeat pouring of the other plates and other stacks of plates.
6. Stack groups on top of each other.
7. Leave undisturbed for at least 15 minutes. Keep plates closed until ready to use.
8. Allow drying in a clean area, undisturbed, for at least 24 hours before use. Plates are good for about 2 weeks if stored in a cool, dark place.

Data Analysis/Conclusion

Evaluate your ability to pour plates with about 15 to 20 mL of LB agar. Consider the final volume (about 20 mL) of agar in the plate, coverage (equally covering bottom), lumpiness (none), contamination (cloudy or fuzziness in culture), and labeling of the plate. Describe which of these tasks you did well, and which you could improve upon and how.

Thinking Like a Biotechnician

1. Name five things you can do to decrease the chance of contaminating a sample.
2. When pouring plates, you notice that the agar is coming out in lumps. Why is this undesirable and what corrective measures can you take?
3. LB agar plates are needed for several days of lab work. If eight sleeves of Petri plates (20 plates/sleeve) are need, each poured with about 20 mL, what total volume of LB agar should you prepare?

Laboratory 4g
Bacteria Cell Culture

Background

For DNA extraction purposes, it is desirable to use a broth culture of cells. The broth culture must be "started" 1 or 2 days in advance, from a plate culture, to ensure that there is a high density of cells in the culture.

The broth culture is started from a single colony grown on agar plates. Using a single colony of identical cells ensures that all cells in the broth culture are identical (see Figure 4.9).

Materials

Laminar flow hood or biosafety cabinet	Incubator oven, 37°C
Lysol® disinfectant	Tubes, 50 mL, sterile, conical
LB agar plates/broth (from Labs 4e and 4f)	Tube racks for 50-mL tubes
E. coli, stock plate	Pipets, 10 mL
Glasses, safety, plastic	Pipet pump, green
Bunsen burner	Water bath, 37°C, shaking
Lab gas lighter	
Inoculating loop, Ni/Cr wire or sterile, plastic, disposable inoculating loops	

Environmental Health and Safety Officer

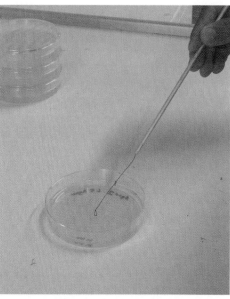

Figure 4.9. Bacterial cell cultures are started on agar Petri plates. Using a sterile inoculating loop on a sterile bench, a sample is streaked out until some cells are spaced individually on the agar. The cells grow into colonies of identical cells. A colony can be used as a starter for a broth culture.
Photo by author.

Part I: Growing a Plate Culture

Purpose

To streak and grow a plate culture with isolated colonies.

Procedure

- Do all work in a sterile laminar flow hood, biosafety cabinet, or countertop.
- Use all standard precautions with the Bunsen burner, including tying back hair, wearing goggles, etc.
- Dispose of any bacteria-contaminated products in autoclave bags and/or 10% bleach solution.

1. Obtain a Petri plate of LB agar. Label the bottom edge of the plate with your initials, the type of media, the sample identification, and the date.
2. If using a metal inoculating loop, flame sterilize (as demonstrated by the instructor) it (see Figure 4.10),

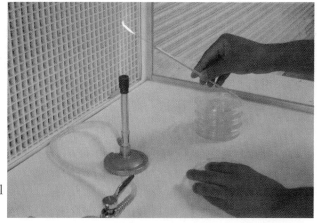

Figure 4.10. Place the wire in the hottest part of the flame (where the blue and orange meet) and allow it to get hot enough to glow red. Start at the base of the wire and have the loop glow last.
Photo by author.

Environmental Health and Safety Officer

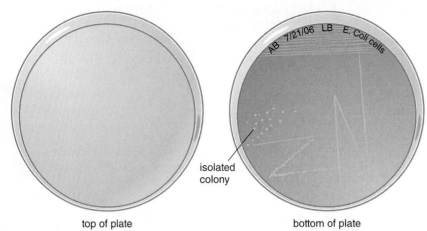

isolated colony

top of plate   bottom of plate

Figure 4.11. Streaking for Isolated Colonies. Use the triple-Z method of streaking, flaming between streakings. This method results in a significant decrease in the number of cells spread each time so that isolated colonies result in the last "Z."

cool it on a spot of uncontaminated agar, and collect a colony of *E. coli* from the stock plate. If using a sterile, disposable plastic loop, remove it from the sterile packet without touch the end loop or contaminating other loops in the packet, then collect a bacteria colony.

3. Streak the bacterial colony onto a sterile LB agar Petri plate (see Figure 4.11).
   a. Be careful to hold the top of the Petri plate over the bottom to minimize contamination.
   b. Streak the sample back and forth across the agar on the top one-eighth of the plate. This is the first set of "Z"s.
   c. Rotate the plate 90°. Flame-sterilize the metal inoculating loop. Cool on uncontaminated agar. If using the plastic loop, discard it into disinfectant and get another sterile loop.
   d. Streak the loop at a right angle through the previous streak. Go through the first streak only once to pick up the fewest bacteria cells possible. Make a "Z"-shaped streak. This is the second "Z."
   e. Rotate the plate another 90°. Flame-sterilize the metal inoculating loop. Cool on uncontaminated agar. If using the plastic loop, discard it into disinfectant and get another sterile loop.
   f. Streak the loop again, at a right angle, through the second "Z" streak. Go through that streak only once to pick up the fewest bacteria cells possible. Make a third "Z." Flame-sterilize the inoculating loop. Place on laminar flow hood counter to cool. If using the plastic loop, discard it into disinfectant.
   g. Replace lid. Place your inoculated LB plate, upside down, in one of the incubation ovens designated by the supervisor.

 37°C

4. Incubate the bacterial plate culture, upside down, for 24 to 36 hours at 37°C.
5. Before leaving the lab area, discard any biological waste in the biohazard bag, disinfect your workspace, and wash your hands.

Data Analysis/Conclusion

Evaluate your ability to isolate individual bacteria cells and grow them into isolated colonies. How many isolated colonies are present in the final "Z"? Describe how you might improve the technique next time. Are any of the colonies good candidates for starting a broth culture?

Part II: Starting a Broth Culture

Purpose

To grow a broth culture to use as a source of cells for DNA isolation.

Procedure

Environmental Health and Safety Officer

- Do all work in a sterile laminar flow hood, biosafety cabinet, or on a countertop.
- Use all standard precautions with the Bunsen burner, (tying back hair, wearing goggles, etc.).
- Dispose of any bacteria-contaminated products in autoclave bags and/or 10% bleach solution.

1. Obtain a Petri plate of LB agar containing isolated colonies, a 50-mL sterile, conical centrifuge tube, and a bottle of sterile LB broth.
2. Flame-sterilize (as demonstrated by the supervisor) the top of the LB broth bottle.
3. Using a sterile 10-mL pipet, transfer 10 mL of LB broth from the bottle to the 50-mL tube.
4. Flame-sterilize (as demonstrated by the supervisor) an inoculating loop, cool it on a spot of uncontaminated agar, and collect a colony of *E. coli* from the streaked plate. If using a sterile plastic loop, collect a colony of *E. coli* from the streaked plate.
5. Holding the tube at a 45° angle, add the colony to the broth, with a twist of the loop, to ensure that most of the colony gets into the broth (see Figure 4.12). Reflame the loop to remove any remaining bacteria. If using the plastic loop, discard it into disinfectant.
6. Incubate the broth culture in a shaking hot water bath or a shaking incubator oven at 37°C for 24 hours (see Figure 4.13).
7. Before leaving the lab, discard any biological waste in the biohazard bag, disinfect your workspace, and wash your hands.

Note: After 24-hour incubation, remove 1 mL of culture and store (-20°C) in a sterile tightly capped 1.7 mL tube for Lab 4l.

37°C

Figure 4.12. Inoculating a Broth Culture. Hold the tube "sideways" to decrease the chance of contaminants falling into the container.

Figure 4.13. In industry, large shaker flask ovens keep cells moving, aerated, and warm, so that they grow and divide at a maximum rate. Photo by author.

Data Analysis/Conclusion

Evaluate your broth culture. Does it look the way you think it should look? Is it cloudy and obviously full of bacteria cells? How do you know? How can you be sure that there are enough of the right kinds of cells? Propose a method for checking that your cell culture is healthy and growing the "right" bacteria at the "right" rate.

Thinking Like a Biotechnician

1. After streaking a plate with a colony of *E. coli* cells and incubating it overnight at 37°C, a technician returns to find no colonies on the plate. List three reasons this could happen.
2. You make 1 L of LB agar and pour it into five media bottles for sterilization. After autoclaving and cooling them, you notice some of the bottles have agar that is not completely solid, while other bottles do have solidified agar, as expected. What should you do? Are any of them usable? If so, which ones?
3. Propose a method to check if a laminar flow hood is still working correctly (filtering out all the bacteria and fungi from the air).

Laboratory 4h
DNA Extraction from Bacteria

Background

Within bacteria cells, DNA and, therefore, genes are found both in the single strand of genomic DNA and in any extrachromosomal plasmids. Either source of DNA may be a source of genes for genetic engineering or gene therapy purposes.

Isolation of either type of DNA includes bursting open the cells, getting rid of contaminant molecules, and precipitating the DNA out of the solution.

To burst open cells, the cell membrane must be removed. Since the major component of a membrane is a phospholipid bilayer, a detergent can be used to dissolve away this "fatty" layer. Several different detergents may be used depending on the type of DNA to be extracted. For bacteria cells, SDS works well. Even household detergents, such as Dawn® and Ivory® (both manufactured by Procter & Gamble), have been used.

When the cells burst, all the cellular contents are released into the collection vessel. The detergent not only removes the lipids, but also precipitates many of the proteins from the membrane and cytoplasm. These proteins drop to the bottom of the vessel and are easy to separate from the DNA. Adding heat speeds the process.

Enzymes may be added to degrade other molecules. For example, RNase is commonly used to decompose RNA contaminant molecules in DNA extractions. Proteases are used to degrade protein contaminants in samples.

Centrifugation can separate the precipitated proteins and degraded cellular debris from the DNA still in solution. The DNA can be drawn out of solution by adding alcohol, usually ethanol (EtOH), or isopropanol. If genomic DNA is desired, the DNA can be spooled onto a glass rod (see Figure 4.14) or it can be pelleted by a high-speed centrifuge. Plasmid DNA is much too small to be spooled. It is precipitated from solution using a series of alcohol washes and centrifugation. Ultimately, plasmid DNA is recovered from one of the pellets left after one of the centrifugations. Plasmid isolation is presented in Chapter 8.

Purpose

Can relatively pure genomic DNA be extracted from *E. coli* bacteria cells?

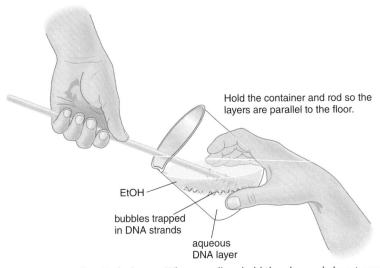

Hold the container and rod so the layers are parallel to the floor.

EtOH

bubbles trapped in DNA strands

aqueous DNA layer

Figure 4.14. Spooling Technique. When spooling, hold the glass rod almost parallel to the floor. Rotate and revolve through the two layers, scooping the DNA threads out and spinning them around the rod.

Materials

E. coli broth cultures (from Lab 4g)	SDS, 10%	Beakers, 50 mL
Pipets, 10 mL	Water bath, 65°C	Ethanol (EtOH), 95%
Pipet pump, green	RNase, 0.1 mg/mL	Glass rods
Tubes, 15-mL, conical	Protease, 0.1 mg/mL	TE buffer (from Lab 4a)
Tube racks for 15-mL tubes	5 *M* NaCl (from Lab 4a)	Pipets, 2 mL
	Centrifuge for 15-mL tubes	Pipet pump, blue

Procedure

Safety Precautions

- Use sterile technique when working with bacterial cultures (see Lab 4g)
- Use all standard precautions with the Bunsen burner, such as tying back hair, wearing goggles, etc.
- Dispose of any bacteria-contaminated products in autoclave bags and/or 10% bleach solution.

1. Using sterile technique, add 10 mL of *E. coli* broth suspension to a 15-mL capped, conical, centrifuge tube.
2. Add 0.5 mL of 10% SDS to the tube with *E. coli*. Invert gently five times (5X) to mix.
3. Incubate tube in a 65°C water bath for 15 minutes.
4. Cool on ice for 5 minutes.
5. If desired, add 0.5 mL of RNase and 0.5 mL of protease to the tube. Invert to mix.
6. Add 0.5 mL of 5 *M* NaCl. Place on ice for 5 minutes.
7. Spin the tube in a tabletop centrifuge for 10 minutes (see Figure 4.15).
8. Gently pipet the supernatant (top layer) to a clean, cold, 50-mL beaker without taking up the loose precipitant of cellular waste. Observe the color and viscosity of the solution. Create a data table in your notebook to record these and other observations.
9. Place the beaker containing supernatant on ice for 5 minutes.
10. Layer 5 mL of ice cold 95% ethanol slowly, with a pipet, down the inside of the beaker. Look at the interface between the alcohol layer and the DNA layer. Do you see any evidence of DNA? Observe the color and viscosity of the solutions and interface. Record these observations into the data table.

Note: Before spooling, add 2 mL of TE buffer to a 15-mL conical tube for use in Step 13.

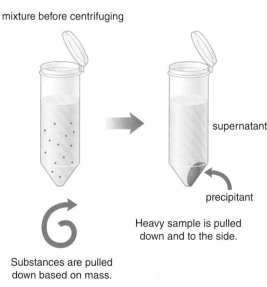

mixture before centrifuging

supernatant

precipitant

Heavy sample is pulled down and to the side.

Substances are pulled down based on mass.

Figure 4.15. **Supernatant/precipitant centrifuge results.**

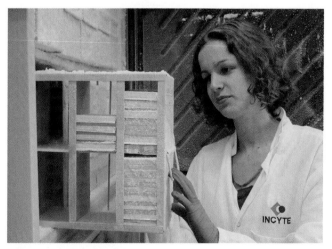

Figure 4.16. **DNA, RNA, and most proteins are temperature-sensitive and may be degraded or denatured by enzyme contaminants (eg, proteases or DNases) at room temperature. To decrease their activity and preserve molecular or cellular samples, most are stored at –20°C or –80°C. This –80°C freezer stores DNA samples for sequencing.** Photo by author.

11. Hold the beaker at a 45° angle and spool the bacterial DNA out of the solution. Slowly rotate a stirring rod clockwise, as well as up and down, and around, through the layers. Rotate and *scoop* at the interface instead of swirling. Every once in a while, pull up the rod and examine the DNA strands.
12. Try to spool all of the DNA strands. Observe and record the characteristics of the DNA spooled sample in the data table.
13. Blot the excess EtOH off the sample and place the DNA into a sterile, capped, conical centrifuge tube containing 2 mL of TE buffer. Immediately, observe and record the characteristics of the DNA sample in the data table.
14. Allow the DNA to go back into solution, over several days to a week, before using it for further analysis. After a week, record the sample's appearance in the data table. Store the samples at 4°C for 2 to 3 weeks. Long-term storage of the DNA samples should be at –20°C (see Figure 4.16).
15. Test the sample for DNA using EtBr dot testing (Lab 4d), G-Biosciences' NUCLEIC dotMETRIC™ kit or by running a gel (Lab 4j or Lab 4k).

4°C

Data Analysis/Conclusion

Describe the quality and quantity of DNA extracted from the bacterial cell sample compared with other DNA samples you have spooled. Discuss how effective the DNA extraction technique is at isolating pure DNA. Give evidence for your statements. Propose variations in the protocol that may lead to improved quantity or purity of the DNA sample.

Thinking Like a Biotechnician

1. Protease is used in this experiment to chop up protein contaminants. There are many different kinds of proteases. One protease that can be purchased at the grocery store is papain, a protease derived from papayas, which is found in meat tenderizers, such as Adolph's® meat tenderizer (by Lawry's Foods, Inc.). How can one know that 1 mg/mL of papain is the best concentration of the protease to use? Describe a simple experiment to determine the best concentration for protease activity.
2. You used 10% SDS in the experiment to explode the bacteria cells and precipitate protein contaminants. One can purchase 20% SDS commercially. How much 20% SDS would you need to have enough to make 2000 mL of 10% SDS?
3. The genomic DNA that was spooled was considerably less in volume than the salmon sperm DNA spooled in a previous lab experiment. What is the reason for the difference in DNA yield?

Laboratory 4i
Making Agarose Gels for Separating and Analyzing DNA Fragments

Background

Agarose gels are typically used to separate and analyze DNA molecules ranging in length from about 500 to 25,000 base pairs (bp). The ability of a gel to separate molecules is called its "resolving power" and is mainly determined by the concentration of agarose in the gel. Most agarose gels have concentrations between 0.6% and 3.0% agarose in buffer.

Agarose gels are prepared by dissolving powdered agarose in a certain volume of electrophoresis buffer. The agarose-buffer mixture has to be boiled for the agarose to go into solution. Powdered agarose may be purchased from a chemical supply house. The buffer may be prepared in the lab or purchased premade, usually as a concentrated stock solution (see Figure 4.17).

The most common agarose gel electrophoresis buffer is 1X TAE (TRIS, Acetic Acid, and EDTA). Although used for decades, the TRIS molecule is a rather poor conductor of electricity. Advances in electrophoresis technology have found some buffering molecules that do a better job of conducting electricity than TRIS. One excellent electrophoresis buffering molecule is lithium borate (LB). Lithium borate conducts electric better and doesn't generate as much heat during an electrophoresis as TRIS does. The result is that LB buffered gels may be run 6–8X faster than TAE gels. Now, many labs use 1X LB buffer to run faster, better gels. Read more about LB buffers at **www.fasterbettermedia.com**. In this lab manual, agarose gel labs provide the option of either a TAE-buffered gel or a LB-buffered gel system.

The concentration of agarose used in a gel depends on the type of molecules to be analyzed. The longer the molecules in a sample, the less concentrated the gel should be. Too high a concentration may impede the movement of molecules through a gel. The lowest practical working concentration of an agarose gel is about 0.6%, or 0.6 g, of agarose dissolved in 100 mL of buffer. This is used when a sample is composed mostly of long DNA fragments.

As the concentration of agarose in a gel increases, the agarose threads are pushed closer together, making it difficult for larger molecules to move through them. A higher concentration gel separates short DNA fragments well. Gels of 0.8% and 1% are typical for plasmid analysis. Gels of higher concentration, up to about 3%, may be used with smaller DNA pieces. A lower concentration gel resolves long DNA fragments, such as genomic DNA, best.

Purpose

To prepare and pour an agarose gel for DNA fragment analysis.

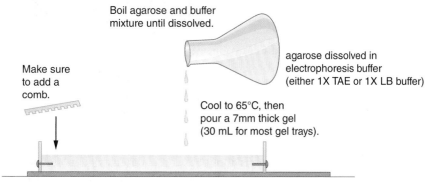

Boil agarose and buffer mixture until dissolved.

agarose dissolved in electrophoresis buffer (either 1X TAE or 1X LB buffer)

Make sure to add a comb.

Cool to 65°C, then pour a 7mm thick gel (30 mL for most gel trays).

Figure 4.17. **Pouring agarose gels.**

Environmental Health and Safety Officer

Materials

Electrophoresis Buffer
   concentrate, TAE (40X or 50X)
   or LB buffer (10X or 20X)
Beakers, 600 mL
Agarose
Balance, tabletop milligram

Weigh boat, 3.5" × 3.5"
Lab scoops
Media bottle, 250 mL
Permanent lab marker pens
Microwave oven
Hot hands protector

Glasses, safety
Gel box, horizontal, for agarose
   gels
Beakers, 50 mL
Water bath, 65°C

Procedure

- A 0.8% gel is prepared in the following procedures since that is the appropriate concentration for resolving a variety of DNA fragment lengths.
- Prior to step 1, prepare 500 mL of 1X electrophoresis buffer from the buffer concentrate provided. The 1X buffer will be used in this and in the following activity. Use the $C_1 V_1 = C_2 V_2$ equation. Record the calculations and recipe in your notebook.

1. Make 100 mL of 0.8% agarose in 1X electrophoresis buffer solution. Determine the recipe for a 0.8% gel, below.

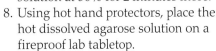

0.8% of 100 mL = _____ g of agarose in a total volume of 100 mL of 1X electrophoresis buffer

2. Obtain a clean 250-mL media bottle and cap. Label it.
3. Weigh out the required mass of powdered agarose in a weigh boat. Add it to the media bottle.
4. Measure out enough 1X electrophoresis buffer to prepare a total of 100 mL of agarose and buffer mixed together. Add the buffer slowly to the agarose in the media bottle, swirling it to mix.
5. Loosely cap the top of the media bottle. Swirl the flask gently to suspend the agarose in the buffer.
6. To dissolve the agarose in the buffer, microwave the suspension for 4 minutes at 50% power.
7. Wearing bottle holders and safety goggles, lift the beaker toward the light (but away from your face), and very slowly and gently swirl it. **Caution: Do not swirl too fast because it could boil over.** Look to see if all the agarose crystals have dissolved. Agarose crystals that do not dissolve will impede molecular motion through the gel and will affect electrophoresis results. If any agarose crystals are still floating in the buffer, reheat the solution at 50% for 2 minutes more.

Environmental Health and Safety Officer

65°C

8. Using hot hand protectors, place the hot dissolved agarose solution on a fireproof lab tabletop.
9. The solution must cool to approximately 65°C before pouring it (see Figure 4.18).
10. Prepare the gel tray found in your gel box for pouring (casting) a 7mm thick agarose gel.

Figure 4.18. If the agarose solution is not to be used immediately, it can be kept hot in a 65°C water bath until it is time to cast the gels.
Photo by author.

Note: Different gel boxes have different types of gel-casting trays. Some trays have gates at the ends that are screwed into an upright position for gel casting. Some gel trays use tape to seal the ends. Some gel trays have rubber gaskets that seal the ends of the tray in the gel box for pouring. Your instructor will show you how your gel tray should be set up for gel pouring.
11. When the agarose solution is about 65°C (just barely cool enough to hold), pour about 30 mL of it into the gel tray. The gel should be about 7mm thick.
12. Quickly place a six-well comb into the notches at the end of the gel tray. Make sure the comb goes into the notches evenly so that all the wells created are of the same size. Check to make

sure that no bubbles get trapped on the comb.

13. Leave the gel to cool for 15 minutes.

14. After the gel has solidified, secure the gates into the "down" position if you are using a gated tray. Or, turn the gel into the correct orientation for the self-sealing tray. Be careful that the gel does not slide off the tray.

15. Place the gel (on the gel tray) into the gel box, resting it on the gel tray stand, so that the sample wells created by the comb will be closest to the negative electrode (black) end.

16. Pour 1X electrophoresis buffer into the gel box and over the gel. The gel must be completely submerged and a continuous volume of buffer should just cover the gel (about 5 mm of buffer should cover the gel) and the electrodes. Too much buffer will result in a slower gel run. This requires about 250–300 mL of buffer.

17. Wait until you are ready to load and run the gel, and then with the gel covered with buffer, gently pull the comb out of the gel. Pull the comb straight up in one smooth motion.

18. Check to make sure the gel wells are not broken or cracked. The gel can be used immediately, or it can be stored (with the comb still in the wells) in the gel box overnight at room temperature or in the refrigerator for several days.

Thinking Like a Biotechnician

1. The agarose gel in this lab is prepared with 1X electrophoresis buffer, not water. What is the reason water is not used?

2. A 7mm gel is recommended for most samples. What are the disadvantages of pouring a gel thicker or thinner than 7mm?

3. E-gels are commercially prepared agarose gels that will run tiny volumes of samples (see Figure 4.19). They require a special e-gel box setup. Go online and find companies that sell e-gels. What concentrations are available, and how many sample wells do the gels have? How much sample will the wells hold?

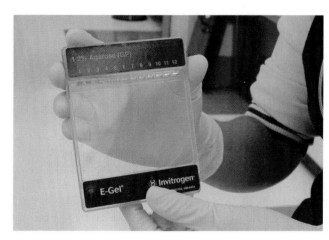

Figure 4.19. **An e-gel cartridge.**
Photo by author.

Laboratory 4j
Using Gel Electrophoresis to Study DNA Molecules

Background

Gel electrophoresis is one of several ways that molecules are studied in labs. The technique uses a gel and an electric field to separate molecules based on size, shape, and/or charge. Most frequently, samples of nucleic acids (DNA and RNA) and proteins are analyzed using gel electrophoresis.

DNA molecules in solution have a net negative charge due to their phosphate groups. Because of the negative charge, DNA molecules are attracted to the positive end of a "running" gel box. The agarose gel material acts as a molecular sieve separating longer DNA strands from shorter ones, thus separating the molecules based on their size.

Pieces of DNA of known lengths, called standards or sizing markers, can be run on a gel. Their size determines how far they travel. By running unknown samples and comparing them to the known sizing standards, technicians can deduce the sizes of the unknown pieces.

In this activity, you will add DNA loading dye (see Figure 4.20) and load the following types of DNA onto a gel: salmon sperm (animal), *E. coli* (bacterial genomic), fungus or plant, plasmid (bacterial extra-genomic), and lambda (viral). The purpose of running these samples is to try to gain more information on the sizes of the DNA molecules from these organisms and how these types of samples appear on a gel.

Purpose

What is the appearance of different DNA samples on an agarose gel?

Materials

Environmental Health and Safety Officer

Microcentrifuge
Gel box, horizontal, for agarose gels
Prepared agarose gel (from Lab 4i)
Electrophoresis Buffer concentrate, TAE (40X or 50X) or LB buffer concentrate (10X or 20X)
Tube rack for 1.7-mL tubes
Reaction tubes, 1.7 mL
Permanent lab marker pens
DNA samples (spooled salmon testes DNA, yeast DNA, spooled *E. coli*, each prepared with 27 µL of sample and 3 µL of 10X DNA loading dye for TAE gels or 6 µL of 5X LB loading dye for LB gels)
Plasmid DNA, 0.1 µg/µL (pre-mixed 90 µL sample + 10 µL of 10X DNA loading dye for TAE gels or 20 µL of 5X LB loading dye for LB gels)
Lambda DNA (uncut), 50 ng/µL (pre-mixed 90 µL sample + 10 µL of 10X DNA loading dye for TAE gels or 20 µL of 5X LB loading dye for LB gels)

Other DNA samples (pre-mixed 90 µL sample + 10 µL of 10X DNA loading dye for TAE gels or 20 µL of 5X LB loading dye for LB gels)
DNA loading dye, 10X (for TAE gels) or 5X LB loading dye (for LB gels)
Micropipet, P-10
Micropipet, P-100
Micropipet tips for P-10
Micropipet tips for P-100
Lambda/*Hind*III DNA sizing standard markers, 50 ng/µL (pre-mixed 90 µL sample + 10 µL of 10X DNA loading dye for TAE gels or 20 µL of 5X LB loading dye for LB gels)
Power supply, 300V
Glasses, safety, plastic
Weigh boat, 5.5" × 5.5"
DNA gel stain (ethidium bromide 0.5 µg/mL or 1X LabSafe Nucleic Acid Stain™)
Deionized water
Gel photo imaging system
Gloves, large

Procedure

Part I: Preparing the Gel and Gel Box for Loading

1. Prepare 400 mL of 1X electrophoresis buffer from buffer concentrate. Record the calculations and diagram the preparation of this dilution.

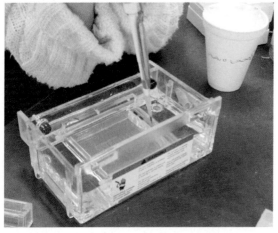

Figure 4.21. Load above the well, not allowing the tip to enter and possibly puncture the well.
Photo by author.

Figure 4.20. Each DNA sample has to have enough loading dye in it so that it will sink into the well. If the loading dye is a 10X concentrate, that means 1 part loading dye is added for every 9 parts of sample.
Photo by author.

2. Prepare a 0.8% agarose gel using 1X electrophoresis buffer (see Lab 4i). Record the calculations and diagram the preparation of the gel. Once the gel is solidified, secured the gel tray gates, if they are present, in the down position. Place the gel tray in the gel box in the correct orientation with the sample wells adjacent to the negative electrode. Be careful to not let the agarose gel slide off the gel tray. Add the 1X electrophoresis buffer to the gel box, covering the gel about 5 mm. Gently remove the comb (under buffer) from the gel.

Part II: Preparing and Loading the Samples

- Position the gel box where it will be "run." Decide which samples should be loaded into which wells.
- Each group may not be running exactly the same samples in their gels, depending on the available samples. In your notebook, draw a diagram of the gel to show the six samples to be loaded and volumes that you intend to load into each well of the gel.

3. Assemble all of the samples, in labeled 1.7-mL reaction tubes, to be loaded into the gel. If the samples do not already have DNA loading dye in them, add loading dye as described in the Materials List.

4. Practice loading 15 µL of practice loading dye (concentrated loading dye diluted to 1X with dH₂O) into Lane 1 (see Figure 4.21). Flush the practice loading dye out with several pipetfuls of electrophoresis buffer.

5. Load 20 µL of a salmon testes DNA/loading dye sample into Well 1 of the gel.

6. Load 20 µL of an *E.coli* DNA/loading dye sample into Well 2 of the gel.

7. Load 7 µL of the Lambda/*Hin*dIII DNA/loading dye sizing standard markers into Well 3 of the gel.

8. Load additional samples already mixed with loading dye into the other 3 wells of the gel. Choose what samples to load depending on what is available. For example:
    - Load another salmon testes DNA sample
    - Load another E.coli DNA sample
    - Load a yeast DNA sample
    - Load a plasmid DNA sample
    - Load an uncut DNA sample
    - Load a plant DNA sample

9. Record on your loading diagram exactly what got loaded and into which well.

Part III: Running the Samples

10. After loading the samples, quickly connect the electrodes to the power supply (red to red, black to black) and run the gel at 110 V, about 65 mA, for 45 to 60 minutes for a TAE gel or at 300V (about 100 mA) for about 12 minutes for a LB gel, until the front loading dye is two-thirds of the way down the gel. Make sure the gel box is conducting electricity. There should be a minimum of 60 mAmp of current, and it should be bubbling at the electrodes. Observe safety precautions for using the gel box and power supply; be sure to turn the power supply off when connecting and disconnecting the electrodes.

11. When the gel has run long enough that the loading dye bands are past the middle of the gel, turn off the power supply and move the gel into a staining tray. The instructor will cover the gel with just enough DNA stain to submerge the gel. Stain the gel for 20 to 30 minutes as instructed. The instructor will pour off the stain. Cover the gel with deionized water and swirl for 20 seconds to destain.
    - Use gloves and goggles when using DNA stains.
    - If using EtBr, the supervisor should do all staining and disposal.

Part IV: Analysis of DNA Fragments

12. Observe the gel on a UV light box (see Figure 4.22). Photograph the gel for analysis. Glue the photo in the middle of a blank notebook page.

13. Label the photograph of the gel data. Label the contents of each well, the size of the standards, and the name and estimated sizes of the bands of unknowns seen in the gel. All bands observed (known and unknown) must be identified. The size of the Lambda/*Hind*III sizing standard fragments (Lane 6), in base pairs, follows.

   Estimations of the unknown fragments can be made by comparing their location on the gel to the location of the known lambda DNA fragments.

23,130	9416	6557	4361	2322
2027	564	125		

Note: The 125-bp band is difficult to see, because the actual amount of DNA in this band is very small.

Data Analysis/Conclusion

Look for distinct bands and smears of DNA in each lane. Estimate the sizes of the molecules in the bands in each lane by comparing each band to a band of known size in the lambda + *Hind*III lane. Do these sizes make sense for what you know about each sample? Explain. Look at other students' gels and data. Are your replications of the extractions and gel running producing results similar to theirs? Why or why not? Of what value is running a sample like this on agarose gels?

Environmental Health and Safety Officer

Environmental Health and Safety Officer

Figure 4.22. **Visualizing of EtBr stained gels is done on a UV light box. Use a camera with a UV filter to photograph the gel.**
Photo by author.

Thinking Like a Biotechnician

1. Give plausible reasons for the following results on your gel.
   a. When stained and visualized on the UV light box, other gels have many bands and smears of DNA. Your gel has no bands, smears, or anything on it. What may have caused these results?
   b. A sample that is supposed to give a straight, single band of high molecular weight, instead has a big smear of DNA down most of the lane. What may have caused this smearing?
   c. All the bands and smears of samples are located right next to the wells and have not moved very far. What may have caused this?
2. On semi-log graph paper, plot the distance the DNA standard fragments traveled from the wells (in mm) on the horizontal axis versus their size (in base pairs) on the vertical axis. Draw a "best-fit" straight line that represents how DNA fragments of different lengths move through the gel. Use this graph to estimate the sizes of the plasmid bands.

Laboratory 4k

Estimating the Amount of DNA in a Sample Using Agarose Gels

Background

It is helpful to be able to estimate the amount of DNA in an experimental sample. Several methods may be used to detect DNA and estimate its concentration or mass in a sample. If there is enough sample volume, the DNA concentration may be estimated using UV spectrophotometry (see in Chapter 7.) Indicator testing, such as that done with the NUCLEIC dotMETRIC™ kit, allows for estimation of the mass of DNA in a sample.

Gel electrophoresis may also be used to estimate or quantify DNA. Running a few microliters of a DNA on an agarose gel can give an estimate of the amount of DNA in a sample. If samples of known concentrations (standards) are loaded onto a gel at a specified volume, then the mass of DNA loaded in those samples will be known. Running unknown samples of the same volume on agarose gels at the same time as the standard samples give a method of estimating the amounts of DNA (mass and concentration) in the unknown samples by comparing the glowing in the stained gel.

Purpose

To prepare a serial dilution of a known sample of DNA for use as a concentration standard.
What is the amount of DNA, measured in µg, in an unknown sample?
What is the smallest amount of DNA, measured in µg, visible (resolved) on a 0.8% agarose gel?

Materials

Microcentrifuge
Gel box, horizontal, for agarose gels
Prepared agarose gel (from Lab 4i)
Electrophoresis Buffer concentrate, TAE (40X or 50X) or LB buffer (10X or 20X)
Beakers, 600 mL
Tube rack for 1.7-mL tubes
Reaction tubes, 1.7 mL
Permanent lab marker pens
DNA samples (spooled

Lambda DNA (uncut), 500ng/ µL, 2 tubes for 16 lab groups
DNA loading dye, 10X (for TAE gels) or 5X LB loading dye (for LB gels)
Micropipet, P-10
Micropipet, P-100
Micropipet tips for P-10
Micropipet tips for P-100
Lambda/HindIII DNA sizing standard markers, 50 ng/µL (pre-mixed 90 µL sample + 10 µL of 10X DNA loading dye

for TAE gels or 20 µL of 5X LB loading dye for LB gels
Power supply, 300V
Glasses, safety, plastic
Weigh boat, 5.5"X 5.5"
DNA gel stain (ethidium bromide, 0.5 µg/mL or 1X LabSafe Nucleic Acid Stain™)
Deionized water
Gel photo imaging system
Gloves, large

Procedure

Note: This activity assumes prior knowledge and experience preparing and running agarose gels. Refer to Lab 4i and Lab 4j if you need help preparing electrophoresis buffer or agarose gels or with loading, running, staining or imaging an agarose gel.

1. Prepare enough 1X electrophoresis buffer to prepare and run a gel. Record the calculations and a diagram to show how you prepared the buffer. Are you using TAE buffer or LB buffer? Find the correct DNA loading dye to use in step 4.
2. Prepare 0.8% agarose in 1X electrophoresis buffer with **either 1 row of 8 wells or 2 rows of 6 wells**. Pour a gel that is 6–7 mm thick. Leave to cool, undisturbed for 15 min.
3. Prepare four DNA samples at different concentrations to use as concentration standard samples. Start with 22 µL of the **uncut** Lambda DNA stock sample at 0.5 µg/µL in your first tube. Then produce 3 more samples by doing a 1:10 serial dilution. Use dH₂O as the diluent solution. The final volume in each should be 20µL. Make these in 1.7 mL tubes. Label them.

Fill in the reaction matrix below to show how each was prepared.

Think about how you will make these. "1:10" means 1 part sample in a total of 10 parts (sample and solvent). How much of which sample and how much diluent do you need in each tube? Diagram how you will make the 3 samples.

Tube #	Dilution from the 0.5 µg/µL stock	Amount of Which Lambda DNA Sample is added to the Tube?	Amount of dH₂O added as diluent to the Tube?	Amount of DNA in tube after preparation of all samples?
1	Undiluted	22 µL, 0.5 µg/µL stock	0 µL	10 µg
2	1:10			
3	1:100			
4	1:1000			

4. Prepare a 5th tube with only 20µL of dH₂O to use as a negative control and two tubes of 20µL of unknown sample (one undiluted and one diluted 1:2).

5. To each of the five known DNA sample tubes and 2 unknown sample tubes, add either 10X DNA loading dye (for TAE gels) or 5X LB loading dye (for LB gels).

   How much of the concentrated loading dye are you adding to each tube? Pipet up and down to mix the sample with the loading dye. Change tips each time you add loading dye to a new tube.

6. Pour 1X electrophoresis buffer over the gel (2 mm over the entire gel). Gently pull the comb up and out to reveal the wells.

7. Into the first row, load all of each of your known standard samples into the wells of the gel, loading Wells 1–5, from highest concentration standard to lowest. Into Well 6 add 10µL of DNA sizing standard prepared by the supervisor. Change tips with each load.

8. Into Wells 3 and 5 of the 2nd rows, add all of the undiluted and diluted 1:2 unknown samples, respectively.

9. Close the gel box and run the electrophoresis at the recommended voltage for the type of electrophoresis buffer used in the gel and gel box **(either 110V/60mA for TAE gels or 300V/80mA for LB gels)**. Record the gel run conditions.

10. Once the gel run is completed, turn of the gel box, gently slide the gel into a large, labeled weigh boat and stain it by the method recommended by your supervisor.

11. Observe and photograph the stained gel and observe the amount of staining for each concentration (and mass) of DNA in the known standards. Study the unknown sample bands. Compare the amount of staining in these as compared to the unknowns. Estimate the concentration (and mass) of DNA of the unknown samples in the gel using the standard known samples as a comparison.

Data Analysis and Conclusion

Report the estimated concentration (µg/µL) of the unknown (undiluted and diluted) samples. Describe how you determined these values. Knowing that 20µL of each unknown sample was used in the gel, what is the mass of DNA (µg) in these samples? Discuss how well your standards shows the range of DNA amounts? Were any of the samples so dilute that the DNA was not visible? List technical errors in setting up the experiment that might lead to erroneous data. Discuss the value of learning how to quantify DNA by this method. How would this technique be valuable to biotechnologists?

Thinking Like a Biotechnician

1. The original stock unknown sample contained a volume of 500 µL. Based on your estimation of the mass of DNA in the unknowns you ran on the gel, what is the total mass of Lambda DNA in the stock unknown sample?

2. Is it possible to estimate the sizes (bp) of the Lambda DNA pieces in the concentration standards by comparing them to the Lambda/HindIII sizing standards? Which known concentration of the Lambda DNA known samples shows a sharp enough resolution to be able to best determine the size of these DNA pieces?

Laboratory 4l

Characterizing *E. coli* Using a Light Microscope and Gram Staining

Background

In Lab 4g and 4h, *E. coli* cells were cultured and their DNA was extracted. How do you know, though, if you've cultured *E. coli* or if you have mistakenly cultured some other bacteria? Scientists study an organism's characteristics, such as structure (morphology), nutritional requirements, and behavior. Once these traits are characterized, it is easier to recognize the organism in the future.

Gram staining provides an opportunity to characterize bacteria based on the cell wall structure. By using a Gram stain, you can identify six different groups of bacteria. There are three shapes of bacteria: coccus (spherical), bacillus (rod-shaped), and spirillum (spiral). Gram staining separates these three groups into two color groups: purple and red. The purple or red color is determined by the bacterium's cell wall type. Bacteria that have a thick cell wall retain the crystal violet stain and are purple in color. Bacteria that have a thin cell wall lose the purple color during decolorization and must be stained with a red counterstain, called safranin. When properly Gram-stained, *E. coli* appear as light red rods (Gram– bacilli) on 1000X.

Purpose

Is there evidence that a bacteria culture contains Gram-negative (Gram–) *E. coli* cells?

Materials

E. coli broth culture, small sample saved from Lab 4g	Immersion oil	Bunsen burner
Microscope, compound, with 100X objective lens	Microscope slide coverslips, glass	Crystal violet stain
Microscope slides	dH$_2$O	Ethanol (EtOH)
	Inoculating loop	Safranin stain

Procedure

1. Make a wet mount of 10 μL of the *E. coli* broth culture. Use the oil immersion lens to observe these unstained bacteria cells. In your notebook, draw and label the cells showing their cell wall, cytoplasm, and nucleoid area (darkened by DNA). Determine and record their length.
2. Do a **Gram stain** of the broth culture cells using these procedures:
   a. Obtain another clean, dry slide.
   b. Add a small drop of distilled water to the slide.
   c. Sterilize an inoculating loop.
   d. Take a small sample of bacteria (10 μL) from the culture.
   e. Smear the bacteria from side to side through the water and across the slide.
   f. Allow the slide to air dry for at least 20 minutes.
   g. "Fix" the slide by passing it through a flame three times.
   h. Add crystal violet stain to the air-dried, fixed bacteria and stain the slide for 1 minute.
   i. Dunk three times in water. Drain.
   j. Add mordant (iodine). Leave on for 1 minute. Dunk and drain.
   k. Decolorize with alcohol by dripping alcohol over the cell-containing area until the color stops flowing off the slide.
   l. Counterstain with safranin. Leave on for 1 minute. Dunk three times in fresh water and drain.
   m. Gently pat the slide dry. Do not use a coverslip. Observe, draw, and identify the bacteria at 400X and 1000X.

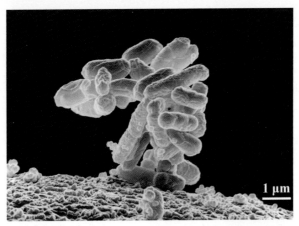

Figure 4.23.   Electron micrograph of a cluster of *E. Coli* bacteria. Each individual bacterium is oblong shaped. **10,000X**

Photo by Wikimediacommons.org.

Thinking Like a Biotechnician

Data Analysis/Conclusion

Do the cells in the culture appear to be Gram– bacilli? Give evidence for your answer. Describe the issues that make it difficult to distinguish tiny bacteria cells through microscopy and Gram staining.

1. Why is it important to have a "Fix" step (2g)? What would happen if you didn't "fix" the sample?
2. When viewing the cells on 1000X, all the cells look melted together and their shape is impossible to distinguish. Explain what may have happened to the cells to change their shape.

5 Protein Isolation and Analysis

A research associate in the Applications Department at Genencor International, Inc tests the activity of a protein, cellulase, on denim material. When a product is manufactured for one use (in the case of cellulase, to soften paper), a company tries to find additional applications (such as decolorizing and softening blue jeans) and, thus, a larger market.
Photo by author.

The importance of proteins in the biotechnology industry is reflected in the expression, "DNA is the show, but proteins are the dough." For the majority of biotechnology companies, proteins are the product they develop, manufacture, and market. These protein products include pharmaceuticals, industrial enzymes, and proteins that are used in research and diagnostic tools.

Even if a biotech company is not in the protein-making business, it is almost certainly using or modifying proteins as part of the research and development of biotechnology instruments or other agricultural, environmental, or industrial products.

Protein studies are essential. In particular, researchers and scientists work on determining the presence, structure, and activity of a protein or group of proteins for application to protein manufacturing.

In the following activities you will learn some of the basic techniques used to study protein structure and function. Specifically, you will learn the following:

- how to test for an antibody-antigen reaction
- how to test for an enzyme's activity
- how to use indicators to test for the presence and estimate the concentration of proteins in a solution
- how to prepare samples for and conduct a vertical polyacrylamide gel electrophoresis (PAGE) for the purpose of determining protein size
- how to extract proteins from animal cells and analyze them using PAGE

The laboratory methods practiced in this chapter will be applied in later chapters to the manufacture of a protein product and the use of proteins in diagnostics.

Laboratory 5a
The Specificity of the Antibody-Antigen Reaction

Background

Antibodies recognize foreign molecules, called antigens. They tag and aggregate them for removal from the body (see Figure 5.1). All antibody molecules have a specific three-dimensional structure critical to their function of recognizing and clumping antigens. Each type of antibody has a unique variable region that matches only certain antigens.

Antigens may be either free-floating proteins or carbohydrate molecules, such as those that cause allergic reactions. More often, antigens are molecules on the surface of cells or viruses that invade the body. Either way, specific antibodies bind with specific antigens and induce an increase in the number of those specific antibodies in the host organism.

Allergens are antigens that specifically induce the formation of immunoglobulin E (IgE) antibodies. An allergic reaction occurs when an excess of IgE molecules stimulate inflammatory response symptoms, such as swelling, redness, and itchiness. You are allergic to the specific antigens that cause this IgE inflammatory response in your body.

When an antigen binds to an antibody molecule, the complex is too small to be seen. However, when hundreds of antibodies bind to hundreds of allergens, they create a network of many millions of molecules (see Figure 5.1). Researchers have used this knowledge to produce tests to identify when a specific antigen is present in a solution.

One method researchers use to test for antigen-antibody binding is called the Ouchterlony test, or Ouchterlony method (see Figure 5.2). To do an Ouchterlony test, an agar or agarose matrix is poured into a test plate. A hole (well) is punched in the center of the matrix, and an antibody-containing solution is added. The antibody solution contains one or more antibodies to suspected allergen antigens. Suspected antigens are placed in wells evenly spaced between the center and the edge of the plate. The solutions are allowed to diffuse outward from the center of the well.

When antibodies diffuse into antigens that they recognize, they bind to them and to each other, causing an agglutination (clumping) reaction. The aggregated antibody-antigen precipitates out of solution and may be visible as a white or colored band at the interface of each diffusion front.

The Ouchterlony method may be used in several applications, including allergy testing where common allergens are tested to determine if a patient has antibodies that recognize an allergen and cause an allergic response.

This test can also be used to screen blood serum for the presence of antibodies and, thereby, learn of prior exposure to an antigen. Screening by antibodies, for example, is used

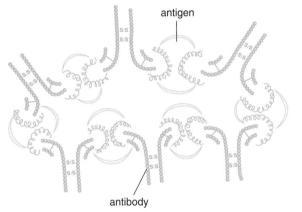

Figure 5.1. Agglutination. Antibodies recognize and clump antigens (agglutination), making it easier for white blood cells (WBCs) to remove the invading particles from the body.

Well punches in an agar or agarose matrix are filled with antibody solution (Ab) or a suspected antigen (Ag).

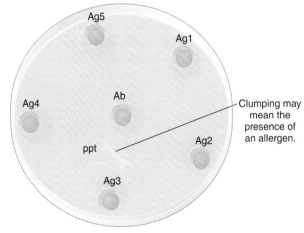

As they diffuse out and meet, if the antibody and antigen match, they bond and clump, forming a white precipitate (ppt).

Figure 5.2. Ouchterlony Test. During an Ouchterlony test, a patient's serum (with his or her naturally occurring antibodies) is placed in the center well. Solutions with known antigens are placed in the outer wells. All molecules diffuse. If an antibody molecule finds an antigen, it will clump and fall out of solution (precipitate).

in human immunodeficiency virus (HIV) testing. Ouchterlony testing may be used to identify an antigen in a solution, when assaying for a protein in a mixture. In addition, the test may be used to determine whether an antibody will bind to a particular antigen. This technique would be useful if one were looking for an antibody to use for affinity chromatography, a method of protein purification.

Purpose

Rocky is scratching his skin raw because he has a rash. Does Rocky have an allergen to his new pork-based dog food? To which food allergens, if any, does Rocky's blood serum have antibodies?

Photo by author.

Materials

Petri plates 60 × 15mm, sterile, 2/3 full of LB agar.
Permanent lab marker pens
Transfer pipets, 3 mL
Prepared antigen solutions (beef and pork samples)
Rocky's blood serum antibody solution
Pipets, 1 mL and Pipet pump, blue, or P-1000 and tips
Caution: Wear goggles and gloves when using chemicals.

Environmental Health
and Safety Officer

Procedure

1. Obtain two Petri plates containing the agar matrix. Label them each with your initials and Trials 1 and 2, respectively.
2. Use a transfer pipet, and while applying a slight suction to the bulb by compressing your fingers, poke wells for samples in the agar in plate No. 1 (see Figure 5.3). A plug of agar will be sucked up into the pipet leaving a sample well. Discard the agar hole punch. Bore five holes around the edge of the Petri plate (see Figure 5.2). Bore one hole in the middle. Label the wells on the plate bottom with the antigen to be added (see step 4).
3. Repeat Step 2 with the other Petri plate.
4. Obtain the antibody and antigen solutions, one with Rocky's blood serum (containing antibodies, one the negative control of deionized water,) and four with extracts of suspected dog food allergens (including beef blood serum, beef-based dog food, pig blood serum, and pork-based dog food).
5. Using a different sterile, 1-mL pipet or P-1000 micropipet, fill the five outer wells with the suspected dog food allergen extracts. Fill the central well with Rocky's blood serum.
   Note: Try to use the same volume of antigen and antibody in each well (ie, 200 µL). However, do not overfill the wells since this will cause the samples to mix on top of the agar.

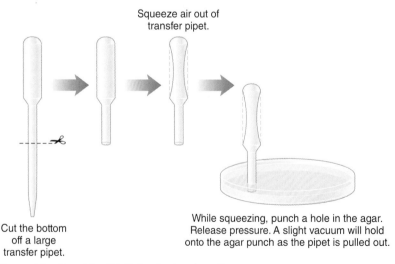

Squeeze air out of transfer pipet.

Cut the bottom off a large transfer pipet.

While squeezing, punch a hole in the agar. Release pressure. A slight vacuum will hold onto the agar punch as the pipet is pulled out.

Figure 5.3. **Punching Wells for Ouchterlony Test.**

6. Leave the plates, undisturbed, overnight. After 24 hours, a precipitin line may appear between one or more of the dog food allergens and Rocky's antibody-containing serum.
7. Record the results of the Ouchterlony test in the form of scale drawings of the Petri plates and a numerical value (5 = strong precipitation; 0 = no precipitation). Calculate average results.
8. Determine which allergens, if any, appear to give a reaction that could cause Rocky's rash.

Data Analysis/Conclusion

Based on the results of the Ouchterlony test, what recommendations might be made to Rocky's owner? What is the reason for testing beef and pork blood samples as well as the dog food samples? Give evidence for these recommendations. Identify some of the errors in the experimental procedure that could lead to fallacious data. What can be done to decrease the likelihood of these errors occurring? Discuss how antibody-antigen recognition and binding may be used in other applications besides allergy testing.

Thinking Like a Biotechnician

1. How likely is it that one Ouchterlony test will give results that lead to the understanding of an organism's allergic response? Explain.
2. Why is the speed of agglutination or precipitation not a valuable piece of data in this experiment?
3. Setting up an Ouchterlony test may be time consuming. Why not just mix two solutions together to see if they clump? Suggest an advantage to having the molecules diffuse through and precipitate in the matrix.

Laboratory 5b

The Action of Different Enzymes on Apple Juice Production

Inspired by labs by Louann Carlomagno, formerly of Genencor International, Inc.

Background

Many industries use enzymes to create better products (see Table 5.1). As you know, the dairy industry uses enzymes to speed the curdling of milk in cheese production. Both naturally occurring enzymes, such as rennin from calf stomachs, and genetically engineered enzymes (eg, chymosin) are used now. These enzymes create desirable products, which are sometimes cheaper, faster, and of higher quality than uncatalyzed products. Speeding up the changes that occur during the curdling process increases cheese production. Of course, this means increased sales for the cheese company, and greater profits for the owners and shareholders.

Table 5.1. **Examples of Marketed Biotechnology Enzymes**

amylase	breaks down starch to sugar; used by fabric, beverage, and biofuel industries
pectinase	degrades the cement between plant cells and softens plant fibers; used in paper-making, coffee/tea extraction, and food-processing
cellulase	decomposes cellulose in plant fiber and breaks down cells; used in the paper-making, textile, and biofuel industries
subtilisin	protein-digesting enzyme; used in detergents to remove protein stains
Purafect® Prime L protease (Genencor International, Inc)	protein-digesting enzyme; used in detergents to remove protein stains
rennin	protein-digesting enzyme; curdles milk for making cheese

As in all industries, apple juice producers want a cheaper, higher-quality product. One goal of juicers is to extract as much juice as possible from every apple. In the 1980s, scientists at the biotechnology company, Genencor International, Inc., found two enzymes that they believed might possibly increase the amount of juice released from apple cells. The enzymes, called pectinase and cellulase, were created in nature by two different fungi. However, neither fungus grew well in the lab. The scientists decided to genetically engineer some fungi, which do grow well in the lab, to produce these enzymes on a large scale. The recombinant enzymes had to be tested to determine their effect on juice yield. If results were favorable, Genencor International, Inc. could scale up production of the recombinant enzymes, harvest the enzymes, and sell them to juice makers to produce a clear, high-quality product (see Figure 5.4).

Figure 5.4. **Clarified Apple Juice.** Photo by author.

The first step in making juice and testing juice enzymes is to mash the apples. Some juice will be released in the mashing process. The mashed apples (chunky applesauce) may then be treated with enzymes to test the effect of each enzyme on the amount of juice that can be extracted.

Purpose

What are the effects of different enzymes on increasing apple juice yield?

Materials for each lab group:

Electronic balance, 0.0001g
Weighing paper
Microcentrifuge tubes, 1.5 mL
Narrow lab spatula
Applesauce, unsweetened
Paper cup

P-1000 micropipets and tips
Microcentrifuge, high-speed, 5000xg
50 mM TRIS, 5mM CaCl$_2$, pH 7.2

Cellulase, 2 mg/mL in 50 mM TRIS, 5mM CaCl$_2$, pH 7.2
Pectinase, 2 mg/mL in 50 mM TRIS, 5mM CaCl$_2$, pH 7.2
Protease, 2 mg/mL in 50 mM TRIS, 5mM CaCl$_2$, pH 7.2

General Procedure:

Each lab group will conduct one replications of the experiment testing the effect on juice yield using an enzyme of interest. The supervisor will assign the enzyme treatment or a negative control group. All groups' trial results will be shared.

Procedure:

1. Label three 1.5 mL tubes to represent the enzyme treatment and the trial (such as P1, P2, P3) and a designation for your lab group.
2. Create a data table (similar to Table 5.2) to collect reaction information and data for your group's trials.

Table 5.2. **Amount of Apple Juice Produced by _____ (your enzyme treatment)**

Trials	Mass of Empty Tube (g)	Mass of Tube with Applesauce (g)	Mass of Tube with Cell Debris (g)	Mass of Juice Extracted (g)	Estimated Volume of Juice Extracted (µL)	Comments
#1						
#2						
#3						
Average						

3. Mix the stock applesauce well. Measure out about 10 mL of applesauce into a paper cup. Bring it to the weighing station.
4. Tare the balance with weigh paper to protect the weigh pan from spills. Weigh the first tube and record it's mass in the data table. Add 1g of applesauce to the tube using the narrow tip of a lab spatula. Record the mass of the tube with applesauce in the table.
5. Repeat step No. 4 with the other tubes.
6. Using a P-1000, add 500µL of the assigned enzyme (or buffer in the negative control) to each tube. Mix for 10 seconds using the micropipet tip. Change tips each time.
7. Cap the tubes and give each tube a 1 second spin in a microcentrifuge to pool the mixture. Let each mixture sit (incubate) at room temperature for 24 hours.
8. After 24 hours, place all 3 tubes into a microcentrifuge in a balanced configuration and spin for 10 minutes at 5000xg (or a medium setting). The fragments of apple cell debris should settle into a loose pellet and the apple juice (apple cell cytoplasm) should pool above it. Look to see if the tubes contents appear similar.

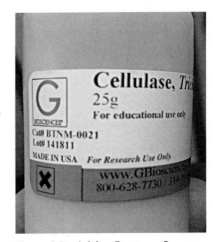

Figure 5.5. **Juicing Enzyme** Enzymes are made in cells and must be isolated (purified) from other cell contents for research and manufacturing purposes. Enzymes of commercial importance are produced in large amounts by biologcal supply companies and often sold in lyophilized (freeze-dried) form such as this cellulase produced in a fungus. Photo by author.

9. Gently open the tube caps being careful to not dislodge each pellet and resuspend it in the juice. Using a P-100 (set at 100μL), withdraw all the juice in each tube, 100μL of juice at a time, and estimate the amount of juice yield from each treatment. Record this data in the table.
10. Once all the juice has been separated from the pellets, reweigh each tube with its cell debris. Record this data in the table.
11. Subtract the tube and debris mass (after the juice has been removed) from the starting mixture to determine the mass of juice extracted. Record this data in the table. Average your results and make them available to other groups in the class.
12. In a data table similar to Table 5.3, collect average data for all enzyme treatment trials in the class.
13. Review the data collected during the experiment. What data best answers the question of how much juice is extracted from samples treated with the different enzymes? Create a bar graph to represent the data that best answers the purpose question.

Table 5.3. Average Amount of Apple Juice Produced by Different Enzyme Trials
(Enzymes at 2 mg/mL in 50 mM TRIS, 5mM CaCl$_2$, pH 7.2, 500μL treatments)

Enzyme	Trial Group	Mass of Juice Extracted (g)	Volume of Juice Extracted (μL)	Comments
Cellulase	#1			
	#2			
	#3			
	Average			
Pectinase	#1			
	#2			
	#3			
	Average			
Negative Control	#1			
	#2			
	#3			
	Average			

Data Analysis/Conclusion

Assume you have completed this experiment for a company. Write a conclusion statement that describes the results of the experiment, and recommend which enzyme treatment should be used for maximum juice production. Discuss how the type of enzyme affects juice yield. Also, discuss any possible errors that may produce misleading or fallacious data and conclusions. Finally, propose further experimentation to your immediate supervisor as well as applications of this information to industry.

Thinking Like a Biotechnician

1. Assuming similar incubation and processing times, describe what might happen to the juice yield if the enzyme volume was doubled or tripled.
2. Sketch what a line graph would look like if the data showed that at some point, adding more of the enzyme did not increase juice yield substantially.
3. Suggest a method to determine the optimum temperature for pectinase activity. Include experimental procedures.

Laboratory 5c
Developing an Assay for Protease Activity

Background

Experimental design is the process by which research scientists prepare an experiment that tests only one variable at a time collecting numerical data that may be statistically (mathematically) analyzed. In a well-designed experiment, a relationship between cause and effect may be established or refuted and other researchers will be able to replicate the experiment to validate the results.

In this experiment, your lab group will design an experiment that tests the activity of a protease. Protease is a term that describes many enzymes that hydrolyze or break the peptide bonds of proteins. In the presence of a protease, long peptide chains are broken down to shorter peptide chains; they may even be broken down all the way to individual amino acids.

Proteases are used in research, manufacturing, and industrial applications. Some examples include the protease, bromelain, found in Adolph's® and McCormick's® meat tenderizers (both by Lawry's Foods, Inc.) and the proteases added to detergents to remove protein stains from clothing (see Figure 5.6).

Like many proteins, proteases are colorless; therefore, assays (tests) must be developed to show that they are present and active at the desired concentration. Proteases are used throughout biotechnology research and development to remove unwanted protein from a sample.

Figure 5.6. **Many meat tenderizers contain the protease, bromelain, purified from pineapples. When bromelain is sprinkled on meat, it breaks down the protein in the muscle tissue. This makes the meat less stringy and increases its tenderness.** Photo by author.

Purpose

To design a valid experiment that determines the pH that produces a maximum of gelatin protein breakdown by the protease, bromelain.

Procedure

1. In teams of four students (or as directed by your instructor), use the Internet to learn as much as you can about bromelain. What is bromelain's structure, how does it function function, in what conditions does it works best?

2. Using your previous lab experiences and reagents, plasticware, and glassware commonly found in the laboratory or a grocery store, design a set of experimental procedures to test the effect of pH on bromelain protease activity to break down gelatin protein. Remember that you are designing a test for protease activity, not proteins in general.

   Before starting, ask yourself, "If bromelain breaks down protein, what can I observe and measure to quantify the reaction?"

   When designing the experiment, make sure you include the following:
   a. Step-by-step instructions, which are short and easy to follow.
   b. All masses, volumes, concentrations,recipes, and sources of all reagents, solutions, and buffers used.
   c. All the equipment needed for the experiment.
   d. All operating conditions.
   e. Trials that include a negative control sample and if appropriate any positive controls.
   f. Trials that include each variable sample.
   g. Multiple replications of each sample.
   h. Method for collecting measurable, numerical data.

3. Type your experiment plan on a computer so that the procedures can be easily edited when your group is given feedback. Title each version of the plan using this format: TeamName_ Protease_V1.doc (V1 = Version 1). Change the version number with each editing. Keep copies of each version. Include all of the following elements in the experimental plan:

- lab team members
- a purpose statement of the experiment
- data table (rough draft) to collect the numerical data produced in the experiment
- list of materials
- procedures (meeting the criteria above)

4. Print a copy of the final version of your experimental plan on paper for your supervisor's review. Be prepared to present it to the class, if requested, on an interactive smart board.

5. Use the protease-assay design rubric (see Table 5.4) to evaluate your own experimental plan and other experimental plans. Two of the plans will be chosen for testing.

Table 5.4. **Protease-assay Design Rubric**

Element	3 Points	2 Points	I Point	0 Points
purpose (objective)	clear, testable purpose statement that leads to measurable data	Purpose statement shows some connection to measurable data.	unclear, untestable purpose statement	No purpose is stated.
materials	list of all ingredients in the experiment	list of most of the ingredients in the experiment	very incomplete or unclear list of ingredients	no list of the ingredients in the experiment
procedures	short, easy-to-follow procedural steps	Some procedural steps are unclear or too long.	Most procedural steps are unclear or too long.	All procedural steps are unclear or too long.
	All volumes, masses, and concentrations of reagents are given.	Some volumes, masses, and concentrations are given.	Most volumes, masses, and concentrations are not given.	No volumes, masses, or concentrations of reagents are given.
	It is clear that everything in each trial is identical, except the variable to be tested.	It is not clear that everything in each trial is identical, except the variable to be tested.	One or two additional variables make it unclear what causes the results of a trial.	Many additional variables make it unclear what causes the results of a trial.
	Trials with either a positive or negative control are included. There are sufficient (at least three) multiple replications of each trial for each variable tested. These are presented individually and as averages.	A trial with a negative, but not a positive, control is included. There are insufficient replications for data to be averaged for each variable tested.	A trial with a positive, but not a negative, control is included. There are no multiple replications of each trial for each variable to be tested.	No trials of positive or negative controls are included. Some variables are tested; some are not.
	It is clear what numerical data are to be measured and how they will be measured.	It is clear which data are to be measured, and how they will be measured but there are no numerical data.	It is not clear which numerical data are to be measured and how they will be measured.	Data to be measured are not stated.
data table (scratch)	The data table is set up correctly (independent variables in the left column, dependent variables in the right columns).	The data table is set up backwards (dependent variables in left column, independent variables in the right columns).	The dependent and independent variables are not clearly shown on the data table.	The data table does not contain independent or dependent variables.
	The data table has a proper title, including the independent and dependent variables, and the subject.	The title is incomplete (missing either the independent or dependent variables, or the subject).	The title is incomplete (missing more than one of the following: the independent or dependent variables, or the subject).	The data table has no title.
	All units of measure are shown.	Some units of measure are shown.	Some units of measure are shown, but may be incorrect.	No units of measure are given (when they should be).
	The data table has cells for individual, as well as average, data.	The data table has cells for individual data, but not for average data.	The data table has cells for average data, but not for individual data.	The data table has no cells for individual or average data.

Laboratory 5d

Using Indicators to Test for the Presence of Protein in Solution

Background

Several protein indicator reagents are available to use to determine the presence and concentration of protein in a solution. Most protein indicators contain copper, which reacts with the arginine molecules in proteins. You may remember using the Biuret reagent (NaOH and $CuSO_4 \cdot 5H_2O$) to test gelatin solutions. Biuret is easy to prepare and cheap, but it is not very stable and many proteins quickly precipitate when tested with Biuret, making it impractical for spectrophotometry use.

Other protein indicators including Lowry Reagent, Bradford Reagent, and Coomassie Blue Reagent are commonly used when the concentration of protein solutions is determined using spectrophotometry. When Bradford Reagent is mixed with proteins at near neutral pH, a blue color develops that is stable for up to 1 hour. The absorbance of colored protein/Bradford mixtures is read at 595 nm.

Known concentrations of protein can be tested with Bradford reagent. The absorbance of the "knowns" is measured and plotted on a concentration versus absorbance graph (standard curve). Samples of unknown concentration can be tested with Bradford, and the absorbance of each is then determined. Using the standard curve, the absorbance gives an approximation of the unknown's concentration.

Using a standard curve to measure protein concentration is a method used throughout the research and manufacturing phases in biotechnology product development. It is a quick method for assessing the presence and concentration of protein in solution.

Purpose

What is the concentration of the protein bovine serum albumin (BSA) in two "unknown" samples?

Materials

1X PBS buffer diluted 1X from 10X PBS stock or prepare from scratch
[1.9mM NaH$_2$PO$_4$ × H$_2$O (monohydrate), 8.1 mM Na$_2$HPO$_4$ (anhydrous), and 150 mM NaCl, pH 7.0]
Balance, analytical
Balance, tabletop milligram
Weigh paper, 7.6 × 7.6 cm
Weigh boat, 3.5" × 3.5"
Lab scoops
Bottle, 1000 mL
Bovine Serum Albumin (BSA)
Reaction tubes, 1.7 mL
Tube rack for 1.7-mL tubes
Tubes, 15 mL capped
Tube racks for 15-mL tubes

Pipets, 10, 5, 2, 1-mL
Pipet pump, green and blue
Bradford reagent (available from G-Biosciences or prepare from scratch: Coomassie Brilliant Blue G-250, 95% ethanol, 85% phosphoric acid (teacher use only, in a chemical fume hood), and Whatman filter paper, #1
Aluminum foil
Media bottle, 125 mL
Micropipets
Micropipet tips
VIS spectrophotometer (Spec 20D+)
13 × 100-mm cuvettes and plug caps
Permanent lab marker pens
Unknown protein samples, U1 and U2

Safety Precautions

Wear goggles and gloves when using chemicals.

Environmental Health and Safety Officer

Environmental Health and Safety Officer

Procedure

Part I: Preparation of Solutions and Stock Protein Sample

1. Prepare 1X PBS, pH 7.0 from scratch or from a 10X PBS stock.
2. Prepare 10 mL of stock BSA in 1X PBS solution (1 mg/mL).
3. Purchase premade Bradford reagent or prepare 1X Bradford reagent as follows:
    Dissolve 100 mg of Coomassie Brilliant Blue G-250 in 50 mL of 95% ethanol. Add 100 mL of 85% phosphoric acid (teacher use only, in a chemical fume hood). When the dye has completely dissolved, dilute to 1L. Wrap bottle in aluminum foil. Store at 4°C for several months. Filter through Whatman #1 paper just before use.

Part II: Preparation of Protein Standards of Known Concentration

1. Prepare to 500 µL volumes of 1, 0.5, 0.25, 0.125, and 0.0625 mg/mL BSA in 1X PBS using the 200 µg/mL stock and the $C_1V_1=C_2V_2$ equation. In your notebook, create a preparation matrix (similar to Table 5.5) to show how the diluted standard protein samples will be prepared. Also, calculate the total amount of protein in each sample.

Table 5.5. **Standard Solutions Preparation Matrix**

Concentration of Diluted Sample Desired (mg/mL)	Volume of 1 mg/mL Stock (µL)	Volume of 1X PBS (µL)	Mass of Protein in Sample (µg)
1.0			
0.5			
0.25			
0.125			
0.0625			
0			

Bradford Assay

2. Warm up the spectrophotometer for 15 to 20 minutes before use.
3. In labeled 13×100-mm tubes, mix 500 µL of each diluted sample with 3 mL of Bradford reagent.
4. Cap each tube with a plug cap and invert each tube one time to mix.
5. Quickly obtain two unknown sample tubes (U1 and U2). Mix 500 µL of each unknown with 3 mL of Bradford reagent. Cap each tube with a plug cap and invert each tube one time to mix. Read the absorbance of all standard samples and unknown samples at 595 nm.

How to Use the Spectrophotometer (Spec 20D+) to Read the Absorbance of Bradford Samples

a. Set the wavelength value on the spectrophotometer to 595 nm.
b. Set the spectrophotometer to 0% T with nothing in the sample holder.
c. Using the 0 µg/mL sample as a blank, set the 100% T to 100%.
d. Measure the absorbance of each known sample at 595 nm. Measure the absorbance of the two unknowns.

6. Record the absorbance and color of each known sample in a data table similar to Table 5.6. Record the absorbance of the unknowns in a separate table.
7. Plot the concentration of each known sample versus its absorbance on an X-Y scatter plot graph. Connect the data points. Do not include the unknown sample absorbance on this graph.

8. Draw a second line, a best-fit straight line averaged through all the known data points. If using Microsoft® Excel®, choose the "Add Trendline" option under the Chart Menu to draw a linear best-fit straight line. If the spec has been calibrated correctly and the concentrations of the samples are not too high or too low, the best-fit straight line should go through the point 0,0.

9. Use the best-fit standard curve to estimate the concentration of each unknown sample by looking where the absorbance of each unknown intersects the line (at what concentration).

10. If Microsoft® Excel® has calculated an equation of the best-fit line, use y=mx+b to determine the absorbance values for the unknowns.

Table 5.6.   The Absorbance at 595 nm of Known Concentrations of BSA mixed with Bradford reagent

Concentration (mg/mL)	Absorbance (au)	Color of Sample	Comments
1.0			
0.5			
0.25			
0.125			
0.0625			
0			

Absorbance, U1 _____   Absorbance, U2 _____

Estimated Concentration, U1 _____   Estimated Concentration, U2 _____

Data Analysis/Conclusion

Report the best estimate of the concentrations of the unknown samples. Discuss how accurate you think the concentration estimates are. Identify and describe two factors that could impact the accuracy of the concentration estimates. Discuss the applications of the Bradford reagent test in a research facility that isolates or manufactures proteins for sale.

Thinking Like a Biotechnician

1. Does a negative Bradford test mean that there is no protein in a sample? Explain.
2. If several of the samples give absorbance values over 2.0 au, how will this affect the slope of the best-fit standard line? As a lab technician, how should you modify the procedures to give values that can be used to create a linear best-fit stand curve?
3. Each of the diluted samples in this procedure was produced by diluting the 1 mg/mL BSA stock sample. Describe how to make 500 µL of each diluted sample using a serial dilution method, where each diluted solution is used to make the next more diluted solution.

Laboratory 5e
Preparing Buffers and Protein Samples for PAGE Analysis

Background

Most of the proteins found in organisms are in solution. For example, insulin is found in the cytoplasm of pancreas cells and is excreted into blood plasma. In a similar manner, salivary amylase is secreted into saliva from the cytoplasm of salivary gland cells. When proteins are purified for study, they are extracted in a buffered solution and then either stored in the buffer, or dried and stored in powdered form.

In the next several activities, you will study proteins using polyacrylamide gel electrophoresis (PAGE). In this activity, a PAGE electrophoresis running buffer is prepared and then used to suspend commercially available proteins in solution for analysis by PAGE. The PAGE running buffer has the buffering compound, TRIS, to conduct electricity and the detergent, SDS, to denature and coat proteins with negative charge. Additionally, a SDS-PAGE sample prep loading dye is prepared that will be used to dilute and load samples into the PAGE gel.

Purpose

To prepare the buffers and stock protein sample needed for a polyacrylamide gel electrophoresis.

Materials

Environmental Health and Safety Officer

Balance, analytical	Boric acid **Caution: Wear**	Glass rods
Balance, tabletop milligram	**goggles and gloves when**	Syringe filter, 0.2 μm
Weigh paper, 7.6 × 7.6 cm	**using chemicals.**	Syringe, plastic, 10 mL
Weigh boat, 3.5" × 3.5"	SDS, 10%	Pipets, 10 mL
Lab scoops	Permanent lab marker pens	Pipet pump, green
Bottle, 1000 mL	Bovine serum albumin (BSA)	Sucrose
TRIS	cellulase	Bromophenol Blue
	Tubes, 15 mL, conical	Beta-mercaptoethanol (BME)
	Tube racks for 15-mL tubes	

Procedure

1. Prepare 1 L 1X PAGE running buffer (also called Laemmli buffer) according to the following steps: Store the unused portions at room temperature.
   a. Measure out the following:

   10 mL of 10% SDS
   (Caution: Powdered SDS is a hazardous inhalant. The instructor should prepare the 10% SDS in a fume hood with the fan off and the glass shield down.)
   11 g of TRIS base
   6 g of boric acid

   Environmental Health and Safety Officer

   b. Get a clean, 1-L bottle and cap. Gently add the dry ingredients to the bottle.
   c. Add 800 mL of dH_2O to the dry ingredients. Mix gently, without foaming, until completely dissolved.
   d. Add the 10% SDS solution.. Mix gently, without foaming.
   e. Fill with dH_2O to a total volume of 1 L.
   f. Label the bottle and store it at room temperature up to 2 months.

   Note: SDS will precipitate out of solution in cool temperatures. If white flecks of SDS are seen in the buffer, gently heat it to about 30°C to resuspend the SDS.

2. In the next activity, two proteins, bovine serum albumin (BSA) and cellulase, will be studied using PAGE. A 5 mL stock of 5 mg/mL solution in 1X PAGE running buffer will be needed for each protein. Calculate the amount of protein (in grams) to be measured out for 5 mL of a 5-mg/mL protein solution. Record the calculation and diagram the solution preparation in your notebook.

_____ mL × _____ mg/mL = _____ mg = _____ g

a. Measure out enough of each protein to make 5 mL of 5 mg/mL solutions (on an analytical balance) and add each to their own 15-mL conical tube.
b. To each tube, stir in the 1X PAGE running buffer slowly making a paste of the protein. Add enough 1X PAGE running buffer to bring the final total volume to 5 mL.
c. Rotate each tube **very slowly** until the protein has dissolved in the buffer (about 5 minutes).
d. Label each tube with the sample name and concentration, date, and your initials. Store for up to 2 weeks at 4°C. For long-term storage, use a syringe filter to sterilize the protein solution (see Figure 5.7).

3. Prepare 50 mL of 2X PAGE Sample Prep Loading Dye without BME. (2X SPLD) using the recipe below. The 2X SPLD is added to samples prior to loading into a gel to make the sample visible and dense (so it will sink into the wells). BME is a denaturing agent that helps linearize peptide chains. If it is used in a loading dye it is best added just prior to use.
a. For 50 mL of 2X SPLD:
   5 g of sucrose
   0.05 g of bromophenol blue
   30 mL of 1X PAGE running buffer
b. Add sugar and bromophenol blue to 1X PAGE running buffer; stir until dissolved.
c. Bring to a final volume of 50 mL. Label and store tightly in a glass or plastic bottle at 4°C.

Thinking Like a Biotechnician

1. 1X PAGE running buffer contains TRIS, boric acid, and SDS. What is the function of each ingredient in this buffer?
2. It takes a bit of mixing to get some proteins to go into solution, while other proteins go into solution more easily. Why?
3. If the protein solution needs sterilization for long-term storage, why not autoclave it?
4. 10X PAGE running buffer is available for purchase. How do you make 300 mL of 1X PAGE running buffer from 10X?

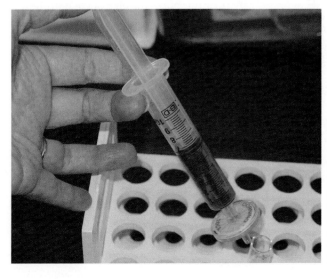

Figure 5.7. **To sterilize small amounts of solution, use a syringe filter. A syringe is filled with the solution to be sterilized. A 0.2-µM filter disc is screwed onto the end of the syringe. A 0.2-µM filter is small enough to separate bacteria and fungi contaminants from the molecules in solution. Gentle pressure pushes the solution though the filter into a sterile tube. If the solution contains proteins, the proteins are small enough to go through the filter, and then the protein solution will be sterile.** Photo by author.

Laboratory 5f
Characterizing Proteins by PAGE

Optimized by Ryan Flatland and Justen Wu, Biotechnology students.

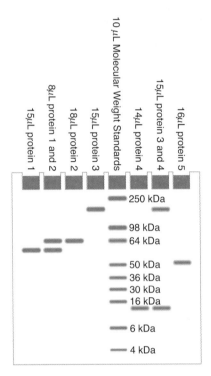

Figure 5.8. PAGE Gel. Running the gel distributes the samples according to molecular weight. Sizing standards in Lane 5 range from 4 to 250 kDa. Through visual inspection, one can estimate the size of unknown bands.

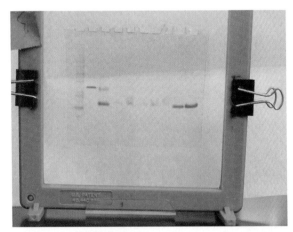

Figure 5.9. Stained PAGE Gel. Coomassie® Blue staining makes peptide bands visible. The standards are in the left lane, and the other nine lanes have one or more peptide bands. A protein composed of more than one polypeptide chain will show a band for each chain.
Photo by author.

Background

One of the first things to learn about a protein is its size and structure. By running a denaturing sizing gel, one can determine the molecular weight and the number of different polypeptide chains of a protein. Molecular weights are reported in kilodaltons (kDa). A dalton (Da) is equal to the mass of one hydrogen atom. For example, 1 kDa is equivalent to 1000 Da. Proteins usually have molecular masses ranging from 10 to 300 kDa.

For size determination, a TRIS-glycine (TG) polyacrylamide gel at a given concentration is used. Premade gels can be purchased. The activity below uses gels with a polyacrylamide concentration of anywhere from 4% to 20%. Samples of unknown molecular weight are loaded into wells. Standard proteins of known molecular weight are run in at least one lane.

Traditionally, PAGE gels are run at 35 milliamps (mAmp) for 1 to 2 hours. New buffers and gel preparations allow for faster running times at higher currents. See manufacturer's recommendations for gel running conditions. The SDS and other denaturing agents in the loading dye and buffer causes the peptide chains to unravel and linearize. If there is more than one type of polypeptide in the protein, it separates from the other peptides. Smaller peptides move through the gel faster than larger ones. The peptides "band out" based on size (see Figure 5.8). After staining the peptides, you can size them by comparing the bands of unknown molecular weight to standards of known molecular weight (see Figure 5.9).

Two proteins are studied in this lab activity. The first is bovine serum albumin (BSA). Serum albumin is the most abundant protein in mammalian blood and is important in blood pressure regulation. The second protein is cellulase which is the enzyme that breaks down cellulose fibers to glucose. Cellulase is important in juice-making and biofuel production. By running pure samples of each protein on a SDS-PAGE gel, the number of polypeptide chains (one or more) in each protein may be determined and the size of each polypeptide chain may be estimated. Knowing that the average size of an amino acid is about 110 kDa, the number of amino acids in each polypeptide chain may be estimated as well.

Purpose

What structural characteristics of BSA and cellulase can be determined from running samples on a SDS-PAGE gel? How is the resolution of the polypeptide bands on the gel affected by the concentration of the sample loaded?

Materials

Environmental Health
and Safety Officer

Balance, analytical
Balance, tabletop milligram
Weigh paper, 7.6 × 7.6 cm
Weigh boat, 3.5" × 3.5"
Lab scoops
1X PAGE electrophoresis
running buffer (from Lab 5e)
5 mg/mL protein solutions
(from Lab 5e)
Permanent lab marker pens
Beta-mercaptoethanol (BME)
Tube rack for 1.7-mL tubes
Reaction tubes, 1.7 mL

Micropipet, P-100
Micropipet tips for P-100
Micropipet, P-10
Micropipet tips for P-10
Microcentrifuge
Dry/heat block, 90°C
LidLock, locking caps for
1.7-mL tubes
Gel box, vertical, for PAGE
PAGE gel, 10% TG, 10 well
Transfer pipets, 3 mL
PAGE gel loading tips
Protein sizing markers, (such as
PAGEmark™ Tri-color protein
ladder [G-Biosciences, Inc.])

Power supply
Petri dishes, 150 × 15mm,
sterile
Methanol, 95%
Acetic acid, glacial
Coomassie® Blue R-250
Lab rotator, 12" × 12"
White light imaging system
Paper, thermal
Printer, thermal
Gloves, large
Glasses, safety, plastic

Procedure

Note: Sharing a single 10-well PAGE gel, each lab group is responsible for studying just one type of protein, either bovine serum albumin (BSA) or cellulase.

1. Prepare 1X PAGE running buffer, Sample Prep Loading Dye, and 5 mg/mL protein samples using the protocol in Lab 5e. Alternatively, PAGE running buffer and sample prep loading dye may be purchased from commercial vendors.

2. Dilute the protein stock solution in the following ratios with 1X PAGE running buffer: 1:2, 1:4, and 1:8.

   - Starting with the 5-mg/mL stock, measure out 50 µL and combine it with 50 µL of 1X PAGE running buffer. Mix. This is the 1:2 dilution. It has a concentration of 2.5 mg/mL. Label this tube "2.5."
   - Measure out 50 µL of the 2.5-mg/mL solution and combine with 50 µL of 1X PAGE running buffer. Mix. This is a 1:4 dilution of the original sample. It has a concentration of 1.25 mg/mL. Label this tube "1.25."
   - Measure out 50 µL of the 1.25-mg/mL solution and combine with 50 µL of 1X PAGE running buffer. Mix. This is a 1:8 dilution of the original sample. It has a concentration of 0.625 mg/mL. Label this tube "0.625."
   - Measure out 50 µL of stock solution. It has a concentration of 5 mg/mL. Label this tube"5."

3. For *your* protein, make up four sample tubes for loading. Select **four new** 1.7-mL tubes and label them No. 1, 2, 3, and 4. Add a letter before the number to identify the protein. Place 25 µL of each concentration into the appropriate 1.7-mL tube (see Table 5.7).

Table 5.7. **Sample Preparation Matrix**

Concentration (mg/mL)	Tube No. for BSA	Tube No. for Cellulase
5	B1	C1
2.5	B2	C2
1.25	B3	C3
0.625	B4	C4

90°C

4. In a running chemical fume hood, prepare the Sample Prep Loading Dye with beta-mercaptoethanol (SPLD-BME). Beta-mercaptoethanol (BME) is an additional denaturing agent, and it ensures that the polypeptide chains completely linearize. Make a stock tube of SPLD-BME by mixing 950 µL of PAGE Sample Prep Loading Dye and 50 µL of beta-mercaptoethanol. Measure out BME in a running fume hood since it is extremely stinky. This PAGE Sample Prep Buffer/Loading Dye/beta-mercaptoethanol must be used immediately or stored at -20°C.

5. Add 25 µL of the SPLD-BME to each of the 25 µL diluted samples, BSA1 through BSA4 or C1 through C4. The samples may be used immediately, however better separation and sharper bands result it the samples are allowed to incubate at room temperature for 40 minutes or at

4°C if not used that day.

6. Prior to loading samples on a gel, further denature each sample by placing them in a 90°C heat block (or hot water bath) for 3 minutes. Be sure to place a lid lock cap on each tube to prevent evaporation, and do not heat for longer than 5 minutes. This step may have to wait until the gel is ready to load.

7. Prepare a PAGE gel and set it up in a vertical gel box as directed by the manufacturer or in the directions below. Use a TRIS-glycine gel. In your notebook, record the gel concentration, the lot number, and the expiration date. **Caution: Wear goggles and gloves.**

Figure 5.10. When setting up a PAGE gel, make sure to evenly tighten the holding clamps. Add buffer to the upper (back chamber) so that the wells are completely covered. Check to make sure the upper chamber does not leak before adding buffer to the lower chamber. The gel is done running when the loading dye is a few millimeters above the bottom slit.
Photo by author.

PAGE Gel and Gel Box Set-up

a. Cut open/drain the preservative from the cassette.

b. Rinse the outside of the cassette 5 times with dH_2O.

c. Rinse the edges of the cassette 5 times.

d. Dry front of gel.

e. Label gel. If the wells are not already labeled, place a number or dot in the center and a line on the bottom of each well. This makes it easier to see the well boundaries during loading.

f. Some prepared gels have tape on the bottom. If tape is present, pull it of the bottom of the gel cassette.

g. Study the gel box to understand how it is put together and which side is the front (see Figure 5.10). Put the gel(s) in the box with the high side facing out, so that the labeled side faces the front of the gel box and the top of the wells are in the inner chamber.

h. Fill the inner chamber of the gel box with running buffer to the height necessary to cover the wells completely. Make sure the inner chamber (the one with buffer covering the wells) does not leak.

i. Gently, remove the comb (that formed the wells).

j. Gently, rinse the wells with at least 3 times their volume of buffer.

k. Fill the front chamber with buffer until the bottom of the gel (where the tape was) is covered.

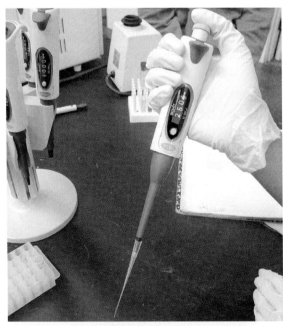

Figure 5.11. Vertical gel loading tips are long and end in a very narrow tip. These long, thin tips fit into the 1-mm gel spacing between the front and back plastic or glass plates that hold the gel.
Photo by author.

8. Hook up the power supply, and run the empty gel for 5 minutes at the current (mA) recommended by the manufacturer. If no recommendations are given, run the gel at 35 mA. to clear preservative from each well.

9. Practice loading a well with 1:2 sample prep loading dye and deionized water before actually loading samples. Load the gel wells with 30 μL of sample using special, long-tipped PAGE gel loading tips if they are available. (see Figure 5.11). Be careful to load all of the sample without overflowing into the adjoining wells (see Figure 5.12).

10. Load 10 μL of molecular weight standards to one of the lanes. Researchers commonly use 15–150 kDa molecular weight standards if several unknown proteins are being studied (see Figure 5.13).

11. As soon as all samples are loaded, run the gel at the current (mA) recommended by the manufacturer. If no recommendations are given, run the gel at 35 mA. for 60 to 80 minutes, until the loading dye reaches the bottom of the

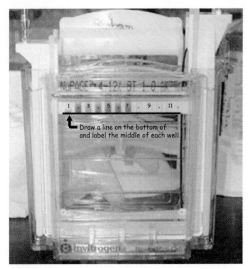

Figure 5.12. Use a permanent marker to number the middle of each well and underline the bottom of the wells. This makes it much easier to see where you are loading a sample.
Photo by author.

Figure 5.14. Set and maintain the current at 35 mAmp and check for bubbling. If the current goes down, make sure there is enough buffer covering the wells in the back reservoir.
Photo by author.

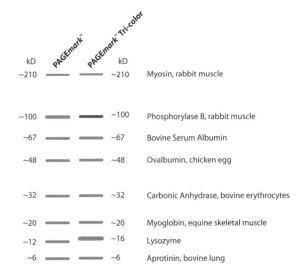

Figure 5.13. Protein Sizing Standard Markers. Unstained or prestained protein sizing standards are available from several suppliers. These from G-Bioscience, Inc. contain eight known proteins that show how peptides, from 6–210 kDa, run on a SDS-PAGE gel.
Photo courtesy of G-Biosciences, Inc.

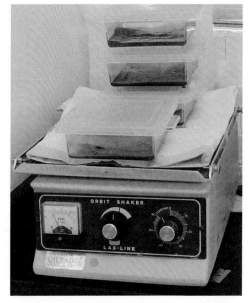

Figure 5.15. Cover the gel with just enough stain for the gel to float and swirl on the orbital shaker.
Photo by author.

gel. Sample preparation loading dye serves as tracking dye (see Figure 5.14).

12. Remove the gel from gel box. Rinse it 2–3 times in deionized water until no soapy residue is seen. Some gel cassettes are designed to be opened using fingers to pry the sides apart. Some gels require a tool to separate the cassette sides. If necessary, use a knife to gently separate the two gel plates holding the gel in place. Loosen the entire edge of the gel from the plate using a knife or spatula. Gently, trim off the well fingers and fat edges of the gel.

13. Using water in a Petri plate for adhesion, drop the gel onto the water. Gently remove the water from the plate by decanting or using a vacuum pump.

14. Add enough Coomassie® Blue staining solution (see the recipe below or use pre-made commercial stain) to just cover the gel. Let it stain for a minimum of 3–7 hours or as

recommended by the manufacturer.. Rotating the staining gel on an orbital shaker is desirable for even staining (see Figure 5.15). Do not stain for more than 12 hours.

Environmental Health and Safety Officer

Note: Prepare stain/destain in chemical fume hood.

Coomassie® Blue Stain
- 800 mL of methanol
- 200 mL of glacial acetic acid
- 1000 mL of dH_2O
- 2 g of Coomassie® Blue R-250

Destain
- 200 mL of methanol
- 150 mL of glacial acetic acid
- 1650 mL of deionized water

15. Funnel off Coomassie® Blue stain into a "used stain" bottle. Cover gel with destaining or dH_2O solution for at least 7 hours, but not more than 24 hours. Change destaining solution several times. Rotating the destaining gel on an orbital shaker is desirable. Add a lab tissue to absorb the stain (stain sink). Change it every 4 hours. Destaining can be sped up by gently microwaving the gel in destain solution at 30% power for 20 seconds and then swirling for 1 minute. Repeat the procedures until the background is light enough to easily distinguish polypeptide bands. The destain may have to be changed periodically (every fifth time).

16. Examine the banding pattern on gel over a white-light box. Use a photo-imaging system to take a photograph of the gel. Make copies for each lab partner. If no photo-imaging system is available, place an acetate sheet over the gel and draw a copy of the gel. Make photocopies for each lab partner.

17. For long-term storage of a gel, dry on gel-drying rack. Follow the directions on the gel-drying kit.

18. Glue the gel image into the center of a notebook page. Label the contents of each lane as diagrammed in the background section. Each well, each standard, and each of the sample bands should be labeled with sizes.

Data Analysis/Conclusion

For each protein studied, identify the number of polypeptide chains present, the molecular weight of each polypeptide chain, and the total molecular weight of the protein. Determine the optimum concentration for visualizing the characteristics of each protein studied. Discuss the sources of error in technique that could lead to fallacious data. Describe several ways in which the PAGE technique can be used in industry.

Thinking Like a Biotechnician

1. A technician sets up and starts a PAGE. Current is flowing, and bubbling is visible at the electrodes. After 30 minutes, none of the samples have moved out of the wells. List three things the technician should check.

2. If a gel has a band significantly darker and fatter than all the other bands on the gel, suggest a few reasons for that result.

3. Every amino acid has a different molecular weight because of different R groups. Using amino acid data from Promega Corp. at **www.promega.com/~/media/files/resources/technical %20references/amino%20acid%20abbreviations%20and%20molecular%20weights.pdf**, one can determine that the average molecular weight of an amino acid is about 110 Da. Use the average molecular weight of an amino acid and the estimated molecular weight of the polypeptide chains in the protein you studied to determine the approximate number of amino acids in each protein.

Laboratory 5g
Studying Muscle Proteins via SDS-PAGE

Background

The function of a cell, tissue, or organ depends on the proteins and other molecules that make up its structure. So, if scientists are trying to understand the function or behavior of a sample, they need to understand the protein composition. Likewise, if scientists were looking for similarities or differences in tissues, they would compare protein content.

In this activity, you will study tissues from a variety of animal muscle samples to identify similarities and differences in protein content. Since a muscle's function is to contract and relax, certain muscle proteins would be expected in all muscle samples. Since different muscle samples are used in different ways, some protein content differences would also be expected.

Mashing and diluting the animal tissue with sample preparation buffer accomplishes the extraction of protein from cells. Samples are loaded onto vertical polyacrylamide gels containing SDS and are electrophoresed. Proteins are denatured with SDS so they will electrophorese in the gel at a rate proportional to their molecular weight. After the gel is stained, the protein-banding pattern for each sample can be compared to determine how many protein polypeptide chains are present and whether there are differences in the peptides. The molecular weight of the unknown protein bands is determined by comparison with protein standards.

Purpose

What variety of proteins is found in the muscle tissue of some animals?

Hypothesis

Using Internet resources, determine some of the proteins known to exist in muscle cells. Try to find their molecular weights, the number of peptide chains, and the number of amino acids per chain for the muscle proteins, so you can predict what to expect on the gel. Record these predictions in your notebook.

Materials

Environmental Health and Safety Officer

Balance, analytical	Tube rack for 1.7-mL tubes	Petri dishes, 150 × 15 mm
Balance, tabletop milligram	Reaction tubes, 1.7 mL	Methanol, 95%
Weigh paper, 7.6 × 7.6 cm	Pipets, 1 mL	Acetic acid, glacial
Weigh boat, 3.5" × 3.5"	Micropipet, P-100	Coomassie® Blue R-250
Lab scoops	Micropipet tips for P-100	Lab rotator, 12" × 12"
Bottle, 1000 mL	Microcentrifuge	White light imaging system
Permanent lab marker pens	Dry heat block, 90°C	Paper, thermal
Beta-mercaptoethanol (BME)	Gel box, vertical, for PAGE	Printer, thermal
Mortar and pestle	PAGE gel, 10% TG, 10 well	Gloves, large
Pipets, 2 mL	Transfer pipets, 3 mL	Glasses, safety, plastic
Pipet pump, blue	PAGE gel loading tips	Fresh animal muscle tissue
Tubes, 15-mL, conical	Protein sizing markers, (such as	samples such as shrimp,
Tube racks for 15-mL tubes	PAGEmark™ Tri-color protein	catfish, chicken, beef
Pipets, 5 mL	ladder [G-Biosciences, Inc.])	
Centrifuge, 15-mL tubes	Power supply	

Procedure

1. Prepare 1X PAGE running buffer, and Sample Prep Loading Dye using the protocol in Lab 5e. Alternatively, PAGE running buffer and sample prep loading dye may be purchased from commercial vendors.

2. In a running chemical fume hood, add beta-mercaptoethanol to prepare the Sample Prep Loading Dye (SPLD-BME). Beta-mercaptoethanol (BME) is an additional denaturing agent,

and it ensures that the polypeptide chains completely linearize. Make a stock tube of 5 mL of SPLD-BME by mixing 4.75 mL of PAGE Sample Prep Loading Dye and 250 µL of beta-mercaptoethanol. Measure out BME in a running fume hood since it is extremely stinky. This PAGE Sample Prep buffer/Loading Dye/beta-mercaptoethanol must be used immediately or aliquoted into 1.5 mL tubes, stored at -20°C.

3. Use a mortar and pestle (or a test tube with a glass rod) to grind 1 g of animal tissue with 2 mL of cold, deionized water for 1 minute. Add 3 mL of 1X SPLD-BME and mix for 30 seconds.

4. Transfer the mixture to a 15-mL centrifuge tube. The total volume in the centrifuge tube should be 5 mL. Add 1X SPLD-BME, as needed, to adjust the volume.

5. Repeat Steps 1 and 2 for each animal tissue sample to be studied.

6. Spin the samples for 5 minutes at medium speed in a lab tabletop centrifuge.

7. Transfer 0.5 mL of the supernatant to a 1.7-mL microtube. Prepare four dilutions of the stock sample (supernatant) using the SPLD-BME as the diluent to make 1:4, 1:8, 1:16, and 1:32 samples. The diluted samples should each have a final volume of 48 µL per tube. The diluted samples will be loaded on the PAGE gels. In your notebook, diagram how the dilutions are prepared.

8. Store the samples in the refrigerator for up to 5 days.

9. Two gels must be set up and run to have enough wells for all four dilutions of all four animal muscle tissue samples. Set up each TRIS-glycine gel (any concentration from 4% to 12%) in a gel box with 1X PAGE running buffer.

10. Denature the proteins in the samples by placing the tubes in a 90°C water bath or heat block for 5 minutes. Seal the tubes tightly (use a locking lid) so they do not open during heating.

11. Load the gel wells. Using a new tip for each sample, load 30 µL of each of the dilutions (1:4, 1:8, 1:16 and 1:32 samples) for a particular animal tissue into Lanes 1 through 4, respectively. Add a set of dilutions for a second animal tissue into Lanes 6 through 9. Use a new tip with each sample. Repeat with the other animal muscle tissue samples in a second gel.

12. Load 10 µL of protein molecular weight sizing standard markers into Lanes 5 and 10.

13. Run the electrophoresis at the current (mA) recommended by the gel manufacturer. If no recommendations are given, run the gel at 35 mA until the loading dye reaches just above the bottom vent of the gel cassette. The SPLD-BME serves as tracking dye.

14. Do the following to prepare the gel for staining (see Figure 5.16): Place the larger side of the gel cassette on a tabletop. Use your fingers or a knife to gently pry the cassette plates apart. The gel will stick to one cassette side or the other. Use distilled water to help detach it from the other plate, if necessary. Gently trim the wells off the gel and loosen the edges of the gel from the plate. Be careful not to rip the gel. Transfer the gel from the cassette into a Petri dish filled with distilled water. Using four gloved fingers, pour off the water while holding the gel in the tray.

Figure 5.16. A technician prepares a gel for staining. The two sides of the gel cassette must be gently pried apart without ripping the gel.
Photo by author.

15. Cover the gel with Coomassie® Blue staining solution (see Lab 5f for recipe). Stain for 3 to 7 hours while rotating the gel on an orbital shaker.

16. Remove Coomassie® Blue stain. Cover the gel with destaining solution. Add a lab tissue to act as a dry sink. Change the tissue every few hours. Leave the destaining solution on the gel for a minimum of 7 hours, or if necessary, use the following accelerated destaining procedure. Be careful to not overly destain the gel.

a. Pour off the existing solution.
b. Add about 50 mL of fresh destain.
c. Put a paper towel in the microwave.
d. Put the Petri dish in the microwave.
e. Microwave for 20 seconds at 30%.
f. Swirl for 1 minute.
g. Repeat steps b through f as necessary. Add fresh stain every fifth time.
h. Pour off the destain and flood with dH_2O.

17. Examine the banding pattern on the gel over a white-light box. Use a photo-imaging system to photograph the gel. If a photo-imaging system is not available, place an acetate sheet over the gel and draw a copy of it. Make photocopies for each lab partner.
18. Dry the gels on a gel-drying rack if long-term storage is desired.
19. Glue the gel image into the center of a notebook page. Label the gel. Label the contents of each well. Label the size of each standard. Label the sizes of the bands in each sample.

Data Analysis/Conclusion

For each sample studied, identify the number of polypeptide chains present and their molecular weights. Are any of the bands unique to a sample? Which bands are common to all samples? Are any of the bands expected, based on what is known to be in muscle cells? Give evidence. Are there any bands that are of particular interest? If so, why? Look at other gels. Are all the replications of a sample identical? Discuss possible errors in technique that could lead to fallacious or misleading data. Propose methods of reducing the likelihood of these errors. Describe several extensions and applications of this preliminary experiment. What future experiments would you suggest to your supervisor and why?

Thinking Like a Biotechnician

1. Do you know the concentrations of protein in the muscle extract samples loaded on the gel? How can you find out?
2. Many proteins have bands of the same molecular weight. If you find a protein band that you believe is a particular protein or polypeptide, how might you confirm it's identity?
3. A lane on a gel has a huge smear in it. What is the most likely cause, and how can the problem be corrected on future gels?

6 Assay Development

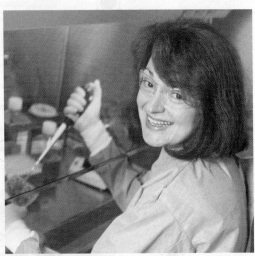

As cell cultures are grown, they must be assayed, or tested, for the presence, concentration, and activity of protein product
Photo courtesy of Cell Genesys, Inc.

Many biotechnology companies produce recombinant protein products. To do so, they must be able to monitor the protein product at all stages in research, development, and manufacturing. Most proteins are colorless and all are submicroscopic. How can researchers or production scientists know that the protein they want to produce is present and active? How can the concentration or effectiveness of a protein product be monitored?

Once a protein is selected as a potential product, researchers must develop methods, called assays, to identify and quantify the protein through production. Assay development and the use of assays are of critical importance during research and manufacturing. Assays for a product's presence, activity, concentration, and stability are just some of the many tests developed and conducted during protein production. If at any time, a product is not performing adequately or a manufacturing procedure is not sufficient, manufacture of the product could be halted. This could cost a company a substantial amount of time and money.

A large portion of a company's scientific staff works on assay development and assay application. Depending on the size of the company and the product of interest, assays might be developed and used right on a lab bench in research and development. More commonly, assays are developed in one department of a company (such as Process Development) but then used in another department (such as Assay Services or Quality Control). Technicians growing cultures and purifying product would then send their samples to Assay Services or Quality Control for testing.

Amylase is produced by several species and catalyzes the breakdown of starch to sugar. Genetically-engineered recombinant amylase was one of the first biotechnology products. Recombinant amylase is commercially important and used in biofuel production and in the foods and textile industries. In the following activities you will learn some methods of assaying for the enzyme amylase. Specifically, you will learn:

- how to test for the presence of amylase's substrate, starch
- how to test for the presence of the product of amylase activity, the sugar, maltose
- how to assess an enzyme's activity by comparing substrate use and product production
- how to measure the presence and concentration of amylase in a solution using a technique called an ELISA
- how to recognize bacterial amylase on a PAGE gel
- how to verify a protein band on a PAGE gel by a technique called a Western blot

The assays presented in this chapter are examples of how the presence or activity of a protein product might be tested. In the next chapter, you will conduct additional assays for protein concentration using spectrophotometry. In future chapters, you will apply the assays used and developed in these chapters to recombinant protein production

Laboratory 6a

Searching for Native Amylase-Producing Bacteria

This lab was developed by Diane Sweeney currently of Sacred Heart Schools and modified by Ellyn Daugherty, Pat Seawell of Gene Connection™, and David Kane, Biotechnology student.

Background

Biotechnology companies have three options for producing a protein, such as amylase, for market. The potential product may be either extracted from nature, grown in the laboratory from existing sources, or genetically engineered into a production cell line and then scaled-up into larger volumes.

Amylase is a product already present in nature. Several species of decomposition bacteria and fungi present in the soil and on plant surfaces produce the amylase enzyme. The soil or plants may be sampled for the presence of amylase-producing bacteria. If naturally-occurring amylase-producing bacteria can be isolated and grown in the lab, then that "native" amylase is a potential product for a biotechnology company. If the bacteria from an existing source can be grown in sufficient quantities for amylase purification and marketing, then R&D costs will be substantially reduced.

Manufacturing costs increase as more time and manpower are used to develop new methods of production. Each of the possible methods of manufacturing a protein must be evaluated in light of the production costs. For amylase, the protein must be grown in "the lab," either from existing amylase-producing bacteria or from genetically engineered bacteria. In this activity, native amylase-producing bacteria will be isolated and evaluated for their potential pipeline use.

To assay for amylase-producing bacteria, agar-containing starch can be inoculated with samples suspected of having amylase activity. If amylase is produced by any of the bacteria colonies growing on the starch agar, then clearings (halos) around the colonies will become visible as the starch is broken down into sugar by the amylase enzyme (see Figure 6.1). If an amylase-producing colony can be characterized and scaled-up to large volumes, it can serve as the production host (or cell line) for commercial amylase.

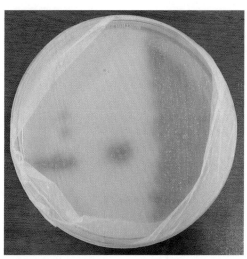

Figure 6.1. **Bacteria colonies growing on starch agar plates. If the cells produce it, amylase diffuses out and breaks down the starch around the colony. The result is clear halos around amylase-producing colonies.**
Photo by author.

Purpose

Which suspect samples contain amylase-producing bacteria?
Can single, amylase-producing bacteria colonies be isolated from nature?
What are the characteristics of the best amylase-producing bacteria?

Materials

Environmental Health and Safety Officer

Balance, tabletop milligram	Magnetic stir bars	Lysol® disinfectant
Weigh boat, 3.5" × 3.5"	Hot plate stirrer	Petri dishes, 100 × 15 mm,
Lab scoops	Hot hands protector	sterile
LB agar base	Media bottle, 250 mL	Loop, inoculating, sterile
Starch, soluble	Permanent lab marker pens	Incubator oven, 37°C
Beakers, 400 mL	Sterilizer/autoclave	Lugol's Iodine, diluted 1:2
Glass rods	Laminar flow hood	with water

Procedure

Caution: Wear gloves and goggles. No eating or drinking.

1. At least 1 day in advance, prepare 250 mL of sterile 2% starch/LB agar and pour it into Petri plates. (Prepare LB agar as described in Chapter 4, but add 2% mass/volume of soluble starch to the dry LB media mix.) Show the media prep calculation and diagram in your notebook.
2. Obtain one 2%-starch/LB agar Petri plate per person. Label (initials and date) the bottom of plate.
3. Using a sterile plastic inoculating loop, sample plants, soil, or other surfaces for amylase-producing bacteria. Select a sample that seems logical for amylase production. (Remember that bacteria with the capability to produce amylase will probably not do so if no starch is present.) Record the source of your sample and why you chose a sample from that location. To obtain a soil or water sample, plunge the inoculating loop into the soil or water. Twist it gently, so as not to break it. Remove it from the soil or water. Shake off any excess dirt or water. For a plant bacteria sample, rub the inoculating loop over the plant surface.
4. Streak the plate with the sample in a "triple Z" arrangement as directed in Lab 4g. Do not "flame" the loop between "Zs."
5. Place the plate, upside down, in an incubation oven at 37°C.
   Caution: Wear gloves. No eating or drinking.
6. After 24 hours, get the Petri plate and observe bacterial growth. Look for colonies and halos around them. Expect hundreds of colonies, but only a few, if any, colonies with halos. To make halos more visible, chill the Petri plates in a refrigerator for several hours. Dilute Lugol's Iodine may be added to turn the starch areas blue-black and better show areas of starch clearing. Be aware that this may kill the colonies or spread bacteria that may be undesirable, should there be interest in keeping the colonies. These unidentified bacteria, though, should not be kept and should be discarded properly after autoclaving.
7. Draw your plate, making sure it is accurate in size and detail. Label the amylase-producing bacteria.
8. Record the characteristics of each amylase-producing colony on a data table. Record the diameter of the colonies and the width of the halos. Record colors, shapes, and textures of the colonies.

Caution: Treat these bacteria with respect. These bacteria are not identified and may be pathogenic. Wear goggles and gloves when handling the plates. Dispose of the plates in the autoclave bag. Wash your hands after handling the plates and disinfect the work surface.

Environmental Health
and Safety Officer

Data Analysis/Conclusion

Determine which colony on your plate, if any, shows amylase production. Is the colony a good candidate for growth as a commercial producer of amylase? Why or why not? Share your data with the colleagues in the class. Pick the three colonies in the class that best show potential for amylase production in the lab. Consider the growth rate and halo characteristics. In a concluding statement, discuss why you have chosen these particular colonies. Also, discuss what the next step in commercial amylase production might be. Finally, discuss the advantages and disadvantages of using these unknown bacteria species as laboratory or manufacturing amylase producers.

Thinking Like a Biotechnician

1. For this assay, which is better: a fast-growing bacteria colony that has a large cloudy halo around it or a slow-growing colony that has a small- to medium-size, very clear halo around it?
2. Propose a method to get any of the bacteria colonies showing the results from question 1 to have additional desirable characteristics?
3. None of these bacteria will be used in our efforts to make large volumes of amylase. Give a good reason and explanation for why these bacteria are less attractive for that purpose than genetically engineering *E. coli* to produce amylase.

Laboratory 6b
How Do You Know When You Have Some Amylase?

Figure 6.2. **Assays take many forms. Here, a technician labels tubes for a colorimetric assay that measures enzymes by the amount of color change in a reaction.**
Photo by author.

Background

If Genencor International, Inc. or another biotechnology company hopes to produce a protein, such as amylase, it must devise a method of identifying amylase in a solution. Scientists must develop tests to show the presence, concentration, and activity of this colorless molecule. The tests are called assays, and assay development is one of the first steps in determining a potential biotechnology product (see Figure 6.2).

Since amylase decomposes starch to sugar molecules, the ability to assay for starch (amylase substrate) or sugar (the result of amylase activity) in a solution is valuable in an amylase production facility.

Purpose

To design an experiment that tests the question: Does a given solution (clear extract) contain the enzyme amylase?

Procedure

1. Spend 10 to 15 minutes with your lab partners discussing how one might test for the presence of amylase. in a solution. Consider the chemical nature and activity of the enzyme. Review how enzymes have been studied and tested earlier in this course to get some idea of how enzyme-activity experiments are conducted. You may need to go online to find out more about how amylase works, or review information presented in the text, if available. You have all the equipment and supplies in the lab available to you, and most chemicals can be ordered from supply houses if they are not already in stock in the lab.

2. Your group is to produce a laboratory proposal for conducting an experiment that tests the question: Does a given solution (clear extract) contain the enzyme, amylase?
   a. Create a list of procedures that outline in a step-by-step fashion how your experiment will be conducted.
   b. Make sure that the procedures outline the independent variable to be tested. The independent variable is the one factor that will differ from one experimental group to another. For example, in an experiment to measure the effect of nitrogen concentration on grass growth, the independent variable is the amount of nitrogen.
   c. Make sure that the procedures outline the dependent variable and how it will be measured (what equipment and units of measure). The dependent variable(s) is the data collected. In an experiment to measure the effect of nitrogen concentration on grass growth, the length of grass blades in centimeters (cm) might be the dependent variable. The dependent variable changes as a result of the independent variable.
   d. Include a negative control group in your experiment. A negative control group is one that lacks the variable being tested. Often, water or a buffer is used in the negative control group to substitute for a volume of reagent. In an experiment to measure the effect of nitrogen concentration on grass growth, a grass group with no nitrogen, and only water substituting for the nitrogen volume, would be the negative control.
   e. Include a positive control group in your experiment if it is appropriate. In a positive control group, the variable being tested is in a form that will give a positive result. In an experiment to measure the effect of nitrogen concentration on grass growth, a grass group with some "recommended" amount of nitrogen might serve as the positive control.
   f. Design a data table (with a title, labels, and units of measure) into which data from the experiment could be collected.

3. Submit the experiment proposal to your supervisor. If the design is valid and reasonable, it will be approved.

Laboratory 6c
Assaying for Starch and Sugar

Background

When testing for amylase activity, the reactant (starch) and product (sugar) of amylase catalysis must be able to be recognized. Starch and sugar molecules in solution may be detected with the use of indicator solutions. An indicator is a chemical that changes color when another chemical is present. Several indicators are used in assays to determine the presence or concentration of a molecule. Some common indicators used in the biotechnology lab include iodine, Benedict's solution, Biuret reagent, phenol red, and Bradford reagent, to name a few.

Iodine (I_3^-) is an indicator of starch molecules (see Figure 6.3). When iodine is caught in long starch molecule coils, it causes a visible color change. Thus, iodine may be used in assays to show the presence of starch in a sample. Iodine can also be used to demonstrate whether starch is being used or removed from the solution.

Benedict's solution is an indicator of some sugars, including glucose and maltose. Benedict's solution contains a copper compound that reacts with the aldehyde group (H-C=O) on open-chain forms of glucose and maltose. These sugars are called aldoses. Depending on the amount of glucose or maltose present, a variety of colors appear during testing.

Since amylase decomposes starch to maltose molecules, the ability to assay for starch and maltose content in a solution is valuable in an amylase production facility.

Figure 6.3. **Plant starch (amylose) is the substrate of bacterial amylase. Corn starch and potato starch are available in grocery stores. For research, soluble starch should be ordered from a chemical supply house, since their product goes into suspension more easily than the other starches.**
Photo by author.

Purpose

How does an iodine indicator show the presence of starch?
What happens when iodine is mixed with other molecules, such as sugar or protein?
How does Benedict's solution show the presence of sugar?
What happens when Benedict's solution is mixed with other molecules, such as starch or protein?

Materials

Environmental Health and Safety Officer

Balance, tabletop milligram	Maltose	Micropipet, P-1000
Weigh boat, 3.5" × 3.5"	Gelatin	Micropipet tips for P-1000
Lab scoops	Tubes, glass, 13 × 100 mm	Vortex mixer
Starch, soluble	Peg racks for 13 × 100-mm tubes	Benedict's solution
Tubes, 15 mL, conical	Pipets, 2 mL	Hot plate stirrer, 7" × 7"
Tube racks for 15-mL tubes	Pipet pump, blue	Beaker, 250 mL
Glucose (dextrose)	Lugol's Iodine Solution	Test tube holder

Caution: Wear goggles and gloves when using chemicals.

Procedure

1. Prepare 10 mL of 2% starch solution in a 15-mL tube. What amount of each ingredient do you need? In your notebook, show the calculations and a diagram of how to prepare the solution.
2. Prepare 10 mL of 1% glucose solution in a 15-mL tube. What amount of each ingredient do you need? In your notebook, show the calculations and a diagram of how to prepare the solution.
3. Prepare 10 mL of 1% maltose solution in a 15-mL tube. What amount of each ingredient do you need? In your notebook, show the calculations and a diagram of how to prepare the solution.
4. Prepare 10 mL of 1% protein (gelatin) solution in a 15-mL tube. What amount of each ingredient do you need? In your notebook, show the calculations and a diagram of how to prepare the solution.

Starch Assay

a. Place 2 mL of the solution to be tested into a test tube.
b. Add 250 µL of iodine solution to the sample.
c. Mix by inverting several times.
d. Record color after mixing.

Aldose Assay

a. Place 2 mL of the solution to be tested into a 13 × 100 mm tube.
b. Add 2 mL of Benedict's solution to the sample.
c. Mix by vortexing for 1 to 2 seconds.
d. Heat in a boiling hot water bath (100 mL of boiling water in a 250-mL beaker) for 2 minutes.
e. Record all the colors that appear while heating in the order they appear.

5. Test the starch solution using the starch and aldose assays.
6. Test the glucose solution using the starch and aldose assays.
7. Test the maltose solution using the starch and aldose assays.
8. Test the protein solution using the starch and aldose assays.
9. Test the water using the starch and aldose assays.
10. In your notebook, create a data table to collect the data from each assay (see Table 6.1). Record the qualitative data in a quantitative (numerical) way. Describe the method used to quantify the data.

Table 6.1. **Results of Iodine and Benedict's Test on Sugars, Starch, and Protein Molecules**

Molecule Tested	Result(s) of Aldose Assay	Result(s) of Starch Assay	Comments
glucose			
maltose			
starch			
protein			
water (negative control)			

Data Analysis/Conclusion

Discuss how these indicator tests may be used during the production of amylase at a biotech company. Include a discussion of the negative control compared with the test groups. Of what value are these assays? What experimental errors may give misleading results?

Thinking Like a Biotechnician

1. How can you tell if a 2%-starch solution (versus some other concentration of starch) gives the best (most comparable) results for the starch assay standard test?
2. The aldose assay may display up to five color changes in the 2-minute reaction time. Propose an explanation for each of the colors that appear during the assay.
3. Drawing on your experience with sugar testing, is there any other indicator system that could be used to assay for the presence or concentration of sugar in this experiment?

Laboratory 6d
Assaying for Amylase Activity

Background

Amylase is an enzyme that catalyzes starch digestion (see Figure 6.4). It is used commercially in several ways: 1) to eliminate starch in products; 2) to produce sugar from starch; 3) in biofuel production. Using amylase to decompose starch is a cheap and effective method, but substantial quantities of amylase must be produced if it is to be used commercially. Similarly, amylase is an economical way to obtain sugar for use in beverages and baked goods since sources of starch, for example, cornstarch, are more readily available than sources of sugar (sugar cane).

Some bacteria and fungi cells in nature make amylase. Several herbivorous mammals synthesize amylase as well. In humans, amylase is made in two organs involved in food breakdown. In the mouth, salivary glands produce and excrete amylase (salivary amylase) to break down the starch in food into smaller units (maltose). The pancreas is another organ that makes amylase. Amylase is produced in the pancreas (pancreatic amylase) and excreted to the small intestines where it breaks down starch to maltose. The equation for the reaction catalyzed by amylase is as follows:

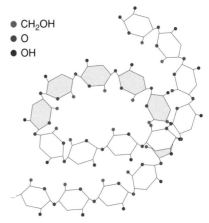

● CH₂OH
● O
● OH

Figure 6.4. Molecular Structure of Starch. Amylose is one type of plant starch. The amylose molecule is very long, composed of hundreds of glucose molecules linked together. Amylase breaks the bond between glucose molecules in the chain to produce the disaccharide, maltose.

$$\text{starch} \xrightarrow{\text{amylase}} \text{maltose} + \text{maltose} + \text{maltose}$$

How might a biotechnologist know that this reaction is taking place? What assay can be used to test for the activity of this enzyme?

Purpose

What is the behavior of the human enzyme, salivary amylase, compared with a 5-mg/mL bacterial amylase solution?

Materials

Environmental Health and Safety Officer

Paper cup
24-well microtiter plate
Pipets, 1 mL, and pump
Balance, weigh boat, lab scoops
Alfa Aesar® modified Soluble starch solution in 100 mM NaH$_2$PO$_4$, 6 mM NaCl, pH 7.0 buffer
Micropipet, P-1000 and tips

Micropipet, P-100 and tips
Lugol's Iodine Solution, diluted 1:2
Glass rods
100 mM NaH$_2$PO$_4$, 6mM NaCl, pH 7.0 buffer
alpha-amylase, 5 mg/mL, in 100 mM NaH$_2$PO$_4$, 6mM NaCl, pH 7.0

Glucose test strips
Tube rack for 1.7-mL tubes
Reaction tubes, 1.7 mL
Benedict's Solution
Dry heat block, 100°C
Lid locks for 1.7-mL tubes

Caution: Wear goggles and gloves when using chemicals.

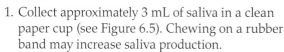

paper cup

3 mL

Figure 6.5. **Collecting Saliva.** Human alpha-amylase is found in saliva. Wait 20 minutes after eating or drinking before collecting saliva. When collecting saliva, remember that it is a biohazard that should be treated in a mature, safe fashion. Disinfect and dispose of all samples and spills after use.

Procedure

Testing for a decrease in starch and an increase in sugar due to amylase activity.

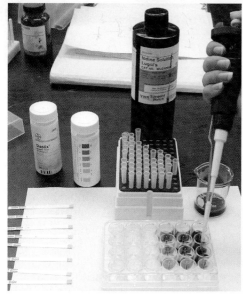

Figure 6.6. **Prepare everything before beginning. Be careful to not cross contaminate samples. Change tips with each measurement.** Photo by author.

1. Collect approximately 3 mL of saliva in a clean paper cup (see Figure 6.5). Chewing on a rubber band may increase saliva production.
2. Obtain a clean, 24-well plate (see Figure 6.6). Read the rest of the procedures, and label the wells that will be used. Before starting, make a diagram in your notebook of what is to be loaded into each well.
3. Place 1 mL of 2% starch solution in the first six wells of Rows A, B, and C. **Be sure to mix the starch solution before you take each sample.** How much 2%-starch solution do you have to make? Record the recipe in your notebook.
4. To Columns 1 and 4 of the wells, add 300 μL of human salivary amylase solution to each of the starch-filled wells. Mix each and wait 1 minute. To Column 4 of the wells, also add 20 μL of iodine. Mix each for 2 seconds with a clean glass rod. Be careful to not cross contaminate.
5. To Columns 2 and 5 of the wells, add 300 μL of 5 mg/mL bacterial amylase to each of the starch-filled wells. Mix each and wait 1 minute. To Column 5 of the wells, also add 20 μL of iodine. Mix each for 2 seconds with a clean glass rod.
6. To Columns 3 and 6 of the wells, add 300 μL of the 100 mM NaH$_2$PO$_4$, 6 mM NaCl, pH 7.0 buffer to each of the starch-filled wells. Mix each and wait 1 minute. To Column 6 of the wells, also add 20 μL of iodine. Mix each for 2 seconds with a clean glass rod.
7. Identify the positive and negative controls in this experiment. Make and record predictions as to what may occur in each well, including the expected color change.
8. Place the 24-well tray on a piece of white paper, out of direct light. Iodine decolorizes in light.
9. Create a data table to record individual sample data and average results for the amount of aldose produced in Columns 1, 2, and 3 and the amount of starch breakdown in Columns 4, 5, and 6. Sugar production is measured using both Benedict's solution and sugar test strips. Starch breakdown is measured by a decrease in the starch-iodine reaction.
   a. After 5 minutes, measure the amount of starch breakdown by recording the degree of lightening of the iodine solution from black to a light red-brown or clear color in the wells of Columns 4, 5, and 6 (5 → 0 rating).
   b. After 1 to 24 hours, measure Measure aldose concentration in Columns 1, 2, and 3 using sugar test strips as directed on the package (see Figure 6.7). Although readings can be made in percent (%) or milligrams per deciliter (mg/dL), for this activity, record the data in mg/dL. A deciliter (dL) is equal to 0.1 L.
   c. After 1 to 24 hours, measure the relative amount of aldose (5 → 0 rating) in the wells of Columns 1, 2, and 3 using a Benedict's solution test. Place 300 μL of sample plus 300 μL of Benedict's solution mixed in a 1.7-mL tube. Place a locking cap on the tube and heat in a 100°C heat block for 2 minutes. **Do not wear gloves when using a hot plate.** Record the color and relative amount of aldose present.

100°C

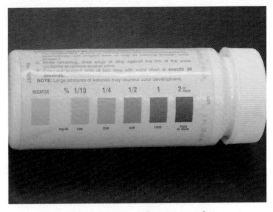

Figure 6.7. Glucose test strips are used to determine the presence and concentration of aldose sugars.
Photo by author.

Figure 6.8. A multichannel pipet speeds setting up the experiment because it allows for pipetting several samples at the same time.
Photo courtesy of Cell Genesys, Inc.

Data Analysis/Conclusion

Discuss the results of the experiment, including the behavior of the human salivary amylase compared with the bacterial amylase solution. Discuss possible errors in experimentation that could lead to erroneous or misleading results. Of what value is this type of assay? Where in industry might it be used?

Thinking Like a Biotechnician

1. Which of these assays should give the "best" (most reliable) results?
2. If an assay (starch or aldose) shows a 100-mg/dL glucose concentration, what is that value measured in percent (%) of glucose? Show the calculations.
3. Why would the use of a multichannel pipet give "better" results (see Figure 6.8)?

Laboratory 6e
Direct ELISA of Bacterial Alpha-Amylase

Optimized by Jonathan Tran, Heidi Pao, and Kevin Sun, Biotechnology students, 2010.

Background

How can a technician know that a particular protein of interest is present in a solution, and how can the concentration of that protein be determined? A technique that is commonly used in research and manufacturing to recognize the presence and concentration of protein in a solution is called an ELISA.

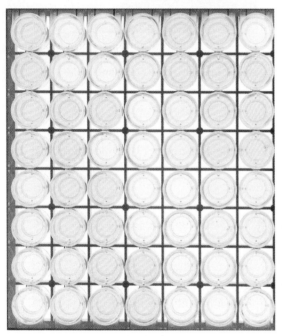

Figure 6.9. **ELISA test plate**
© Science Photo Library/Photo Researchers.

ELISA stands for enzyme-linked immunosorbent assay. In an ELISA, an antibody is used to recognize (immuno-, from immunological) and bind (-sorbent) a particular molecule (called an antigen), let's say amylase. Both the antibody and antigen are colorless, so an enzyme that can cause a colored reaction is attached onto the antibody (enzyme-linked). In this way, when an antibody with its enzyme attaches to an antigen, a reagent can be added and converted by the enzyme to a measurable color. (see Figure 6.9)

ELISAs are used to show the presence and concentration of specific proteins during protein production and purification. Two types of ELISAs, direct and indirect, are commonly used in research and manufacturing. The difference between them is that a direct ELISA uses a single antibody to recognize an antigen and an indirect ELISA uses two antibodies.

In this direct ELISA, a single, specific antibody (anti-α-amylase) binds with a specific antigen molecule (α-amylase). Conjugated onto the antibody is the enzyme horseradish peroxidase (HRP), which causes a colorimetric reagent, tetramethylbenzidine (TMB), to change colors from clear to blue. To stop the reaction, acid is added to denature the HRP enzyme. The TMB turns to a stable yellow color in acid. When the conjugated antibody is bound to the antigen and the reagent changes colors, a technician can measure the color change and infer the presence and concentration of the antigen (amylase).

Purpose

What is the concentration of bacterial α-amylase in unknown samples as determined by a direct ELISA?

Materials

Environmental Health
and Safety Officer

Peroxidase Conjugated IgG Fraction of anti-α-amylase (from *Bacillus amyloliquefaciens*) [Rabbit] available from G-Biosciences, prepared/diluted (1:30,000) anti-α-amylase-HRP antibody in 1X PBS. For 32 trials, mix 4 μL of Ab in 1X PBS to 120 mL, then add 600μL of 10% Tween 20.

α-amylase from *Bacillus subtilis*, available from G-Biosciences, 5 mL of 5 mg/mL in 1X PBS

Two samples of amylase (unknown concentrations), U1 and U2 (prepared by the instructor)

Plastic wrap

1X PBS Buffer [1.9 mM NaH$_2$PO$_4$ × H$_2$O (monohydrate), 8.1 mM Na$_2$HPO$_4$ (anhydrous), and 150 mM NaCl, pH 7.4]

Bovine serum albumin (BSA)

Tween 20, 10% solution

96-well Nunc-Immuno™ MaxiSorp™ ELISA plate or equivalent

0.5M HCl

TMB solution

Micropipets and tips

Tubes, 15 mL, conical, sterile, and rack

Reaction tubes and rack, 1.7 mL and 5 mL

Aluminum foil

Procedure

Day 1

Part I: Pre-Lab Preparation of Reagents

1. Prepare 200 mL of 1X PBS, pH 7.4, from 10X stock or using the recipe in the Materials List. Store at room temperature.
2. To a 50-mL sample of 1X PBS, add 250μL of 10% Tween 20 for the final washes at Part II, Step 12.
3. Using the 5 mg/mL stock amylase solution, prepare 5 mL of 0.5 mg/mL. Use the 0.5 mg/mL amylase in 1X PBS to prepare a 1:4 serial dilution to make 8 tubes containing at least 500μL each of 1:4; 1:16; 1:64; 1:256; 1:1024; 1:4096; 1:16.384; and a 1:65,536. Save the remaining 5 mg/mL amylase stock solution in 1 mL volumes (aliquots) and freeze them at -20°C for use in future lab activities (such as Lab 6f).
4. In your notebook, record how each of the dilutions was prepared. Place all tubes on ice or store for up to 1 week at 4°C. In your notebook record the concentration of these samples in μg/mL.
5. Prepare 100 mL of blocking solution (100 mL of 5% BSA in 1X PBS solution + 500μL of 10% Tween 20). Place on ice. The blocking solution is only good for a few days.
6. Measure 4.5 mL of diluted (1:30,000 dilution) anti-α-amylase-HRP antibody in 1X PBS/10% Tween-20 into a 5-mL sterile tube. Store on ice.
7. Measure 5 mL of 0.5X TMB solution into a 5-mL sterile tube. Wrap in foil and store on ice.
8. Place 1.5 mL of 0.5M HCl into a 1.7-mL tube.

Part II: Experimental Protocol

1. Obtain a 96-well Nunc-Immuno™ MaxiSorp™ ELISA plate.
2. Label nine columns for the amylase samples: 1:4; 1:16; 1:64; 1:256; 1:1024; 1:4096; 1:16,384; 1:65,536; and –C (negative control = 1X PBS buffer).
3. Label three rows "A, B, and C". These labels mark the three replications of each of the different amylase concentrations. Put lab group initials and the date on the plate next to well G12.
4. Label Wells E6, E7, and E8 as "U1" for the testing of three replications of U1.
5. Label Wells G6, G7, and G8 as "U2" for the testing of three replications of U2.
6. Add 125 μL of the appropriate amylase sample to each well. Change micropipet tips each time. Gently tilt the plate once to swirl. Cover with foil. Incubate at room temperature on an orbital shaker for 15 minutes. What mass of protein is in each well? Record the mass of the well samples in your notebook.
7. Use a micropipet to remove all of the contents of each well. Change tips for each sample. Then, make sure all of the wells are dry by repeatedly hitting the inverted plate on a pile of paper towels. Repeat at a clean spot on the paper towel until all of the samples have been removed from all the wells.
8. Add 250 μL of blocking solution to each well. Gently tilt once to swirl. Cover. Incubate at room temperature on an orbital shaker for 30 minutes. Remove all of the blocking solution, first using a micropipet, then by hitting against a paper towel pile. Add 250 μL of blocking solution to each well. Swirl for 1 minute. Continue with the procedures. If time is an issue, you can leave covered plates overnight at 4°C.

Day 2

9. Remove all of the blocking solution, first using a micropipet, then by hitting against a paper towel pile.
10. Rinse each well 5 times with 250 μL of blocking solution. Gently swirl at room temperature for 1 minute before removing each wash.
11. Add 125 μL of the diluted HRP-linked anti-amylase antibody to each well. Gently tilt once to swirl. Cover with foil. Incubate at room temperature on an orbital shaker for 15 minutes.
12. Remove all of the antibody, first using a micropipet, then by hitting against a paper towel pile. Rinse 5 times with 250 μL of 1X PBS/Tween 20. Gently swirl at room temperature for 1 minute before removing each wash.

13. Quickly add 125 µL of 0.5X TMB solution to each well. Cover the ELISA plate with aluminum foil so that no light shines on the plate. Check in 1-minute intervals for evidence of a color change. The HRP oxidizes the TMB molecules, causing them to change from clear to blue.

14. Keep checking the degree of blueness in each well in intervals of 1 minute or until the samples are blue but the control is clear or very light blue. Have the HCl acid ready to add. Before the negative control starts turning blue, go to the next step.

15. Quickly add 30 µL of 0.5 *M* HCl to each well. Swirl the contents of the well before changing tips and adding acid to the next well. The acid turns the blue TMB to a yellow color and denatures the HRP so that no further reaction occurs, and the yellow color is stable for a few hours. The amount of yellow color, compared with the negative control, is an indication of the amount of protein that the ELISA antibody recognizes.

16. In a data table in your notebook, record the degree of yellow color for all the replications of each test (0 = no yellow/clear; 5 = lemon yellow).

17. Photograph the plate from the top and from the side for another record of the yellow change in the wells.

18. Use a P-1000 to transfer all of each sample for a given concentration into a 1.7-mL reaction tube. Pool the samples at each concentration with the samples of another group whose yellow coloring is similar to yours.

19. Use a UV spectrophotometer to take absorbance readings of your samples at 475 nm. Use the negative control sample as the spectrophotometry blank. Record the absorbance data on a data table.

20. Create a best-fit linear graph that shows the relationship between the known concentrations of amylase (in µg/mL) and their absorbance.

21. Use the best-fit linear graph to estimate the concentration of U1 and U2. If the graph was produced in Microsoft® Excel®, determine the equation of the line (y=mx+b) using "Add Trendline" (on the Chart menu) and use it to calculate the concentration of each unknown.

Data Analysis/Conclusion

Evaluate your ability to perform an ELISA that distinguishes between different concentrations of the protein amylase. Were the different concentrations appropriately yellow, or in the case of the negative control, not yellow? Explain the coloration in the multiple replications of each sample. Are the ELISA results "good enough" to estimate the concentration of the two unknown samples? If so, what is the best estimate of their concentration?

Thinking Like a Biotechnician

1. After developing an ELISA, all wells are colored. Give three reasons that all wells, including the negative control would be colored.

2. A lab technician makes a micropipeting mistake and accidentally adds too much antibody when making the 1:30,000 dilution. The actual concentration of the diluted antibody is closer to 1:3000. How might that pipeting error affect the ELISA results?

3. Explain what might happen if the pH of the 1X PBS was at pH 5.5 instead of pH 7.4.

Laboratory 6f
Recognizing Bacterial Amylase on a PAGE Gel

Background

In a recombinant amylase production facility, samples are taken from cell cultures as well as protein purification and analyzed for the presence, concentration, and activity of the enzyme. Along with indicator assays, SDS-polyacyrlamide gel electrophoresis is routinely used to recognize the protein of interest (amylase) in those samples. On a SDS-PAGE gel, a particular protein will show a characteristic banding pattern of its polypeptide chain(s).

The protocol for running proteins on a SDS-PAGE gel is fairly standard and was presented in Lab 5f. Samples are suspended in a sample preparation buffer containing a detergent (SDS) and a denaturing agent (such as DTT or BME) to linearize the proteins in the sample. Samples are further denatured by subjecting them to high heat just prior to loading them on the gel. Depending on the protein, 10 µg – 100 µg amounts of the protein may be resolved (clearly seen) on a gel. Samples are prepared and loaded at different concentrations and volumes with the goal of seeing a distinct band(s) at the protein's known molecular weight (size).

In this activity, the bacterial amylase of interest has a single polypeptide chain and a molecular weight of approximately 55 kDA (See Figure 6.10). Creating amylase standard samples of known concentration and running them on a gel will give the technician "polypeptide band fingerprint" of the protein. Then, when samples collected during research and manufacture (unknown samples) are run on a similar gel, a technician can confirm the presence of amylase and estimate its concentration in the original collected sample.

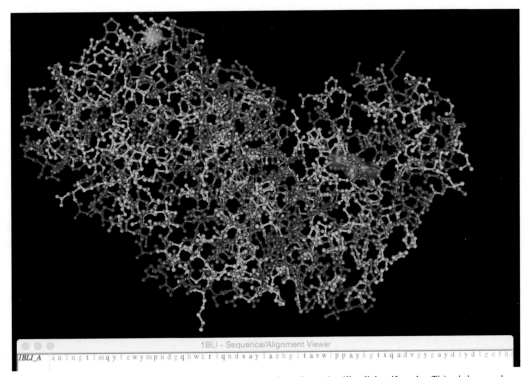

Figure 6.10.   Three Dimensional Model of Alpha-Amylase from *Bacillus licheniformis*   This alpha amylase molecule has a single polypeptide chain composed of 483 amino acid residues. The amino acids are color-coded in the model. This amylase molecule's molecular weight is approximately 55 kDa. On a SDS-PAGE gel, the protein denatures to its primary structure and appears as a single band at approximately 55 kDa.
Courtesy of *Molecule World*, Digital World Biology, LLC.

Purpose

- Does running known bacterial amylase samples on an SDS-PAGE gel, confirm that it has a single polypeptide chain and a molecular weight of 55 kDa?
- What amount (mass in µg) of amylase in the loaded samples gives the best resolved single 55 kDa band (a single dark, think band)?
- What is the approximate mass of amylase in the 8 mL unknown sample provided by the Supervisor?

Materials

Bacterial amylase stock sample, frozen sample prepared in the Lab 6e or fresh sample (5 mg/mL amylase in 1X PBS, pH 7.0)

Unknown bacterial amylase sample (U), 8 mL, provided by Supervisor

1.7-mL microcentrifuge tubes

1X PAGE electrophoresis running buffer (see recipe in Lab 5f or dilute from 10X concentrate)

2X PAGE sample prep buffer (see recipe in Lab 5f or use commercial brand)

BME (to add to 2X PAGE sample prep buffer, if no other reducing agent such as DTT, has been added)

SDS-PAGE molecular weight protein sizing standard markers

Microcentrifuge

P-20, P-200 micropipets with standard and PAGE loading tips

TRIS-glycine gel (10 well, 10% preferred)

Vertical gel box

Power supply, 300V

Heat block, 90°C

Lid locks

Coomassie Blue protein stain and destain (recipe in Lab 5f or commercial brand)

Staining dishes (such as 150 × 15-mm Petri dishes)

Photo-imaging system

Procedure

Note: Prepare 1X PAGE running buffer and 2X Sample Prep Loading Dye (SPLD) before beginning.

1. Aliquot 70 µL of 5 mg/mL stock amylase sample from the class sample. Label the tube and keep it on ice.
2. Get a tube of the unknown sample (U) from your Supervisor (50 µL). Keep it on ice.
3. In a chemical fume hood, prepare 2X Sample Prep Loading Dye with BME (SPLD/BME) by aliquoting 950 µL of SPLD (from Lab 5f) and 50 µL of BME into a labeled 1.5 mL tube. Pipet up and down gently to mix. Tightly seal this tube.
3. Prepare amylase standard samples of known mass by diluting the 5 mg/mL stock amylase sample in 2X SPLD/BME according to the following sample matrix. Add the buffer first, then the stock amylase and add SPLD/BME last. Pipet up and down once to mix. Label them with the mass of amylase they contain. Store all samples at 4°C until ready to use.

Table 6.2. **Amylase Concentration Standard Sample Preparation Matrix**

Amylase in known standard samples (µg)	5 mg/mL Amylase Stock in Sample (µL)	2X SPLD/BME in Sample (µL)	Amount of IX PAGE Running Buffer (µL)	Total Sample (µL)
75	15	15	0	30
50	10	15	5	30
25	5	15	10	30
12.5	2.5	15	12.5	30
6.25	1.25	15	13.75	30
0	0	15	15	30

4. Prepare 3 dilutions of the unknown amylase samples provided by the Supervisor according to the following sample matrix. Add the buffer first, then the unknown amylase sample and add SPLD/BME last. Pipet up and down once to mix. Store all samples at 4°C until ready to use.

Table 6.3. Unknown Amylase Samples Preparation Matrix

Tube Label	Unknown Amylase Sample (µL)	2X SPLD/BME in Sample (µL)	Amount of IX PAGE Running Buffer (µL)	Total Sample (µL)
U 1:1	15	15	0	30
U 1:2	7.5	15	7.5	30
U 1:4	3.75	15	11.25	30

5. Prepare and place a SDS-PAGE vertical gel in a vertical gel box (refer to Lab 5f, if needed). Make sure the orientation of the gel exposes the wells to the inner chamber. Rinse the wells with 1X PAGE running buffer. Fill the inner and out chambers of the gel box with 1X PAGE running buffer. In your notebook, record the % concentration of the gel, the lot number, and the expiration date.

6. Immediately before loading the samples onto a gel, seal the tubes tightly using lidlocks, then denature the proteins in all the samples by placing the tubes in an 90°C heat block for 3 minutes only. This step might have to wait if the gel is not ready to be loaded.

7. Hook up the power supply, and run the empty gel for 3 minutes at a minimum of 35 mA to warm it up and to make sure current is flowing.

8. Load the gel wells with 30 µL of each known sample using special, long-tipped PAGE gel loading tips, if they are available. Use a new tip with each load. Load them in the following order:

Well 1	Well 2	Well 3	Well 4	Well 5	Well 6	Well 7	Well 8	Well 9	Well 10
75	50	25	12.5	6.25	0	markers	U 1:1	U 1:2	U 1:4

Be careful to load all of the sample without overflowing into the adjoining wells.

9. Into Well #7, load only 10 µL of Protein Molecular Weight Sizing Standard Markers standards. **Note:** Prestained sizing standards are available from several suppliers. Be sure to have an image of the sizing standard markers that are used available for gel analysis.

10. As soon as all samples are loaded, run the gel at the manufacturer's recommend current or voltage until the loading dye reaches the bottom of the gel. Sample preparation buffer/ loading dye serves as tracking dye. Once the power is turned on, check for bubbling. If the current goes down, make sure there is enough buffer covering the wells in the back reservoir.

11. Remove the gel from gel box. Following the manufacturer's guidelines, gently separate the two gel plates holding the gel in place. Loosen the gel from the plate using a squirt of running buffer if needed.

12. Using water in a Petri plate for adhesion, gently drop the gel onto deionized water in a large Petri dish or staing tray. Rotate the gel in the water for 1 minute. Gently remove the water from the plate by decanting or using a vacuum pump.

13. Add enough Coomassie Blue staining solution to just cover the gel. Stain for the manufacturer's recommended time or a minimum of 3 hours if using Coomassie Blue stain solution that was prepared using the Lab 5f recipe. Rotating the staining gel on an orbital shaker is desirable for even staining.

14. Remove Coomassie Blue stain, and cover gel with destaining solution or dH_2O for at least 7 hours or a manufacturer's recommended time. Change destaining solution several times and usings a lab wipe tissue as a stain sink will speed destaining (see Lab 5f). Rotate the destaining gel on an orbital shaker if available. Destain until the background is light enough to easily distinguish polypeptide bands. The destain may have to be changed periodically.

15. Examine the polypeptide banding pattern on gel on a white-light box. Use a photo-imaging system to take a photograph of the gel. Make copies for each lab partner.

16. Paste the gel photograph into your lab notebook and label all the sample wells. Record the size (in kDa) of the sizing standard marker bands that are visible. Label at least on amylase band in one of the known concentration standard samples. Record its approximate size in kDa.

17. If the unknown samples show an amylase band, label one. Identify the amount (mass in µg) of amylase in the loaded samples that best shows a single dark, think band of amylase at 55 kDa band. Place an asterisk (*) by that band on the gel photograph.

Data Analysis/Conclusion

In a concluding statement discuss whether you can confirm that known bacterial amylase samples contained a single polypeptide chain with an approximate size of 55 kDa? Describe the difference in the resolution of bands in samples with different amounts of amylase. Give evidence and explanations for your findings. Based on the dilutions and volumes loaded plus the resolution of the unknown samples, determine the approximate total mass of amylase in the 8 mL unknown sample provided by the Supervisor. Average that mass determination with calculation by other groups in the class. How close is your group's amylase mass determination in the unknown sample as compared to the class average? Discuss technical errors that could lead to misleading data. Describe how using PAGE and estimating the mass of a protein is used in the production of a biotechnology product such as amylase.

Thinking Like a Biotechnician

1. If 25 µL of an unknown amylase sample (not including loading dye) is loaded on a SDS-PAGE gel, and the band that resolves is determined to have approximately 40 µg of protein, what is the approximate concentration of amylase in the loaded sample?
2. A sample suspected to have amylase in it is collected during cell culture. It is assayed for amylase activity and a moderate amount is shown. Samples are run on an SDS-PAGE but no bands in any dilutions appear. Explain why this may happen and what should a technician do about it?

Laboratory 6g
Western Blot to Identify Alpha-Amylase

Developed by Wesley Chow, Joanne Dai, Jodi Sato, Biotechnology students, 2009–2010.

Background

Studying proteins on a denaturing SDS/polyacrylamide gel can reveal the approximate molecular weight and number of polypeptides in a protein. Once the banding pattern for a protein is known, it can be used to identify the protein in future samples.

However, since there are so many proteins with similar molecular weights, a method to identify a specific protein on a gel is valuable. The Western blot technique allows for the recognition and visualization of a particular protein on a PAGE gel. In a sample of hundreds of proteins, as in cell extracts or in broth cultures, a Western blot can recognize bands of a particular protein in a mixture (Figure 6.11).

Western blotting utilizes antibody-antigen specificity. A PAGE gel with samples containing a protein of interest is run. At the end of the gel run, a positively charged membrane (ie, nitrocellulose) is laid over the gel and the gel/membrane sandwich is placed in a transfer box. When current is applied, proteins on the gel move to the membrane (blot). Antibodies can be used to recognize the blotted proteins.

Antibodies (ie, anti-alpha amylase) can be purchased that recognize the unique structure of a specific antigen molecule (ie, alpha-amylase) and bind to it. Using antibodies that have attached colored markers, enzymes, or other reporter molecules, a technician can visualize an antigen of interest on the blot.

Figure 6.11. **A Western blot with proteins of decreasing concentration from left to right. The colorless proteins are visible on the blot because an antibody, carrying an enzyme that causes a clear reagent to turn blue, recognizes the protein antigen and binds to it.**
Photo by author.

For this blot, a PAGE gel is run with samples of amylase at different concentrations. The gel is blotted onto a nitrocellulose membrane using a Western-blot transfer unit. The membrane is treated with an anti-alpha amylase antibody that binds only to alpha-amylase. The antibody has an enzyme [horseradish peroxidase (HRP)] attached to it. When tetramethylbenzidine (TMB) is washed over the blot, HRP changes the TMB from clear to blue, and blue bands are visible on the membrane where amylase is found.

Purpose

What concentrations of alpha-amylase can be identified on a Western blot?

Materials

Environmental Health and Safety Officer

Gloves and safety goggles
TRIS-HCl
Sodium dodecyl sulfate (SDS)
Glycerol
pH meter, pH paper, and pH buffers
1 M HCl
10% NaOH
Pipets and pumps
Micropipets and tips
Media or storage bottles
TRIS

Glycine
Beta-mercaptoethanol (BME)
Bromophenol blue
Reaction tubes, 1.7 mL, sterile and racks
Calcium chloride, anhydrous
Methanol, 99%
Sodium chloride
Tween 20
Bovine serum albumin (BSA)
EDTA

Anti-amylase antibody-HRP (Peroxidase Conjugated IgG Fraction of anti-α-amylase, from *Bacillus amyloliquefaciens*) [Rabbit] available from G-Biosciences
Amylase, Scholar Chemistry
Deionized water, sterile
10-well, 10% TRIS-glycine (or Bis-TRIS) PAGE gel
Gel box, vertical, for PAGE with transfer unit

Power supply | Western blot transfer kit | Plastic wrap
Lid locks for 1.7-mL tubes | sponge blotting pads | Aluminum foil
Dry heat block, 90°C | Filter paper, 12.5 cm | Beakers, 50 mL
Transfer pipets, 3 mL | Nitrocellulose paper | Graduated cylinder, 25 mL, 12/
PAGE gel loading tips | Forceps | CS
Protein sizing standard markers | Petri dish, 150 × 15 mm | Digital camera
1 M TRIS | TMB |

Procedure
Day 1

Part I: Pre-Lab—Buffer, Reagent, and Sample Preparation (for about 10 Western blots)

1. Prepare 100 mL of 4X TRIS-HCl/SDS buffer, pH 6.8.
   a. Put 6.05 g TRIS base in 60 mL H_2O.
   b. Adjust pH to 6.8 with 1 M HCl.
   c. Add dH_2O until the total volume is 80 mL.
   d. Add 0.4 g SDS (weigh and add to solution in fume hood, shield down, fan off, do not inhale).
   e. Add dH_2O until the total volume is 100 mL.
   f. Store at room temperature for up to 1 month.
2. Prepare 6X SDS Loading Dye Buffer (SLDB)/BME.
   a. Use 7 mL of 4X TRIS-HCl/SDS buffer, pH 6.8.
   b. Add 3 mL glycerol (30% in final sample).
   c. Add 1 g SDS (10% final) (weigh and add to solution in fume hood, shield down, fan off, do not inhale).
   d. In a (running) chemical fume hood, add 0.5 mL βME (5%).
   e. Add 12 mg bromophenol blue (0.12%).
   f. Add dH_2O until the total volume is 10 mL.
   g. Gently mix until all ingredients are in solution.
   h. Store in 0.5 mL aliquots at -20°C.
3. Prepare 1 L of 10X PAGE Running Buffer.
   a. Use 30.3 g TRIS base.
   b. Add 144 g glycine.
   c. Fill to 750 mL with dH_2O.
   d. Add 10 g SDS (weigh and add to solution in fume hood, shield down, fan off, do not inhale).
   e. Add dH_2O until the total volume is 1L.
   f. Store at room temperature for up to 1 month.
   (*Dilute to 1X before using it in vertical gel electrophoresis.*)
4. Prepare 1.5 L of Western Blot Transfer Buffer.
   a. Use 8.7 g TRIS base.
   b. Add 43.5 g glycine.
   c. Add dH_2O until the total volume is 1L.
   d. Add 300 mL methanol (Add methanol right before use since methanol evaporates quickly.)
   e. Add dH_2O to a total of 1.5 L.
5. Prepare 1 L of 10X TBST buffer (0.5 M TRIS Base, 9% NaCl, 0.5% Tween 20, pH 7.6).
   a. Use 61.0 g TRIS base.
   b. Add 90.0 g NaCl.
   c. Fill to 700 mL with dH_2O.
   d. Adjust the pH to 7.6 with HCl.
   e. Add 5 mL of Tween 20.
   f. Add dH_2O to a total of 1L.
6. Prepare 100 mL of Blocking Buffer (3% BSA in 1X TBST).
   a. Use 3g of Bovine serum albumin.
   b. Add 1X TBST until the total volume is 100 mL.

c. Mix gently until all the BSA goes into solution.
(*May be stored for up to 2 days at 4°C.*)
7. Prepare 1L of Stop Solution (10 m*M* TRIS-HCl, 0.1 m*M* EDTA, pH 8.0)
   a. Use 1.576 g TRIS-HCl.
   b. Add 0.0292248 g EDTA.
   c. Add dH$_2$O to a total of 750 mL.
   d. Adjust the pH to 8.0.
   e. Add dH$_2$O to a total of 1L.
   f. Store at 4°C.
8. Prepare a 1:30,000 dilution of anti-amylase antibody-HRP (Peroxidase Conjugated IgG Fraction of anti-α-amylase, from *Bacillus amyloliquefaciens*) [Rabbit] available from G-Biosciences).
   a. Measure 3 µL stock anti-amylase antibody conjugated with HRP.
   b. Mix the antibody with 90 mL of blocking solution.
   c. Store for up to 2 days at 4°C.
9. Prepare 5 mL of 0.08 µg/µL of amylase sample solution (8 µL of 50 mg/mL amylase stock in 5 mL of 1X PAGE running buffer). Store for up to 2 days at 4°C.
10. Prepare samples of diluted amylase as per the Table 6.2 dilution matrix. Store samples for up to 2 days at 4°C.

Table 6.2. **Amylase Sample Dilution Matrix**

Concentration (µg/µL)	Amount from 0.08 µg/µL (µL)	6X SDS Loading Dye Buffer/BME (SLDB/BME) (µL)	IX PAGE Running Buffer (µL)
0.04	24	6	24
0.02	12	6	36
0.01	6	6	42
0.005	3	6	45
0.0025	1.5	6	46.5
0	0	6	48

Day 2

Part II: Run PAGE for Western blot

1. Set up a 10-well, 10%-Bis TRIS or TRIS-glycine (TG) gel. Do not use NuPage® gels unless you use NuPage® buffers). Run the gel for 5 minutes at 35 mAmp.
2. Place locking lids on amylase samples and heat them at 90°C for 5 minutes prior to loading.
3. Quickly load samples into the gel according to the Table 6.3 loading matrix.

Table 6.3. **Amylase Sample PAGE Loading Matrix**

Well #	Sample	µL to Load
1	SDS Loading Dye Buffer/BME	8
2	Protein Standard #1	10
3	0.04 µg/µL amylase	20
4	0.02 µg/µL amylase	20
5	0.01 µg/µL amylase	20
6	0.005 µg/µL amylase	20
7	0.0025 µg/µL amylase	20
8	Protein Standard #2	10
9	Negative control	15
10	SDS Loading Dye Buffer/BME	8

4. Run at 35 mAmp (or 100 V) for about 1 hour until the blue dye reaches the bottom of

the gel. If the current decreases, use a transfer pipet to periodically add 1 *M* TRIS to the electrophoresis chambers.

5. Fill a large Petri dish with transfer buffer. Remove the gel from the cassette and transfer it to the Petri dish. Cut a tiny piece off the top left corner of the gel. Do not let the gel sit in transfer buffer for more than 10 minutes.

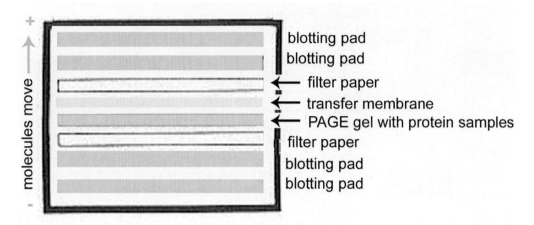

Figure 6.12. **Western Blot Gel Transfer Membrane Sandwich.**

Western Blot Transfer Procedure

1. Using forceps, take out a piece of nitrocellulose membrane.
2. Cut a small piece off the top right corner of the nitrocellulose membrane. Using a pencil, label the top of the membrane with your initials.
3. Submerge the nitrocellulose membrane completely in the transfer buffer for at least 10 minutes.
4. Soak two pieces of filter paper in transfer buffer for 5 minutes.
5. Carefully remove the gel from the Petri dish.
6. Wearing gloves, lay down one blotting pad on the negative side of the transfer cassette.
7. Lay down one piece of filter paper on the blotting pad. Use a pipette to roll the filter paper to ensure there are no air bubbles.
8. Place the gel exactly on top of the wet filter paper so the cut corner of the gel is on the top left of the filter paper.
9. Carefully place the nitrocellulose membrane on the gel so that the cut corners match up. This should position the pencil label on the gel side of the membrane. You may not move the membrane once it is placed, so make sure it is nice and wet. Using a 15-mL tube, roll over the sandwich once to push out air bubbles and then do not move it.
10. Place another piece of filter paper and two more blotting pads on top of the membrane and close the transfer cassette with the positive side (see Figure 6.12).
11. Place the membrane sandwich cassette in the transfer unit, and fill it with transfer buffer. Transfer at approximately 65 mA for 1.5 to 2 hours or at 20V overnight.
12. After the transfer has been completed, disassemble the transfer cassette and using forceps, move the nitrocellulose membrane to a staining tray (large Petri dish), protein-side facing up.
13. Add 20 mL of blocking buffer to the membrane and rotate at room temperature for 1 hour. Or, leave the membrane in the blocking buffer and place at 4°C to be visualized the next day.

Part III: Western Blot Staining/Visualization

1. On the membrane, where the protein standard that is closest to the size of amylase is, *carefully* cut a small incision on the side of the membrane to mark the standard bands. DO NOT cut these bands off; just cut a small notch to leave a placeholder in the side of the membrane since the standard may wash off during the visualization process.
2. Remove the blocking buffer and rinse the membrane 5 times with 20 mL of blocking solution for 1 minute each. Discard each wash.
3. Cover the membrane with 20 mL of 1:30,000 diluted anti-amylase antibody-HRP solution. Pour the solution on one side of the Petri dish, then slowly tilt it so that the solution moves over the membrane. Wrap the staining tray (containing the membrane) in foil.
4. Rotate the membrane with antibody solution at room temperature for 1 hour. After 1 hour, discard the solution.
5. Wash 5 times with 20 mL of 1X TBST for 1 minute each. Remove each rinse.
6. Before adding the colorimetric reagent (TMB) to the membrane, find a designated area where photographs of the membrane can be taken without moving the membrane. A brightly lit area with a large piece of plain white paper is good. Have a digital camera ready.
7. Cover the membrane with 20 mL of TMB solution. Pour the solution on one side of the Petri dish, then slowly tilt it so that the solution moves over the membrane. Swirl the membrane one time, but then keep the membrane as still as possible to allow the blue TMB to deposit over the amylase samples.
8. Immediately cover with foil and check every 2 minutes for color development.
9. When the bands of anti-amylase antibody-HRP/TMB are dark enough to clearly see the difference in amylase concentration, quickly photograph the membrane. Then, pipet the solution off the membrane and photograph the membrane again.
10. Add 50 mL of stop solution and gently lift the membrane out of the dish. Place on filter paper, photograph again, and let dry.

Data Analysis/Conclusion

Evaluate your ability to perform a Western blot that distinguishes between different concentrations of amylase in solution. Were the different concentrations of amylase appropriately blue? What concentrations of amylase were visible on the blot? What was the lowest concentration to be detected? Look at other blots. How does your blot result compare to the results of others? Of what value is Western blotting in protein research and manufacturing?

Thinking Like a Biotechnician

1. After developing the blot, no bands are visible anywhere on the membrane. List several reasons why few or no bands may be visible on the blot?
2. Describe why having just the right concentration of antibody in the blot is important. What might the blot look like if too much antibody is added?
3. This Western blot takes a whole day to complete (if you work all the way through). Suggest a step in the protocol where a change may still give the expected results but might cut down the overall time to completion. Explain what effect the change may have on the blot bands.

7 Using the Spectrophotometer for DNA and Protein Assays

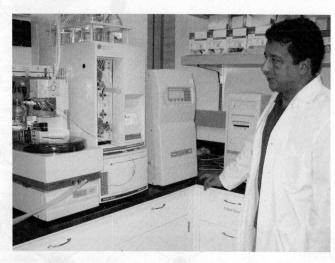

Scientist Dr. Eric Memarzadeh uses an HPLC (high performance liquid chromatography) to separate proteins in a mixture. One of the components of the HPLC is an ultraviolet (UV) spectrophotometer. The UV spec measures the absorbance of light by the proteins in the sample once they have separated. A molecule has a characteristic wavelength of light at which it absorbs the most light. That wavelength is used to identify each of the molecules in the mixture and estimate the concentration of each.
Photo courtesy of Eric Memarzadeh.

The spectrophotometer (spec, for short) is one of the most valuable instruments in a biotechnology facility. With a spec, a technician can characterize and quantify the amount of a molecule in a solution.

A spec works on the principle that every molecule absorbs light energy but not the same amount of the same kind of light. The wavelength at which a molecule absorbs the most light can be used to recognize the molecule in a solution. Since more molecules will absorb more light, the amount of molecules in solution (concentration) can be determined based on the amount of light absorbed by a sample, as compared to solutions of known concentration.

In the following activities you will learn how to operate a spectrophotometer and how to use it to determine DNA and protein concentration. Specifically, you will learn:

- the parts of a visible spectrophotometer and how changing the wavelength setting changes the color of light on a sample.
- how to determine the wavelength of maximum light absorbance for a sample (lambda$_{max}$)
- how to use a VIS spectrophotometer, if a protein is colorful, to determine its concentration in solution
- what pI is and its role in preparing a buffer to maintain a protein at a specified pH
- how to isolate a protein from solution using ammonium sulfate precipitation
- how to use a UV spectrophotometer to determine the presence and concentration of a colorless protein in solution
- how to determine the concentration of an unknown protein solution using a best-fit standard curve
- how to determine the concentration and relative purity of a DNA sample

Stand-alone spectrophotometers or specs built into instruments, such as an HPLC or ELISA plate readers, allow biotechnologists to keep track of their protein product during research and manufacturing. In future chapters, you will use spectrophotometers to recognize and quantify several of the proteins you will be studying, including those made during recombinant protein production.

Laboratory 7a
Learning To Use the Spectrophotometer

Background

A spectrophotometer uses light (*photo*) to measure (*meter*) molecules. To understand how to use a spectrophotometer, it is helpful to understand something about the nature of light and how it interacts with molecules.

The sun produces a spectrum of several different types of radiant light energy (electromagnetic radiation), including radio waves, microwaves, x-rays, and visible light waves. Sunlight is energy and, therefore, it can be used to "perform work," including reactions, such as photosynthesis in plants, in which sunlight energy works on water and carbon dioxide molecules to produce carbohydrates. Dye in fabric is another example of how light energy can affect molecules. Think about when you wear a pair of dark blue pants. If you sit outside under a shady tree, the material stays relatively cool to the touch. On the other hand, if you sit in the sun, the dark blue material becomes hot in the sunlight because the blue molecules absorb high-energy light waves.

All types of light energy travel through space in waves. Light waves comes in different forms and colors, including blue light, violet light, ultraviolet light, red light, and infrared light, to name a few. The colored light (waves) that we see is part of the visible light spectrum (VIS). We see light as different colors because of differences in the wavelengths of the light waves (see Figure 7.1). A wavelength is the distance between the crest, or top, of light waves and is measured in nanometers (nm). Wavelengths of 350 to 700 nm make up the visible (you can see them) spectrum. The photoreceptors in our eyes can detect these wavelengths of light. Which of the three wavelengths of light shown in Figure 7.1 would be visible to our eyes?

We cannot see the actual light waves for several reasons, including that the light wavelengths are too tiny. However, we can see color. This is because the nerve cells in our eyes are stimulated by certain colors, or light wavelengths. In other words, each of the wavelengths of light (blue, green, red, etc) affects our eyes' light detectors differently.

Different wavelengths store varying amounts of energy. The shorter the wavelength, the more energy that particular color of light contains. Think about the waves that hit a beach. If they arrived faster, would they hit you with more, or less, total energy in a minute than waves that were spaced farther apart? Which of the wavelengths of light shown in Figure 7.1 has the most energy?

The visible part of the light spectrum is shown in Figure 7.2. Light that is not visible to the human eye includes x-rays (around 100 nm), UV light (around 250 nm), and infrared light (over 700 nm). Draw the light spectrum in your notebook and include the light that is not in the visible spectrum.

White light contains all the wavelengths of visible light. Colored molecules can either absorb or transmit part or all of this light energy. Substances appear to be a certain color because of

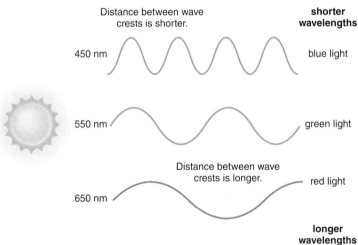

Figure 7.1. **Light travels in waves.**

The Visible Spectrum

The wavelength of different colors of light energy

Figure 7.2. **Visible Spectrum.** Wavelengths below 350 nm and above 700 nm are not usually visible to the human eye, but they may be visible to other organisms, such as bees, which see UV light. This is a "typical" visible spectrum since the actual wavelengths of light visible to each person varies due to age and genetics.

the light energy they do *not* absorb. The light bounces off the molecules (transmitted/reflected), hits your eye, and you see it as a certain color. A red T-shirt appears red because dye molecules in the material reflect red wavelengths.

The VIS spectrophotometer can be used to measure the amount and type of colored light (wavelength) absorbed or transmitted by molecules or cells in solution. This can reveal important information about the nature of the molecules being studied. Since the light energy that a molecule absorbs may be used to run chemical processes, such as photosynthesis, absorbance information can also help us understand reactions in cells. In addition, absorbance data are used to recognize and determine the concentration of molecules or cells in solution.

In this lab activity, you will learn how a VIS spectrophotometer works. In subsequent activities, you will use both VIS and UV specs to study molecules in solution.

Purpose

What wavelengths of the visible spectrum are visible to you in the VIS spectrophotometer in your lab? What is your own personal visible spectrum?
How is it different from your lab partners' and the typical visible spectrum in Figure 7.2?

Materials

Spectrophotometer, Spectronic 20 D+ or similar VIS spectrophotometer
Filter paper, 12.5 cm
Tubes, glass, 13 × 100 mm (cuvette)

Procedure

Turn on the spec and let it warm up for at least 20 minutes before beginning step 2.

1. To understand how the spectrophotometer works, do the following:
   a. Familiarize yourself with the model of spectrophotometer in your lab.
   b. In your notebook, draw a simplified version of the VIS spectrophotometer available in your facility.
   c. Find and label all the parts: power switch, wavelength control, 0% transmittance knob, 100% transmittance knob, sample holder, filter lever (if there is one), display, and the absorbance and transmittance mode settings. If necessary, your instructor will help you find them.
2. Cut a strip of white paper to fit into a spectrophotometer cuvette (13 × 100-mm spec tube). Then, insert it into the tube. Gently, place the cuvette in the sample holder so that the inside of the fold faces the light source (see Figure 7.3).
3. Set the mode to "transmittance." Turn the 100% transmittance knob to the right until it stops. Don't force it past the stopping point. Leave the sample holder open and cup your hands around the opening. Look through your hands into the sample holder.
4. Have your lab partner set the wavelength at 600 nm and adjust the tube so that you see the maximum amount of orange light on the paper.
5. Turn the wavelength knob slowly **in each direction** and record the range of wavelengths at which you see different colors. Make a data table to record these data.

   a. Do you see other or "in-between" colors?
   b. At which wavelength(s)?
   c. Add these to your data table.

6. Make sure that all partners repeat steps 4 through 5.

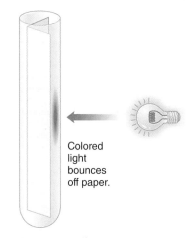

Figure 7.3. **Filter paper in cuvette. Light of a specific wavelength reflects off the filter paper. By turning the wavelength knob, you can determine the color of each wavelength.**

Colored light bounces off paper.

Create a graph that shows the range of colors at different wavelengths. Experiment with bar, column, line, and X-Y scatter graphs until you have one that shows your data well. Make sure that both the wavelength axis and the data plot run continuously from 350 nm through 700 nm. Color-code the data plot.

   Write a paragraph that describes how your personal visible spectrum is similar to or different from the "typical" visible spectrum in Figure 7.2 and your lab partners'.

Thinking Like a Biotechnician

1. What are the approximate wavelengths of the colors, blue-green, mustard-yellow, and red-orange?
2. What factors may affect the range of your visible spectrum?
3. What nerve cells are responsible for color vision? Use the Internet to learn where these cells are located and how they function to produce colored vision.

Laboratory 7b
Using the Spectrophotometer to Study Molecules

Background

Some molecules are colored and some are not. Whether or not a molecular solution exhibits color depends on how the molecules interact with light waves. A red hemoglobin solution reacts differently in light than does a green chlorophyll solution.

As a practical example, a blue sweater is blue because the dye molecules in the yarn react with light waves in a certain way. In the case of blue dye molecules, most of the light waves of the visible spectrum are absorbed by the dye molecules, except for the blue ones (around 475 nm). The blue light waves bounce off the dye molecules and hit the nerve cells in your eye, sending a signal to your brain. The result is that you "see" blue.

If a leaf appears green, it is absorbing most of the colors of light, except for the green wavelengths. The leaf uses the absorbed light energy to make food for itself in the reactions of photosynthesis.

When using a spectrophotometer to study molecules, the technician shines light on a sample. The light is either absorbed by or transmitted through the molecules. The transmittance is measured in percentages, which range from 0% to 100%. If a solution's transmittance is 100%, that means that all of the light waves hitting it are transmitted through the solution, and none of the molecules in the solution are absorbing the light energy.

The absorbance of light by molecules in solution is reported in absorbance units (au). The maximum amount of absorbed light that can be detected by a typical VIS spectrophotometer has a value of 2 au. Therefore, absorbance values fall between 0 and 2 au. The absorbance of a sample is also called the optical density (OD) of the sample. This term is a relic of the days before computerized spectrophotometers determined the concentration of samples automatically. The denser the sample, as with cells growing in broth culture, the higher the absorbance value and OD.

In this activity, three different colored solutions are studied to determine which wavelengths of light they absorb and which of these wavelengths provides the most absorbance ($lambda_{max}$).

Purpose

How much light is absorbed, at different wavelengths, by molecules of different colors?
What are the $lambda_{max}$ and the $lambda_{min}$ (wavelength of minimum light absorption) for each solution?
How is the color of light related to a molecule's ability to absorb light energy?

Materials

Food colorings (1:500 mL H_2O)	Tubes, glass, 13 × 100 mm	Spectrophotometer, Spectronic
Pipets, 5 mL	Peg racks for 13 × 100-mm	20 D+ or other visible
Pipet pump, green	tubes	spectrophotometer

Procedure

1. Place 4 mL of red solution in a cuvette tube.
2. Prepare a "blank" with 4 mL of tap water. A blank has everything the sample contains except the molecule that you are studying. It tells the spec to ignore everything in the sample except the molecules being studied.
3. Use the spectrophotometer to determine the amount of light absorbed by the red solution at different wavelengths..
   If using a Spec 20D+, follow the steps below to calibrate (set) and use the spectrophotometer. It is necessary to re-calibrate the spectrophotometer every time the wavelength is changed. If using a different model of VIS spectrophotometer, follow the instructions in the user's manual.

Spec 20D+ Spectrophotometer Use

    a. Make sure the spectrophotometer has warmed up for at least 20 minutes. Turn the 100% transmittance knob to the center of its turning range.

    b. Set the mode to "transmittance" and the wavelength to 400 nm.

    c. Check to see that the sample holder is empty and closed.

    d. Use the zero control knob/button (knob on the left) to set the transmittance to 0%.

    e. Wipe fingerprints from the blank, insert it, and set the transmittance to read 100% (knob on the right).

    f. Wipe fingerprints from the red solution sample tube, insert it, change the mode to absorbance, and read the absorbance value.

    g. Repeat steps b. through f. for every 10 nm up to 620 nm.

4. In your notebook, record the absorbance data for the red solution in a data table.
5. Make a line graph to show the absorbance data at different wavelengths. This curve is the absorption spectrum for the red solution.
6. Repeat steps 1 through 5, but use the green food-coloring solution.
7. Add the data for the green solution to your red solution data table and graph.
8. Repeat steps 1 through 5, but use the blue food-coloring solution.
9. Add the data for the blue solution to your red and green solutions data table and graph. You should end up with a data table showing the absorbance of the three different colored solutions at different wavelengths, and a graph with three different colored lines.

Data Analysis/Conclusion

What are the lambda_{max} and the lambda_{min} for each solution? Does each absorbance spectrum make sense for what is expected? How so or not? Explain differences in the lambda_{max} for a solution from one lab group to another. What is the practical value of knowing the lambda_{max} and lambda_{min} for each solution? How can this information be of value in the future to protein researchers and manufacturers?

Thinking Like a Biotechnician

1. Study the peaks and valleys of each absorbance spectrum. Does the red sample absorb non-red light while transmitting red wavelengths? What about the blue and green spectra? Explain.
2. What factors affect the height of a peak on an absorbance spectrum? Sketch a scratch graph showing the pattern you would predict for the relative absorbance spectra for red solutions at 1X, 0.5X, and 0.25X.
3. Sketch an absorbance spectrum that would be expected if you were studying carotene, the orange pigment in carrots.

Laboratory 7c
Using the Spectrophotometer to Study the Protein, Amylase

Background

Amylase, like other molecules, interacts with light waves and absorbs or transmits light energy of various wavelengths. If set at an appropriate wavelength, a spectrophotometer can detect amylase in a solution as the amylase molecules absorb light energy. The more amylase molecules in solution, the greater the absorbance should be.

Amylase molecules absorb light of some wavelengths better than others (just as the different dye solutions did in Lab 7b). If one is to detect small amounts of amylase in solution, it is best to know at which wavelength the amylase molecules absorb the most light (λ_{max}). This wavelength will be the most "sensitive" to the presence of amylase.

Like most proteins, amylase molecules are colorless and, in buffer, they absorb light only in the UV range, actually at 280 nm. Spec 20 D spectrophotometers are VIS specs, and they do not detect in the UV range. To use the Spec 20 D to detect amylase, (or some other colorless protein), the amylase can be mixed with a protein indicator solution, that changes colors when protein is present. Bradford reagent is a protein indicator that reacts proportionally with the protein to give a blue product.

To determine the lambda$_{max}$ for amylase (+ Bradford protein reagent), we must produce an absorption spectrum for the Bradford-amylase pair and see where the peak of light absorption is (see Figure 7.4). The lambda$_{max}$ will then be used to detect amylase molecules in solution in future experiments.

A Bradford assay can be used to estimate the approximate protein concentration (Lab 7d) prior to running protein samples on gels (see Labs 6f and 9e). Bradford reagent contains Coomassie® Blue G250 dye molecules, which react primarily with the arginine amino acid residues in proteins.

Purpose

What is the absorption spectrum for amylase (+ Bradford protein reagent)?
What is the lambda$_{max}$ for the amylase (+ Bradford protein reagent) mixture?

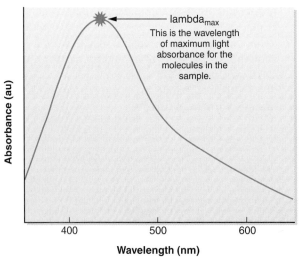

Figure 7.4. Lambda$_{max}$ Graph. For research and manufacturing, knowing the lambda$_{max}$ of a sample is valuable. Once the lambda$_{max}$ has been determined, the spec is set to that wavelength, and used to determine the presence and concentration of the molecule of interest in the sample.

Materials

Amylase buffer (100 mM NaH$_2$PO$_4 \times$ H$_2$O, 6 mM NaCl, pH 7.0) or use 1X PBS buffer
Amylase, 5 mg/mL (in 100 mM NaH$_2$ PO$_4 \times$ H$_2$O, 6 mM NaCl, pH 7.0 buffer)
Micropipet, P-1000   Pipet pump, green
Micropipet tips for P-1000   Permanent lab marker pens
Tubes (cuvettes), glass, 13 $\times$ 100 mm   Bradford reagent, 1X
Plug caps for 13 $\times$ 100-mm tubes   Spectrophotometer, Spectronic 20 D+ or other
Peg racks for 13 $\times$ 100-mm tubes   VIS spectrophotometer
Pipets, 5 mL

Safety Precautions

Environmental Health and Safety Officer

- Wear goggles and gloves when using chemicals.
- Use lab matting or a paper towel to cover the lab tabletop while conducting the experiment.
- Use a wet paper towel for small spills.
- If exposed to acid or base, rinse the affected area with large amounts of water.

Procedure

Note: If the 5 mg/mL amylase solution has not already been made, prepare 100mL of amylase buffer (100 mM NaH$_2$ PO$_4 \times$ H$_2$O, 6 mM NaCl, pH 7.0) or use 1X PBS buffer. Then use it to make 5 mL of 5 mg/mL amylase solution. Record all calculations for the solution preparation. Label the unused amylase and unused buffer and store them at 4°C for later use (Lab 7d).

1. Prepare tubes to determine the absorption spectrum for amylase as follows:
   a. Prepare a sample tube by placing 0.5 mL of a 5 mg/mL amylase solution into a cuvette. Add 3 mL of 1X Bradford reagent. Mix gently, but thoroughly, and let stand for 1 minute and no more than 3 minutes.
   b. Prepare a blank by placing 0.5 mL of buffer into a cuvette. Add 3 mL of 1X Bradford reagent. Mix gently, but thoroughly, and let stand for 1 minute and no more than 3 minutes.
2. Use the spec to determine the amount of absorbance at each of 16 wavelengths by following the steps below or the directions in the spectrophotometer user's manual.
3. In your notebook, record the absorbance data for the amylase-Bradford mixture in a data table.

Spec 20D+ Spectrophotometer Use

1. Make sure that the spec has warmed up for at least 20 minutes. Turn the 100% transmittance knob to the center of its turning range.
2. Set the wavelength to 540 nm. Do not read the absorbance of wavelengths lower than 540 nm. Do you know why?
3. Check to see that the sample holder is empty and closed.
4. Use the 0% T control knob to set the amount of transmittance to 0%.
5. Wipe fingerprints from the blank, insert it, and set the transmittance to 100% with the 100% T knob.
6. Wipe fingerprints from the sample tube, insert it, and read the absorbance value.
7. Repeat steps 2 through 6 for every 5 nm up to 615 nm.

Data Analysis/Conclusion

Graph the absorbance data as a line graph. This line is the absorption spectrum for the amylase-Bradford mixture. What is the lambda$_{max}$ for the amylase-Bradford mixture? What is the lambda$_{min}$ for the amylase-Bradford mixture? Of what value are these wavelength data? Describe how and when these data may be used in the R&D or manufacturing of a protein. Discuss any errors in technique that might lead to an incorrect determination of the lambda$_{max}$.

Thinking Like a Biotechnician

1. Instead of a nice, smooth, bell-shaped curve, the absorbance spectrum for a molecule has one point that is "spiked up" to about 0.8 au above the rest of the graph. What might cause this?
2. Amylase is a colorless molecule; thus, Bradford reagent was used in this experiment to make it visible in the VIS spec. Name at least one disadvantage to using the Bradford reagent on a suspected amylase sample.
3. Propose a method to detect colorless amylase in a sample and still be able to recover it, unaltered, for future use.
4. Bradford reagent is one protein assay indicator. While you are familiar with another protein assay, the Biuret protein assay (Lab 2a), there are two more indicator assays that are commonly used. One is the BCA (bicinchoninic acid) protein assay and the other is the Lowry protein assay. Use the Internet to learn more about each of these assays and compare them to the Bradford assay. Create a chart that lists what each assay does, how it is conducted, and the advantages and disadvantages of each.

Laboratory 7d
Determining the Concentration of Amylase in Solution

Background

Often, the goal of a biotechnology company's product pipeline is to manufacture a protein. The company must synthesize enough of the protein to market it at a profit.

The proteins are made in cells, usually ones that have been transformed with recombinant DNA (rDNA). The protein-making cells are grown in huge fermentation tanks. Often, the protein is released into the fermentation broth where the cells are grown, although sometimes the proteins are held within the cell. Either way, the protein has to be isolated from all the other thousands of proteins made by a typical cell.

Separating a protein of interest from other unwanted molecules is called purification. The biotech company wants purified proteins that are active, stable, and of a relatively high concentration. When proteins are purified from solutions (cytoplasm fermentation broth, etc), the product must be checked to see whether the protein is present and how much is present. At every step in the manufacture of a protein, the concentration must be determined. Protein concentration is usually measured in milligrams per milliliter (mg/mL) or micrograms per milliliter (µg/mL).

Since the protein molecules are submicroscopic, we must measure them using indirect methods. To determine the concentration of a solution, one produces a standard curve that plots the absorbance of solutions at *known* concentrations. First, the technician prepares solutions of known concentrations and reads their absorbance at a given wavelength. The technician produces a "best-fit" straight line, representing how the concentration affects the absorbance by the molecule being tested. The absorbance of an *unknown* solution is then determined. From the "best-fit" straight-line standard curve, the concentration of the unknown solution is determined based on where the absorbance value intersects the standard curve (see Figure 7.5).

If the protein of interest is colorless, it must be measured in a UV spectrophotometer (see Lab 7g). Alternatively, a protein indicator must be added, colorizing the sample, so that it can be measured in a VIS spec (as in this lab activity).

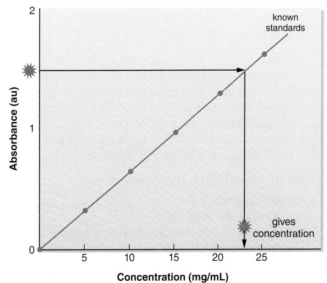

Figure 7.5. **Standard Curve of Protein Concentration versus Absorbance.** The absorbance of a sample is directly proportional to the number of molecules present (concentration).

Purpose

What are the concentrations of two unknown amylase solutions?

Materials

1X PBS (100 mM NaH$_2$PO$_4$ × H$_2$O, 6 mM NaCl, pH 7.0 buffer) (from Lab 7c)

Amylase stock solution, 5 mg/mL (from Lab 7c)

Tube rack for 1.7-mL tubes

Reaction tubes, 1.7 mL

Micropipet, P-1000

Micropipet tips for P-1000

Permanent lab marker pens

Pipets, 1 mL

Pipet pump, blue

Pipets, 5 mL

Pipet pump, green

Tubes, glass (cuvettes),
13 × 100 mm

Bradford reagent, 1X

Plug caps for 13 × 100-mm tubes

Peg racks for 13 × 100-mm tubes

Spectrophotometer, Spectronic 20 D+ or other
VIS spectrophotometer

Amylase unknowns #1 and #2

Caution: Wear goggles and gloves when using chemicals.

Procedure

Note: If the 5 mg/mL amylase solution has not already been made, prepare 100mL of amylase buffer (100 mM NaH$_2$PO$_4$ × H$_2$O, 6 mM NaCl, pH 7.0) or use 1X PBS buffer. Then use it to make 5 mL of 5 mg/mL amylase solution. Record all calculations for the solution preparation. Label the unused amylase and unused buffer and store them at 4°C for later use.

Environmental Health
and Safety Officer

Part I: Sample Preparation

1. Prepare a serial dilution of the *known* samples starting with the 5 mg/mL of amylase stock solution as follows:

   a. Label five 1.7-mL tubes No. 1 through 5.
   b. Add 0.5 mL of buffer to each of the test tubes No. 2 through 5.
   c. To test tube No. 1, add 1 mL of the stock 5 mg/mL amylase solution. Mix gently. Record the concentration of this sample in your notebook.
   d. Take 0.5 mL of the protein solution in test tube No. 1 and add it to test tube No. 2. Mix well.
   e. Take 0.5 mL of the solution in test tube No. 2 and add it to test tube No. 3. Mix well. Record the concentration of this sample in your notebook.
   f. Continue making these dilutions with the remaining test tubes. After preparing test tube No. 5, discard the extra 0.5 mL so that all tubes No. 1 through 5 contain the same volume of solution. Record the concentration of these tubes in your notebook. What type of serial dilution have you performed (ie, 1:2, 1:3, 1:4, or 1:5)?

2. Transfer 0.5 mL of each of these known concentrations to a labeled 13 × 100-mm tube. Add 3 mL of Bradford protein reagent to each. Mix well. Wait 1 minute and no more than 3 minutes.
3. Label two more 13 × 100-mm cuvettes "unknown No. 1" and "unknown No. 2." Add 0.5 mL of the appropriate unknown amylase solution to each tube. Add 3 mL of Bradford protein reagent to each unknown. Mix well. Wait 1 minute and no more than 3 minutes.
4. In another 13 × 100-mm cuvette, prepare a blank with 0.5 mL of buffer plus 3 mL of Bradford protein reagent. Mix well. Wait 1 minute and no more than 3 minutes.

Part II: Absorbance Data Collection

5. Read each tube's absorbance at lambda$_{max}$ for an amylase-Bradford reagent mixture (the lambda$_{max}$ for amylase + Bradford reagent determined in Lab 7c).
6. In your notebook, create a data table to store the absorbance data for all the amylase samples of known concentration (amylase protein standards). In another data table, record the absorbance of the unknown amylase samples.

Data Analysis/Conclusion

7. Make a **very large** graph with concentration on the x-axis and absorbance on the y-axis. Make a "best fit" straight line of the **known** concentration samples versus their absorbance values. **Note:** If you are creating the graph using Microsoft® Excel®, pull down "Chart" on the "Menu," select "Add Trendline," and select "Linear Regression." It will add a "best-fit" straight line for you. Double-click on the "Best-fit Trendline." Select "Options." Click on "axis through 0" and "show equation of the line." This will determine the "equation of the line" to be used later.

8. Using this best-fit standard curve, estimate the concentration of your "unknowns." Show (draw in) where the absorbance value for each "unknown" intersects the following: the y-axis, the "best-fit" straight line, and the x-axis (refer to the Background section of this lab). Record these estimates of the "unknown's" concentration in the data table of unknown amylase samples from step 6.

9. In industry, the concentration of a sample is calculated mathematically using the linear regression equation (equation of the line) below. This method allows technicians to determine the concentrations of many "unknowns" quickly.

$$y = mx + b$$
$y =$ the absorbance of the unknown sample
$m =$ the slope of the best-fit straight line
$x =$ the concentration of the unknown sample
$b =$ the y-intercept

Notes: The equation of the best-fit standard curve line was determined and placed on the graph in above in step 7. For your line, what is the slope of the line and what is the y-intercept?

> You might expect the slope to be close to 1 since the rise of your line should be close to the run of the line if the absorbance increases proportionally to the concentration.

> You would expect the y-intercept to be close to 0 since a concentration of 0 mg/mL should give a 0 au absorbance reading.

> Use $y = mx + b$ to calculate the concentrations of the unknown samples, and add these data to your data table. Using $y = mx + b$ is easy since the line equation gives you "m" and "b" and you have determined "y" for each unknown in step 5.

10. Collect the concentration determinations for each unknown ($y = mx + b$) from the other groups in the class (multiple replications). Put these values into a new data table. Calculate the average concentration of each sample for all the replications of the experiment. These averages are the best guess of the true concentrations of the "unknowns."

> How good are your data? Are they accurate, reliable? How well does your data "match" the multiple replications of the experiment? Compare your values to the averages, the mean, and the range of values.

11. In the lab during R&D, if data are within 10% of the value expected, they are often considered "close enough." Determine the amount of deviation your measurements have (in %) from the average values. To do this, use the following equations.

$$\frac{\text{your sample's value} - \text{the class' average for the sample}}{\text{the class' average for the sample}} \times 100 = \frac{\underline{\quad}\% \text{ deviation for unknown}}{\text{No. 1 from the class average}}$$

$$\frac{\text{your sample's value} - \text{the class' average for the sample}}{\text{the class' average for the sample}} \times 100 = \frac{\_\_\_\% \text{ deviation for unknown}}{\text{No. 2 from the class average}}$$

Is your determination of each "unknown's" concentration "close enough"?

12. Commonly, sample data are analyzed to see how much they deviate from average data. Scientists usually consider data within 1 deviation above or below the average to be valid. Determine the standard deviation (SD) of each group of amylase samples (multiple replications) using the following formula.

$$\text{Standard Deviation} = \sqrt{\frac{\Sigma(\text{Average} - \text{sample reading})^2}{\text{\# of samples}}}$$

If you are using Microsoft® Excel® for your data table, it is relatively easy to calculate the SD for a group of numbers. Highlight an empty cell, and enter the following equation:

= STDEV (highlight the numbers you want to analyze)

Press "Enter." Add and subtract the SD to your class average. Do your own samples' data fall within the SD?

The range of acceptable concentration determinations is the average, + and - the SD. For example, if the average for a group of data is 4.8 mg/mL, and the SD is 0.7, then the range of acceptable data is 5.5 mg/mL down to 4.1 mg/mL. If a sample does not fit in this range, then the data either do not support the hypothesis or they are erroneous.

Should your individual determinations of the "unknown's" concentration be accepted as valid? The smaller the SD for the collection of samples, the more reproducibility there is in the measurements. With a small SD, you can have confidence that the group of measurements reflects the concentrations of the samples.

Thinking Like a Biotechnician

1. Without using the spectrophotometer, how can you estimate the concentration of amylase in the unknown samples?
2. On the best-fit standard curve, all the points fall on a straight line except the 5 mg/mL sample. It is much lower than the rest of the line. Why might this be? Should the value be used in the standard curve?
3. A set of proteins is studied in the spectrophotometer. The linear regression ($y = mx + b$) gives a slope of $m = 0.93$ and the y-intercept (b) is zero. An unknown sample's absorbance is measured at 0.66 au. What is the approximate concentration of the unknown sample?

Laboratory 7e

Determining the pI of the Milk Protein, Casein

This lab was developed by Simon Holdaway, The Loomis Chaffee School, Windsor, CT and modified by Ellyn Daugherty.

Background

The isoelectric point (referred to as pI) is the pH at which an amino acid or protein does not migrate in an electric field. At the pI, the molecule has no net charge (it is neutral), it becomes insoluble and will fall out of solution (it precipitates).

For many biotechnology processes it is important to know a protein's pI. When preparing a protein solution, pH values that are close to the pI of the protein of interest are avoided since that pH would cause protein precipitation and a loss of biological activity. This is why scientists use buffered solutions. Buffered solutions protect against pH changes and keep a protein at a pH that is not near the pI. When preparing protein solutions, a scientist uses the pI of a protein to select a buffer that keeps the pH far enough away from the pI to avoid these precipitation problems.

To understand and determine the pI of a protein, a bit of protein structure review is needed. Remember that peptides are large molecules composed of small molecules (amino acids) attached like beads on a chain. When peptide chains fold into functional units they are called proteins.

The amino acids in a protein have some amount of electrical charge to them (See Figure 7.6). Amino acids are polar molecules (with ends of opposite charge) and carry weak charges on their amino (N) terminus and carboxyl (C) terminus ends. However, when chained together only the amino acid terminus at the very ends of the peptide are exposed and they have little effect on the protein's overall charge.

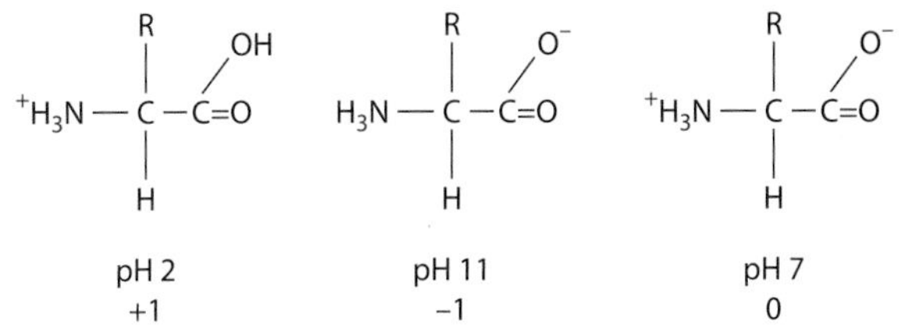

Figure 7.6. **Generic Amino Acid With Charges At Different pH Values**

On the other hand, each amino acid has a R group and the different R groups may be charged or uncharged (see Table 5.1 in the text). As the pH changes, the charged R groups may gain or lose H+ or OH- ions to the solution, with the end result being an excess of + charge as a solution's pH decreases or an excess of – charge as a solution's pH goes up. Since the R group charges vary with pH, changes in pH cause changes in the overall charge of a protein, its shape, and function.

If the pH changes in a protein solution to a value where the total of charges on all the amino acids approach zero, the protein will precipitate out of solution (the protein becomes hydrophobic). This is known as the isoelectric point, and the pH at which this occurs is the pI. *For a protein to stay functional it must stay in solution at a pH that is not its pI.*

In this activity, you will determine the pI of the milk protein, casein. Casein is the most common protein in mammalian milk and contributes to milk's relatively high protein content. Casein is an important source of amino acids for a growing infant. To determine the pI of casein, a casein solution will be brought to a high pH (very alkaline). At a high pH many of the amino acid R groups will have a negative charge so the casein will be dissolved in the solution. As the pH is lowered, by adding acetic acid, the negative charges will be lost and eventually, at the pI, the protein will have no net negative charge and will precipitate out of solution.

Purpose

How does pH affect the solubility of the milk protein, casein?
What is the pI of casein?

Materials

Balance, tabletop milligram
Weigh paper or weigh boat
Lab scoops
Casein powder
1.0 M NaOH
Beakers, 250 ml
Beakers, 100 mL (3 per group)

10ml pipet and pipet pump
Magnetic stirrer & magnet (or
  glass rod)
Lab stand and buret clamp
Titration buret
1.0 M acetic acid
Funnel, plastic

Wide range pH paper (pH 1–14)
pH meter
Narrow range pH paper
  (pH 4–7)
Glasses, safety or goggles
Gloves
Paper towels

Procedure

Environmental Health
and Safety Officer

Caution

- Wear goggles and gloves when using all chemicals and throughout this entire experiments
- Place the titration apparatus and solutions over paper toweling or lab mats to absorb any spills.
- Wipe spills immediately with a wet paper towel.

1. In a 250 mL beaker, prepare 100 mL of 5mg/mL casein solution in 1.0 M NaOH. Record the equation of the calculation of how to prepare this solution. The casein should dissolve to produce a slightly yellow, slightly turbid solution. If the casein does not dissolve immediately try warming the solution to 37°C.
2. Using a 10 mL pipet and pump transfer exactly 20.0 mL of casein solution and to a 100 mL beaker. This will be the titration vessel.
3. Setup the titration buret using the clamp and lab stand. If possible, perform this step with the titration vessel on a magnetic stirrer.
4. Close the tap on the titration buret, then using the funnel, carefully fill the buret with 25 mL of 1.0 M acetic acid.
5. Measure the starting pH with wide range pH paper. If you are using a pH probe place the probe into the casein solution. Turn on the magnetic stirrer, but be careful to adjust the position of the beaker on the stirrer so that the stirrer bar does not hit the pH probe. Position the titration buret so that it is just above the 100 mL beaker.
6. Note the starting volume on the titration buret. In a data table similar to Table 7.1 below, record this along with pH data collected in the experiment, in your lab notebook.
7. Carefully add 15.0 mL of 1.0 M acetic acid to the beaker. Be sure to stir the casein solution while you are adding acid. It is expected that there will be no significant change in either the appearance of the beaker, or the pH value.
8. From this point forward in the experiment, add acetic acid in 1.0 ml aliquots, stirring. Look closely at the reaction in the beaker since small volumes at some pHs can produce large pH changes.

Table 7.1. **The Effect of pH on Protein Solubility, Trial #_____**

Volume of 1.0M Acetic Acid Added (ml)	pH	Observations or Changes in Protein Solution
0.0		
10.0		
15.0		
16.0		
17.0		
18.0		
18.5		
19.0		
19.5		
20.5		
21.0		
21.5		
22.0		
23.0		
24.0		
25.0		

9. Continue to add acetic acid in 1.0 ml aliquots. After each addition, stop and observe the beaker. Do you see any changes? Record these observations in the data table. Measure the pH of the solution using the pH meter probe.
10. When you begin to see a milky white precipitate form in the beaker stop adding acetic acid and record the volume on the buret and the pH of the solution. The precipitate means the casein is close to its isoelectric point and the pH is close to the pI. Record the estimated pI based on this first trial. Often the actual pI is overshot because the technician doesn't actually recognize precipitation.
11. Set the first beaker aside and repeat the protocol (Trial 2) attempting to narrow down the actual pI. In this 2nd trial, slowly add enough acetic acid to get to within 1 pH unit of the 1st trial pI. Then, add small volumes of the acetic acid, recording changes in pH until a 2nd trial value of pI is determined. Record these measurements and observations in a 2nd trial data table.
12. Set the 2nd beaker aside and repeat the protocol a third time attempting to narrow down the actual pI even more. In this 3rd trial, slowly add enough acetic acid to get to within 1 pH unit of the 2nd trial pI. Then add small volumes of the acetic acid, recording changes in pH until a 3rd trial value of pI is determined. Record these measurements and observations in a 3rd trial data table.
13. Observe all 3 beakers, is there an obvious difference in the amount of casein precipitated. Which beaker do you think is closest to the actual pI? Explain your answer.

Data Analysis and Conclusion

Survey the data collected from multiple groups in the class. What is your best estimate of the actual pI of casein, based on a class average? Explain your answer giving supporting evidence. Include a description of what happens to the charges of the protein in the solution, as well as its 3dimensional structure, as the pH changed in the beaker. Explain how a scientist might use the pI of casein when conducting other protein studies or assays on casein.

Thinking Like A Biotechnician

1. Would you expect casein to be soluble (go into solution) or insoluble at pH 3? Explain your answer.
2. Suggest a method for isolating the precipitated casein from the solution in the beaker.
3. With isolated casein, how could you get it to go back into solution so that it might be used for other experiments?

Laboratory 7f

Spectrophotometry to Monitor Protein Purification by Ammonium Sulfate Precipitation

This lab was developed by Simon Holdaway, The Loomis Chaffee School, Windsor, CT and modified by Ellyn Daugherty.

Background

Most proteins may be precipitated (salted out) and isolated from solution using high concentrations of salt followed by centrifugation. Ammonium sulfate is the precipitant solute most frequently used in the "salting out" of proteins.

There are several advantages and a just a few disadvantages to the use of ammonium sulfate precipitation. Ammonium sulfate is good for salting out because

1. at saturation, it is a solution of sufficiently high molarity that it causes the precipitation of most proteins.
2. it does not produce much heat during a precipitation, so proteins are not expected to destroyed.
3. its saturated solution has a density that is low so it does not interfere with the sedimentation of most precipitated proteins during centrifugation.
4. its concentrated solutions prevent or limit most bacterial growth.
5. in solution it protects most proteins from denaturation.

A limitation in the use of ammonium sulfate for protein purification is that the concentration of precipitant protein may only be a few times more than in the original solution. In addition, not all proteins may be salted out by ammonium sulfate.

(Scopes, R.K, "Protein Purification: Principles and Practice" and Englard, S and Seiften, S, "Methods in Enzymology" Vol 82., Chapter 22, Precipitation Techniques, 1993)

In this activity, ammonium sulfate will be used to salt out and purify hemoglobin from solution. Hemogloblin is a colored protein easily measured in solution via visual spectrophotometry. Using the Lambda$_{max}$ for hemoglobin, the yield of a hemoglobin precipitation may be measured.

Purpose

How does ammonium sulfate concentration affect the yield of hemoglobin precipitated from a solution?

Materials

Hemoglobin (Bovine)	VIS Spectrophotometer	Spectrophotometer
1X PBS buffer	Centrifuge, clinical, for 15 tubes	cuvettes (tubes)
Ammonium Sulfate	15 mL centrifuge tubes	10 mL pipets
Micropipets and Tips	and racks	Magnetic stirrer, stirrer bar

Procedure

1. Prepare or obtain 100 mL of 1X PBS buffer. Use the recipe in Lab 7c. In your notebook, record how you prepared the solution.
2. Prepare a 100% saturated solution of ammonium sulfate by dissolving 76.7g of $(NH_4)_2SO_4$ in 100 mL of dH_2O. Slowly add the ammonium sulfate to the solution, pausing then stirring to let the crystals dissolve before adding more ammonium sulfate.
3. Prepare 40 mL of 2 mg/mL hemoglobin solution in 1X PBS. The hemoglobin will dissolve easily and the resulting solution should be reddish-brown with no undissolved material. In your notebook, record how you prepared the solution.
4. Prepare 5 mL of 1mg/mL of hemoglobin in 1X PBS by diluting the 2 mg/mL hemoglobin.
5. Turn on the spectrophotometer and allow to warm up.

6. Prepare a 1X PBS buffer blank, and measure the absorbance of the hemoglobin solution at every 10 nm from 350 nm to 500 nm. Graph the absorbance spectrum data and determine the Lambda$_{max}$ of hemoglobin.
7. Transfer 10 mL of the 2 mg/mL hemoglobin solution to a clean spectrophotometer cuvette.
8. In 15 mL centrifuge tubes, prepare each of 3 dilutions of saturated (100%) ammonium sulfate solution in the 2 mg/mL hemoglobin solution. Using the Table 7.2 reaction matrix below, add the indicated amount (5.0 mL) of hemoglobin to each tube and then slowly add in the indicated volumes of saturated (100%) ammonium sulfate solution. Swirl to mix. Label the three tubes 33%, 50% and 75%.

Table 7.2. **Ammonium Sulfate Precipitation of Hemoglobin Reaction Matrix**

Volume of 2 mg/mL Hemoglobin (mL)	Volume of $(NH_4)_2SO_4$ (mL)	Final $(NH_4)_2SO_4$ (%)
5.0	2.5	33
5.0	5.0	50
5.0	7.5	75

9. Let the tubes incubate on ice for 10 minutes. During this time prepare three centrifuge balance tubes (each with the same volume as the corresponding hemoglobin tube).
10. Load the tubes into a clinical or research centrifuge and spin at maximum speed for 20–30 minutes. (Note: minimum of 400g required, higher speeds produce higher yields)
11. Discard the supernatant into trash beaker, being careful not to disturb the reddish pellet at the bottom of the tube. Depending on the speed of the centrifuge this may be a true pellet on the bottom of the tube, or a reddish smear down the side of the tube.
12. Resuspend the pellet in 5.0 mL of 1X PBS. Vortex the samples for 30 seconds to ensure complete resuspension of the hemoglobin.
13. Using the 1X PBS blank from step 6, zero the spectrophotometer at the Lambda$_{max}$ of hemoglobin.
14. Create a data table to collect absorbance data for each of the resuspended hemoglobin samples (produced by precipitation using different concentrations of ammonium sulfate).
15. Measure the absorbance of the resuspended hemoglobin samples at the Lambda$_{max}$ of hemoglobin. Record the results in the data table.
16. Create a bar graph that shows how the concentration of saturated (100%) ammonium sulfate solution affects the yield of hemoglobin isolated from a 2 mg/mL solution.

Data Analysis & Conclusion

Using the quantitative data obtained from the spectrophotometer discuss how effective the different concentrations of ammonium sulfate were at causing the hemoglobin to precipitate out of solution. If one concentration appeared to be more effective than the others, how much more effective was it? Did you and your partner have the same results as others groups? Why or why not? List technical errors in setting up the experiment that might lead to erroneous data. Given that different proteins have different properties, including solubility, how might this technique be valuable to biotechnologists trying to isolate and purify a protein product?

Thinking Like A Biotechnician

1. Ammonium sulfate precipitation is a key purification technique in biotechnology. It is cheap, fast and effective. Bovine serum albumin (BSA) is another common blood protein. BSA precipitates out of solution at 40% ammonium sulfate concentration. With this information, how would you separate a solution of hemoglobin from BSA? Design a procedure to capture as much pure hemoglobin as possible with no contaminating BSA. Would your procedure purify all the original hemoglobin? Why or why not?
2. Hemoglobin is an unusual protein because it is colored in solution. This makes it easy to track the progress and success of the purification by measuring the protein concentration directly in the spectrophotometer. However, most proteins are not colored in solution and thus cannot be measured directly. Suggest ways a biotechnologist might monitor the purification progress of an ammonium sulfate precipitation experiment if the protein of interest was colorless in solution?

Laboratory 7g
Using the UV Spec to Study Colorless Protein Samples

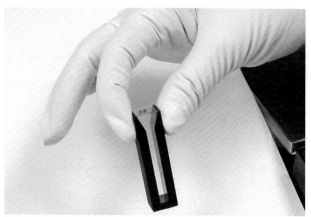

Figure 7.7. Quartz cuvettes or UV-quality disposable plastic cuvettes are often used in a spec. if DNA is being studied at 260 nm. Quartz, glass, or plastic cuvettes can be used if a measurement is made at or above 280 nm. Since the UV cuvettes hold much less sample than the cuvettes for the Spec 20 D, less sample is wasted. In addition, samples that are studied without indicator solution are retrieved and available for future use.
Photo by author.

Background

Proteins that have color can be visualized in the visible spectrum using almost any spectrophotometer. Determining the lambda$_{max}$ is rather simple and predictable if a protein's color is obvious. Yet, most proteins are colorless. However, if you add an indicator, the protein becomes colored and can be seen with a VIS spec. Most indicators, though, alter the protein so the sample cannot be retrieved for other uses. Being able to visualize a colorless protein is valuable in that the sample can be retrieved unaltered. A UV spectrophotometer is used to measure colorless proteins. Like a VIS spec, a UV spec shines light (wavelengths of 350 nm or less) on a sample and determines the amount of light transmitted through the molecules. A deuterium lamp produces the UV light. Special low-volume, high-quality cuvettes are used in UV specs (see Figure 7.7).

The lambda$_{max}$ for colorless proteins can be determined on a UV spectrophotometer, and the lambda$_{max}$ can be used to determine the concentration of the colorless proteins in solution.

Purpose

To prepare absorbance spectra for different concentrations of the same colorless protein, amylase.
To determine the lambda$_{max}$ for the colorless protein, amylase.
To create a standard curve for known concentrations of amylase.
To estimate the concentration of 2 unknown amylase solutions.

Materials

Amylase stock solution, 5 mg/mL (from Lab 7c stock)
100 mM NaH$_2$PO$_4 \times$ H$_2$O, 6 mM NaCl, pH 7.0 buffer (from Lab 7c)

Tube rack for 1.7-mL tubes	
Reaction tubes, 1.7 mL	UV/VIS spectrophotometer
Permanent lab marker pens	UV spectrophotometer cuvettes
Micropipet, P-1000	Pasteur pipets, 9"
Micropipet tips for P-1000	Pasteur pipet bulbs
	Amylase unknowns #A and #B

Procedure

Each UV spectrophotometer operates slightly differently. Make sure you know which cuvettes to use and how to clean them. Make sure you know how to "blank" a sample. Familiarize yourself with how to navigate through the dialog box of the spectrophotometer you are using and how to direct the spectrophotometer to collect an absorbance spectrum.

Note: If the 5 mg/mL amylase solution has not already been made, prepare 100mL of amylase buffer (100 mM NaH$_2$ PO$_4 \times$ H$_2$O, 6 mM NaCl, pH 7.0) or use 1X PBS buffer. Then use it to make 5 mL of 5 mg/mL amylase solution. Record all calculations for the solution preparation. Label the unused amylase and unused buffer and store them at 4°C for later use.

1. Prepare 4 mL of a 1 mg/mL amylase solution by diluting the 5 mg/mL amylase solution in the 100 mM NaH$_2$PO$_4$ × H$_2$O, 6 mM NaCl, pH 7.0 buffer used in Lab 7c. Show the calculations and solution prep diagram for this dilution.
2. Using a 1:10 serial dilution of the amylase solution and the buffer as a diluent, prepare two additional samples to test. The additional samples should have a concentration between 0.1 mg/mL and 0.01 mg/mL
3. Use the UV spec to determine an absorbance spectrum for each of the three protein samples. Follow the spec's instructions to do a scanning absorbance spectrum or collect absorbance data for each sample at every 20 nm between 200 and 340 nm (UV light wavelengths.
4. Determine which concentration gives the "best" lambda$_{max}$ absorbance spectrum. The best would have an obvious lambda$_{max}$ at around 1.1 au and obvious lambda$_{min}$ points.
5. Dilute the sample from step 4 that gave the best lambda$_{max}$ another 1:2, 1:4, 1:8, 1:16. Use these samples to collect absorbance data vs. concentration at lambda$_{max}$. Your spec may be able to do this for you using a single protein concentration assay program.
6. Plot a best-fit straight-line standard curve of amylase concentration vs absorbance. Determine the equation of the best-fit straight-line.
7. Determine the absorbance of each amylase unknown, and use y=mx+b to determine each sample's concentration.

Data Analysis/Conclusion

Create a three-line line graph showing the absorbance spectrum for each amylase solution (from step 4). Color-code and label each line. Determine the lambda$_{max}$ for each sample. What can be said about the lambda$_{max}$ for amylase? How are the lines on the graph similar, and how do they differ from each other? Is this expected? Why or why not? How are these determinations important when studying protein samples? Compare your determinations of the unknowns' concentrations to other groups' data. How much confidence do you have in your data?

Thinking Like a Biotechnician

1. When analyzing a 1 mg/mL amylase absorbance spectrum, most of the absorbance values peak at 2 au. Why is this a problem in determining the lambda$_{max}$ of the sample? What should be done?
2. When analyzing the 1 mg/mL amylase absorbance spectrum, most of the absorbance values peak at under 0.1 au, and most are under 0.02 au. Why is this a problem in determining the lambda$_{max}$ of the sample? What should be done?

Laboratory 7h

Determining the Concentration and Purity of DNA Samples

Background

A UV spectrophotometer (or a fluorometer) can be used to study the concentration and purity of DNA samples in solution. These instruments measure DNA concentration and purity by measuring a solution's absorbance of UV light (the optical density, or OD) at specified wavelengths. Spectrophotometers can detect microgram per milliliter (µg/mL) concentrations, while a fluorometer can measure nanogram per milliliter (ng/mL) concentrations.

To determine the concentration of a DNA solution, the OD (absorbance) is measured in absorbance units (au) at 260 nm. Since 50 µg/mL of DNA in solution gives an OD of 1 au, measuring a sample's absorbance and using the following formula (the DNA Concentration Equation) will give an approximate concentration of a sample in µg/mL:

$$\frac{50 \ \mu g/mL}{1 \ au} = \frac{sample \ concentration \ (\mu g/mL)}{Sample \ OD_{260} \ (au)}$$

or

DNA Concentration Equation

$$Concentration \ (\mu g/mL) \ = \ Abs_{260} \times 50 \ \mu g/\mu L$$

For example, a 1-mL sample known to contain DNA is placed in a calibrated UV spectrophotometer. The absorbance is read at 260 nm and is determined to be 0.305 au. What is the approximate concentration of DNA in the sample?

$$\frac{50 \ \mu g/mL}{1 \ au} = \frac{X \ \mu g/mL}{0.305 \ au} = 0.305 \times 50 \ \mu g/mL = 15.25 \ \mu g/mL \ of \ DNA \ in \ the \ sample$$

To determine the concentration of a sample using the DNA Concentration Equation with confidence, one must have some idea of the approximate DNA concentration of the sample to start. This is because the absorbance readings in a spec are most accurate between an OD of 0.1–1.1 au. If a sample is too concentrated or too dilute, the OD values may be skewed.

Samples should be diluted or concentrated as needed to bring the OD readings within the 0.1–1.1 au range. If a sample gives absorbance readings above 1.1 au, it should be diluted with TE buffer or deionized water until the sample has an OD between 0.1–1.1 au. If a sample is too dilute, it may be concentrated using a centrifuge concentrator tube.

Running an agarose gel gives a technician another way of assaying the approximate DNA mass or concentration of a sample since 1 µg of DNA gives a nice band on a gel. Proteins and RNA are common contaminants in DNA samples. A UV spec can determine the relative purity of DNA in a sample by comparing the absorbance (OD) of a sample at 260 nm (the wavelength of DNA absorbance) and 280 nm (the wavelength of protein absorbance). This is called an A_{260}/A_{280} reading.

DNA Purity Equation

$$\frac{OD_{260} \text{ nm}}{OD_{280} \text{ nm}} = \frac{\text{relative amount of DNA}}{\text{relative amount of protein}}$$

For example, a 1-mL sample is placed in a calibrated UV spectrophotometer. The OD is read at 260 nm and is determined to be 0.305 au. The OD is also read at 280 nm and is determined to be 0.193 au. What is the A_{260}/A_{280} reading?

$$\frac{OD_{260 \text{ nm}}}{OD_{280 \text{ nm}}} = \frac{0.365 \text{ au}}{0.193 \text{ au}} = 1.54$$

If the 260/280 ratio is approximately 1.80, the DNA sample contains a significant amount of DNA and it is considered fairly clean or pure. The closer the 260/280 ratio is to 2.00, the more RNA contamination is suspected. More protein contamination is suspected as the ratio approaches 1.50 or less.

For the sample above, it appears to be contaminated with a significant amount of protein. Before using it for further analysis, it might be treated with a protease or some other protein removal treatment. Determining an A_{260}/A_{280} value is so common that some spectrophotometers have an A_{260}/A_{280} program built in.

Purpose

What is the actual concentration and relative purity of pAmylase DNA in commercially available samples?

Materials

pAmylase2014 plasmid DNA sample (G-Biosciences), approximately 0.2 µg/µL	Deionized water	TE buffer, pH 8.0
	Pasteur pipets, 9"	Reaction tubes, 1.7 mL and rack
	Pasteur pipet bulbs	
UV-VIS spectrophotometer and cuvettes	Permanent lab marker pens	Methanol
	Micropipets and tips	

Procedure

Part I: Pre-Lab

1. Prepare dilutions of the stock pAmylase sample, thought to be approximately 0.2 µg/µL in TE buffer, pH 8.0. Make enough dilutions until you have three samples that would be expected to be in the 0.1 to 1.1 au range. Diagram and label how these diluted samples were produced. For most UV-VIS spectrophotometers, the cuvettes used require a minimum of 500 µL of sample unless an adapter for smaller volumes is available.
2. Prepare and calibrate the UV-VIS spectrophotometer for use. Turn on the spec and allow it to initialize. Each brand of spec has different operating procedures and comes with a user's manual that describes how to warm-up and initialize it.
3. For DNA UV spectrophotometry, quartz cuvettes or special plastic UV cuvettes must be used. Verify that the cuvettes for the spec you are using are appropriate for measuring down to 260 nm.
4. Have samples 1, 2, 3 and a blank of TE buffer in a rack at the spectrophotometer. Have methanol and deionized water available for cleaning the cuvette before and after you use the spec. Have 9-inch Pasteur pipets and pipet bulbs available for transferring samples between the cuvette and the sample tubes. Take care to not break the Pasteur pipet tips off in the cuvette.

5. Review how to read samples on the spec at 260 nm and 280 nm (fixed wavelengths) or how to use pre-programmed programs to collect A_{260}/A_{280} readings. (At the end of these procedures, Genesys® 10 UV-VIS Spectrophotometer Use and DU-530® UV-VIS Life Science Spectrophotometer Use instructions are given as examples).

6. Read through Procedure Parts II and III, and create the data tables needed to collect and analyze the absorbance data. Have columns for sample numbers, expected starting concentrations, A_{260} absorbance data, concentration values, A_{280} purity/contamination data, and comments/inferences.

Part II: Concentration Determinations

1. Using the "Fixed Wavelength" program (or equivalent), set the UV spectrophotometer to a wavelength of 260 nm.

2. Zero the absorbance (0% absorbance = 100% transmittance) using 1 mL of TE buffer as a "blank." If using a quartz cuvette, rinse the cuvette with methanol (for cleaning) and deionized water prior to adding the blank (see Figure 11.11).

3. Remove and discard the TE buffer blank making certain that no solution is left in the cuvette.

4. Add sample 1 to the cuvette (between 0.5 – 1.0 mL of sample). Read the absorbance (OD) and record its value in a pAmylase Plasmid DNA Concentration data table.

5. Remove all of sample 1 from the cuvette and replace it back in its sample tube.

6. Add sample 2 to the cuvette (between 0.5 – 1.0 mL of sample). Read the absorbance (OD) and record its value in the data table.

7. Remove all of sample 2 from the cuvette and replace it back in its sample tube.

8. Add sample 3 to the cuvette (between 0.5 – 1.0 mL of sample). Read the absorbance (OD) and record its value in the data table.

9. Remove all of sample 3 from the cuvette and replace it back in its sample tube.

10. To clean the cuvette, add methanol to cuvette and discard. Then add deionized water and discard.

11. Use the DNA Concentration Equation to calculate the concentration of DNA in each sample. Add these values to the data table.

12. If the sample was diluted, multiply each concentration value by the amount the sample was diluted (by the dilution factor). The actual absorbance data, diluted samples' concentrations, calculated concentrations for the undiluted samples, and your inferences about the data (how close the calculated concentrations match the expected concentrations) should all be represented as separate columns on the data table.

Part III: Purity Determinations

Note: Some UV spectrophotometers have preprogrammed A_{260}/A_{280} programs. If the spec you are using has this feature, all A_{260}/A_{280} reading can be taken at one time. If not, take all the readings of your samples at the A_{260} reading, then reread your samples at A_{280} as described below.

1. Set the wavelength to 280 nm.

2. Calibrate the UV spectrophotometer at 280 nm using the TE buffer as a blank.

3. Add sample 1 to the cuvette (between 0.5 – 1.0 mL of sample). Read the absorbance (OD) and record its value in a pAmylase Plasmid DNA Purity data table.

4. Remove all of sample 1 from the cuvette and replace it back in its sample tube.

5. Add sample 2 to the cuvette (between 0.5 – 1.0 mL of sample). Read the absorbance (OD) and record its value in the data table.

6. Remove all of sample 2 from the cuvette and replace it back in its sample tube.

7. Add sample 3 to the cuvette (between 0.5 – 1.0 mL of sample). Read the absorbance (OD) and record its value in the data table.

8. Remove all of sample 3 from the cuvette and replace it back in its sample tube.

9. To clean the cuvette, add methanol to cuvette and discard. Then add deionize water and discard.

10. Determine the relative purity of each DNA sample by calculating a value from the ratio of the absorbance of each diluted sample at 260 nm to the absorbance at 280 nm (A_{260}/A_{280} reading).

11. Record these purity/contamination values in the data table along with inferences about how pure the sample may be and what, if any, contamination may be present.

Genesys® 10 UV-VIS Spectrophotometer Use Instruction

1. Turn on the spec (with the sample chamber closed) and allow it to warm-up and calibrate.
2. Make sure the cuvette is clean and in the proper orientation.
3. Set the wavelength by pressing the "Set nm" key and putting in the desired value. Then hit "Enter." Other programs are available and may take some exploring to determine how to use them.
4. Add a "blank" solution as needed.
5. Press "Measure Blank" to read the absorbance of the blank.
6. Remove the blank solution completely and add your sample.
7. Read the absorbance of a sample. It will come up automatically once the blank is set. Re-blank every time the wavelength is changed.
8. Use the "Enter" or "ESC" keys as needed.

Beckman DU530 Life Science UV-VIS Spectrophotometer Use Instructions

1. Turn on the spec (with the sample chamber closed) and allow it to warm-up and calibrate.
2. Make sure the cuvette is clean and in the proper orientation.
3. Select the program, usually "Fixed λ." Other programs are available and may take some exploring to determine how to use them.
4. Press through a program following the prompts. In Fixed λ, select "Options," then "Go to λ." and set the wavelength by selecting λ1 and using the "CE" key to erase the previous wavelength value. Then enter the desired λ. Exit back two screens and proceed with blanking.
5. Add a "blank" solution as needed.
6. Press "Blank" to read the absorbance of the blank. Remove the blank solution completely and add your sample.
7. Add your sample and press "READ." Remove your sample.
8. Re-blank every time the wavelength is changed. Use the "Enter" or "Exit" keys as needed.

Data Analysis/Conclusion

What are the calculated values for the concentration of each of your starting samples? How close are they to the expected values? Do the data support that the starting pAmylase sample concentration was actually at 0.2 µg/µL? Is the deviation from that expected result within a 10% error?

Thinking Like a Biotechnician

1. What happens to the absorbance reading, concentration, and purity calculation if the DNA is at too high of a concentration, for example, at 1 mg/mL? What must be done to solve this problem?
2. If an A_{260}/A_{280} purity reading were calculated to be 2.8, what should the technician think?
3. If a sample has a high A_{260} reading (greater than 1.4 au) and a high A_{280} reading, how should a technician handle this?

8 Recombinant Protein Production

Using a microscope, a biotechnologist checks the health of cells in liquid media. Genetically engineered mammalian cells, such as those growing in these cultures, are used to grow complex human proteins. Bacteria cells can be engineered to produce simpler proteins.
Photo courtesy of Cell Genesys, Inc.

Advances in molecular biology in the early 1970s, including the ability to create and transfer recombinant DNA (rDNA) molecules into cells, revolutionized both science and industry. Using special enzymes and special cell-culture techniques, scientists could create new combinations of genes and place them into specific cell lines that would produce proteins coded by the newly inserted DNA. New and improved cells and organisms, with hundreds of new agricultural and pharmaceutical benefits, were and are still being created.

The first genetically modified organisms were bacteria that made rather simple proteins of pharmaceutical interest, such as growth hormone and insulin. Later, scientists used genetically engineered fungi and mammalian cells to manufacture complex enzymes and antibodies. In the 1980s, several plants were transformed with rDNA giving them traits that improved yield and quality.

In the following activities, you will learn how to use rDNA molecules to transform bacteria into protein factories. Specifically, you will learn how to:

- use restriction enzymes to characterize an rDNA sample
- transform bacteria cells into amylase producers
- distinguish between transformants (genetically engineered cells) and nontransformants
- grow and monitor a cell culture of transformed cells
- extract rDNA plasmids from transformed cells

Once cells are transformed, they must be grown in large enough volumes to yield marketable amounts. This occurs in manufacturing during fermentation, scale-up, and protein purification. These manufacturing techniques are presented in lab activities in the next chapter. Although bacterial transformations are performed in these activities, many of the transformation techniques are similar to those involved in the genetic engineering of other organisms.

Laboratory 8a

Restriction Analysis of the Lambda Phage DNA Sequence

Background

Lambda (λ) phage DNA, cut using the *Hin*dIII restriction enzyme, is universally used as a DNA sizing standard. The uncut lambda DNA is 48,502 bp long. When *Hin*dIII is used to digest, or cut, the lambda DNA molecule, eight restriction fragments result with lengths shown in Table 8.1.

Seven of the eight fragments produced during the lambda/*Hin*dIII restriction digestion are easily visualized on an agarose gel (see Figure 8.1). Since the standard bands are of known size, the sizes of other unknown DNA fragments can be estimated by comparing the distance they travel on a gel to the distance traveled by the lambda/*Hin*dIII standard fragments on the same gel.

Table 8.1. **Lambda/HindIII Sizing Standards.** The lambda/*Hin*dIII sizing standards are used on agarose gels when separating medium-sized pieces of DNA. Pieces containing fewer than 500 bp are not likely to be seen.

Lambda/*Hin*dIII Restriction Fragments (bp)
23,130
9416
6557
4361
2322
2027
564
125

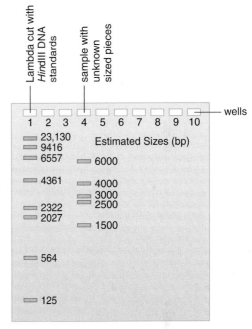

Figure 8.1. **Lambda/HindIII Sizing Standards on Gel.** The lambda/*Hin*dIII standards are used to estimate the sizes of other bands on the gel. Sizing standards are also called markers. Other DNA sizing standards are available for use on agarose gels. Find some online by searching for "DNA ladders."

Purpose

Do the restriction fragments produced during a lambda DNA/*Hin*dIII digestion match the bands present in the commercially available lambda DNA + *Hin*dIII standard markers?

What are the number and lengths of restriction fragments produced during a lambda DNA/ *Eco*RI digestion?

Given the bands in each digestion, evaluate each for use, as a possible sizing standard, to determine the lengths of other DNA fragments. Is one better suited as a sizing standard than the other? If so, why?

Materials (per team)

Note: This Materials List is for classrooms using TAE buffer for horizontal electrophoresis. If using LB buffer for electrophoresis, see the * Alternative LB Buffer System note below and the materials and procedure steps marked with an asterisk* for alternative directions.

Tube rack for 1.7-mL tubes
Reaction tubes, 1.7 mL
Permanent lab marker pens
Ice bucket
Micropipet, P-10
Micropipet tips for P-10
Micropipet, P-100
Micropipet tips for P-100
Lambda DNA, uncut, 500 µg/mL,
  diluted 1:10 in TE buffer prior to use
Electrophoresis buffer, 1X TAE
*Alternative LB Buffer System - Use 1X LB
  Buffer instead of 1X TAE Buffer for agarose gel
  preparation and for the electrophoresis running
  buffer. Use the 5X LB Loading Dye instead of
  the blue 10X or 6X DNA Loading Dye
CutSmart® Restriction Enzyme Reaction Buffer
  (NEB), 10X

*Eco*RI-HF® enzyme (NEB), 20,000 units/mL
*Hind*III-HF® enzyme (NEB), 20,000 units/mL
Nuclease-free, sterile deionized water
Microcentrifuge
Water baths, 37°C and 60°C
Agarose
Gel box, horizontal, for agarose gels
Power supply, 300V
Lambda/*Hind*III Digest Standard Sizing Markers
  Stock Solution, 500 µg/mL, diluted 1:10 in TE
  buffer prior to use
Ethidium bromide, 0.5 µg/mL (or 1X LabSafe
  Nucleic Acid Stain™)
Gel photo imaging system
DNA loading dye, (10X or 6X)*
Gloves, large
Glasses, safety, plastic
Weigh boat, 5.5" × 5.5"

Safety Precautions

- EtBr is a hazardous chemical. 1X LabSafe Nucleic Acid Stain™ is considered a safer alternative.
- EtBr is to be used by the supervisor only.
- Wear goggles and gloves while in an area where EtBr (or other chemicals) is used.

Procedure

- **Keep reagents on ice.** The reagents and enzymes are temperature sensitive.
- **Use sterile technique.** DNA is easily destroyed by contaminant enzymes. Contaminants might also inhibit restriction-enzyme performance.
- **Pipet slowly and carefully.** You are using tiny volumes of reagents. These are easily measured incorrectly.

Part I: Preparing Digests

1. Label four **sterile** 1.7-mL reaction tubes as specified on the reaction matrix. The restriction digests will take place in these tubes. Keep tubes on ice unless otherwise directed.
2. Add reagents to each reaction tube as shown in Table 8.2. Pipet each reagent directly into the solution that is already in the tube. Make sure to watch the end of the pipet tip to ensure that all of each reagent is added. Change tips for each delivery. Buffer goes into the tube before enzyme. **Always add enzyme last.** The CutSmart® Restriction Enzyme Reaction Buffer is for use with NEB restriction enzymes. If using another brand, make sure to use the buffer recommended for the specific restriction enzymes.

Table 8.2. **Lambda Restriction Digestion Reaction Matrix**

Labeled Tubes	Sterile H$_2$O (µL)	CutSmart® Restriction Enzyme Reaction Buffer (µL)	λ DNA (µL)	Enzyme (µL)	Total Reaction Volume (µL)
H	6	2	10	2 *Hind*III-HF®	20
E	6	2	10	2 *Eco*RI-HF®	20
+C	8	2	10	—	20
−C	16	2	—	2 *Hind*III-HF®	20

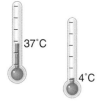

3. Tightly close the caps on the tubes. Give a 1- to 2-second pulse in the microfuge to mix and pool the reactants. (Be sure the tubes are in a balanced arrangement on the rotor!)
4. Incubate the restriction digests at 37°C for 10–15 minutes.
5. Store the digests at 4°C until they are used in gel electrophoresis.

Part II: Analyzing the Digests

6. Prepare a 0.8% agarose gel in 1X TAE buffer* with the six-toothed comb set into the end slots. Record the recipe you used in your notebook. Allow 15–20 minutes for the gel to solidify.

   *Alternative LB Buffer System - Use 1X LB Buffer instead of 1X TAE Buffer for agarose gel preparation and for the electrophoresis running buffer in Steps 6–8.

7. Place the solidified gel in the gel box in the correct orientation.
8. Cover the entire gel with 250–300 mL of 1X electrophoresis buffer. Gently remove the gel comb.
9. Get an empty reaction tube for preparing the sizing standards. Label it "Std."
10. Into tube "Std," place the following and mix:

    4 µL of lambda DNA/*Hind*III (stock standard marker pieces of known size), 50 µg/mL + 6 µL of nuclease-free, sterile deionized water

11. Heat the Std tube (as well as all the sample tubes) at 60°C for 3 minutes and then place them on ice until you are ready to add loading dye (step 12) and load it into a gel.
12. Line up tubes in a rack, in the order they will be loaded. Add 2 µL of 10X DNA loading dye (3 µL if using 6X DNA loading dye) to each sample tube.* Add 1 µL of 10X DNA loading dye (2 µL if using 6X DNA loading dye) to the "Std" tube.* Change tips each time.

    *Alternative LB Buffer System - Add 4µL of 5X LB Loading Dye to each sample tube. Add 2 µL of 5X LB Loading Dye to the lambda DNA/HindIII standard + water tube.

13. Give the tubes a 1- to 2-second pulse in the microfuge to mix and pool reactants. Tightly cap all tubes and place them into a 60°C heat block for just 3 minutes (prior to loading).
14. Load the entire contents of each tube into a well of your gel. Load Tube H into Well 1, Tube E into Well 2, and continue in the order the tubes were prepared. Load the entire contents of the "Std" tube into Well 5. Change tips each time.
15. Run the gel at 115 V* for approximately 45 minutes, or until the loading dye travels at least halfway on the gel.

    * Alternative LB Buffer System - Run the LB gel at 300V (about 85mA) for 10–15 minutes or until the orange tracking dye is 1 cm from the end of the gel.

16. After the gel has run, stain it with EtBr (see below) or with 1X LabSafe Nucleic Acid Stain™ (see the instructions that comes in the packaging). Or, if time is short, move the gel into a weigh boat and zipper-type plastic bag, and store it in a tiny bit of buffer overnight until there is time to stain and photograph it.

EtBr Staining

For EtBr staining:
Hand the tray with the gel in it to your instructor who will add EtBr solution (for staining) for 20 to 30 minutes. **Remember the safety precautions. Only the instructor should use EtBr. Wear goggles and gloves when in the presence of EtBr.**

The instructor will pour off the EtBr and fill the staining tray with deionized water. Let sit for 2 minutes, then pour off the water.

Environmental Health and Safety Officer

17. Photograph your gel for a permanent record. Place the photo in the data section of your notebook. Identify and label the known lambda/*Hind*III standard sizing fragments (Std tube). The size of these known standard fragments, in base pairs, follows:
    23,130 9416 6557 4361 2322 2027 564 (125—may be difficult to see)
18. On the photograph, label the well of each lane and identify what was loaded into each well.
19. Estimate the size of the unknown bands by comparing them to the known lambda fragments. Record these values in a data table in your notebook, and label them on the photograph, on the bottom of each of their lanes.

Data Analysis/Conclusion

Study the bands in the "H" lane. These are the bands produced by your *Hind*III digestion of the λ DNA. The bands in this lane should match the bands in the "Std" lane. Do they? Why or why not? If so, how were they produced? If not, list three reasons that the banding pattern might not be the same in these lanes.

Study the bands in the "E" lane. These are the bands produced by your *Eco*RI digestion of the λ DNA. If you determine the size of all the bands in the *Eco*RI lane, what amount should their total equal? Should any of the bands in the *Eco*RI lane match the bands in the "Std" or "H" lanes? Do they? Why or why not? If so, how were they produced? If not, explain why not.

Do all groups in the class have similar banding pattern data? Why or why not? Discuss the possible errors that could lead to varying results, for the same digestions, from one team to another.

Evaluate the usefulness of each of the digests (the lambda/*Hind*III digest and the lambda/*Eco* RI digest) in producing bands that allow accurate sizing of other unknown DNA fragment samples. Explain in-depth what makes for a good sizing standard and why one of these digests is better than the other for this purpose.

Thinking Like a Biotechnician

1. What is the purpose of the +C and -C tubes? Did they give expected results? Should there have been any other "C" tubes? If so, what would be in them?
2. A technician runs the samples of the restriction digestion, and, in one lane, there are almost twice the number of bands expected. Give a possible reason for the extra bands.
3. A technician needs smaller sizing standards than the ones produced from a lambda/*Hind*III digestion. She wants to create a smaller sizing standard. There is another restriction enzyme, *Hae* III, in the –20°C freezer. It cuts DNA more often than *Hind*III (since it has a shorter, more common recognition site). A lambda/*Hae* III digestion is performed, and the samples are run on a gel. Smaller bands are seen. How might the technician estimate the size of these pieces?

Laboratory 8b
Restriction Digestion Used to Verify the pAmylase2014 Plasmid

This lab was developed with the assistance of Simon Holdaway, The Loomis Chaffee School.

Background

Amylase is an enzyme that speeds the breakdown of starch to sugar. If genetic engineers see a need for large-scale production of the amylase enzyme to supply to several industrial customers, they can produce it in the lab.

One approach is to find naturally occurring bacteria (eg, *Geobacillus stearothermophilus*) or fungi that make amylase. They could grow these "wild" bacteria or fungi and then extract the amylase protein from them. Often, though, the naturally occurring bacteria or fungi grow too slowly, or their production of amylase is too low for commercial use. Also, there is the possibility that a native amylase-producing bacterium could be dangerous or pathogenic.

Scientists already have, in culture, bacteria and fungi that they know how to grow safely in large quantities. These "model" organisms can be coaxed to produce proteins in large amounts. The bacterium grown by most genetic engineering companies is *E. coli*. One of the fungi is *Trichoderma*. If these model organisms can be given the foreign DNA that codes for amylase production, they might produce large amounts of amylase. They could be transformed into amylase producers. The amylase these genetically engineered cells make could then be isolated, purified, and sold for a profit.

To engineer cells to make amylase, one needs to construct a vector that can carry the amylase gene into the cells. To make a recombinant plasmid coding for amylase production, the amylase gene (just over 1600 bp) is excised from a native source and pasted into an existing plasmid (pUC57). The new plasmid might be called pAmylase2014, pAmy2014 for short, since it contains the amylase gene (see Figure 8.2). Along with the amylase gene, pAmylase2014 would contain an ampicillin-resistance (Amp^R) gene since that was already present in the precursor plasmid vector, pUC57. If a bacteria cell, such as *E. coli*, receives this plasmid, it will gain two new phenotypes, amylase production, and ampicillin resistance.

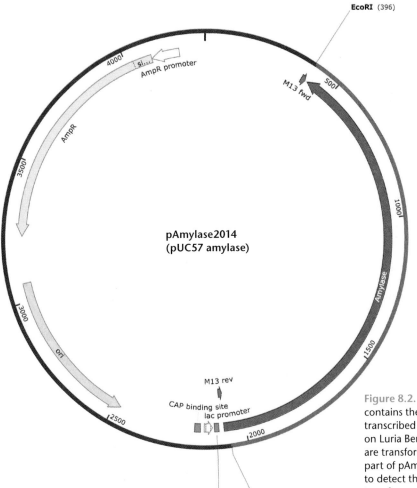

Figure 8.2. pAmylase2014 Plasmid. pAmylase2014 contains the amylase gene. In cells, the amylase gene is transcribed and amylase is produced. Starch clearing occurs on Luria Bertani (LB) starch agar plates around colonies that are transformed with pAmylase2014. An Amp^R gene is also part of pAmylase2014. The Amp^R gene allows a second way to detect that the plasmid got into cells, since only *E. coli* cells transformed with the Amp^R gene will grow on ampicillin agar. Map by Simon Holdaway.

Before we transform *E. coli* cells with pAmylase2014 DNA, we want to confirm that the DNA we are using has the characteristics of pAmylase2104. This can be done by restriction digestion. The pAmylase2014 plasmid has a size of approximately 4300 bp. It contains a single restriction site for the *Hind*III restriction enzyme. It also contains a single restriction site for the *Eco*RI restriction enzyme. The products of the restriction enzyme digestion can be seen on an agarose gel.

Purpose

When a suspected sample of pAmylase2014 is cut by restriction enzymes, do the resulting DNA fragments indicate that the sample has the characteristics of pAmylase2014?

Materials

Note: This Materials List is for classrooms using TAE buffer for horizontal electrophoresis. If using LB buffer for electrophoresis, see the * Alternative LB Buffer System note below and the materials and Procedure steps marked with an asterisk* for alternative directions.

Tube rack for 1.7-mL tubes
Reaction tubes, 1.7 mL
Permanent lab marker pens
Ice bucket
Micropipet, P-10
Micropipet tips for P-10
Micropipet, P-100
Micropipet tips for P-100
pAmylase2014 plasmid, 0.2 µg/µL
CutSmart® Restriction Enzyme Reaction Buffer (NEB), 10X
Electrophoresis buffer, 1X TAE
*Alternative LB Buffer System - Use 1X LB Buffer instead of 1X TAE Buffer for agarose gel preparation and for the electrophoresis running buffer. Use the 5X LB Loading Dye instead of the blue 10X or 6X DNA Loading Dye.

*Hind*III-HF® enzyme (NEB), 20,000 units/mL
*Eco*RI-HF® enzyme (NEB), 20,000 units/mL
Mixture of *Hind*III-HF®/*Bam*HI-HF® enzymes
Nuclease-free, sterile deionized water
Microcentrifuge
Water bath, 37°C
Agarose
Gel box, horizontal, for agarose gels
Power supply 300V
Lambda/*Hind*III, Digest Standard Sizing Markers Stock Solution 500 µg/mL
Ethidium bromide, 0.5 µg/mL (or 1X LabSafe Nucleic Acid Stain™)
Gel photo imaging system
DNA loading dye, (10X or 6X)*
Gloves, large
Glasses, safety, plastic
Weigh boat, 5.5" × 5.5"

Safety Precautions

Environmental Health and Safety Officer

- Wear goggles and gloves while in an area where EtBr (or other chemicals) is used.
- EtBr is a hazardous chemical.
- EtBr is to be used only by the supervisor. 1X LabSafe Nucleic Acid Stain™ is considered a safer alternative.

Procedure

- **Keep reagents on ice.** The reagents and enzymes are temperature sensitive.
- **Make sure the restriction buffer is at the correct concentration.** If necessary, change the volumes accordingly.
- **Use sterile technique.** DNA is easily destroyed by contaminant enzymes. Contaminants might also inhibit restriction enzyme performance.
- **Pipet slowly and carefully.** You are using tiny volumes of reagents. These are easily measured incorrectly. Small pipeting errors can have a significant impact on the results.

Part I: Preparing Digests

1. Label five sterile 1.7-mL reaction tubes, A through E. The restriction digests will take place in these tubes. Keep the tubes on ice.
2. Add reagents to each reaction tube as shown in Table 8.3. Pipet each reagent directly into the solution that is already in the tube. Make sure to watch the end of the pipet tip to ensure that all of each reagent is added. Change tips for each delivery. Buffer goes into the tube before the enzyme. **Always add enzyme last.** The CutSmart® Restriction Enzyme Reaction Buffer is for use with NEB restriction enzymes. If using another brand, make sure to use the buffer recommended for the specific restriction enzymes.
3. Tightly close the caps on Tubes A through E. Give each tube a 1- to 2-second pulse in the microfuge to mix and pool reactants. (Be sure the tubes are in a balanced arrangement.)
4. Incubate the restriction digests at 37°C for a 10–15 minutes.
5. Store the digests at 4°C until they are used in the electrophoresis.

37°C   4°C

Table 8.3.   **pAmylase2014 Restriction Digestion Reaction Matrix**

Tubes	Sterile H$_2$0 (μL)	10X Restriction Buffer (μL)	pAmylase2014 (μL)	Enzyme(μL) (μL)	Total Reaction Volume (μL)
A	12	2	4	2 HindIII-HF®	20
B	12	2	4	2 BamHI-HF®	20
C	12	2	4	2 mixture	20
D	16	2	—	2 mixture	20
E	14	2	4	—	20

Part II: Analyzing the Digests

6. Prepare a 0.8% agarose gel in 1X TAE buffer* with the six-toothed comb set in the end slots. Record the recipe you used in your notebook. Allow 15–20 minutes for the gel to solidify.

   *Alternative LB Buffer System - Use 1X LB Buffer instead of 1X TAE Buffer for agarose gel preparation and for the electrophoresis running buffer in Steps 6–8.

7. Place the solidified gel in the gel box in the correct orientation.
8. Cover the entire gel with 250–300 mL of 1X electrophoresis buffer. Gently remove the gel comb.
9. Label an empty reaction tube "Std."
10. Into the "Std" Tube F, place the following:

    4 μL of 50 μg/mL lambda DNA/HindIII (standard marker pieces of cut DNA of known size) + 6 μL of nuclease-free, sterile deionized water

11. Heat the Std tube (as well as all the sample tubes) at 60°C for 3 minutes and then place them on ice until you are ready to add loading dye (step 12) and load it into a gel.
12. Line up tubes in a rack, in the order they will be loaded. Add 2 μL of 10X DNA loading dye (3 μL if using 6X DNA loading dye) to each tube A–E.* Change tips each time. Add 1 μL of 10X DNA loading dye (2 μL if using 6X DNA loading dye) to the "Std" tube.

    *Alternative LB Buffer System - Add 4μL of 5X LB Loading Dye to each sample tube. Add 2μL of 5X LB Loading Dye to the lambda DNA/HindIII standard + water tube.

13. Give the tubes a 1- to 2-second pulse in the microfuge to mix and pool reactants. Tightly cap all tubes and place them into a 60°C heat block for just 3 minutes (prior to loading).
14. Load the entire contents of each tube into a well of your gel. Load Tube A into Well 1, B into Well 2, etc. Change tips each time. Add the entire contents of "Std" tube to Well 6.

15. Run the gel at 115 V* for approximately 1 hour until the loading dye goes at least halfway on the gel. While you wait, draw a diagram in your notebook showing the sample that was loaded into each lane, and the concentration and voltage of the gel run.

    *Alternative LB Buffer System - Run the LB gel at 300V (about 85mA) for 10–15 minutes or until the orange tracking dye is 1 cm from the end of the gel.

16. After the gel has run, stain it with EtBr (see below) or move the gel into a weigh boat and store it in a tiny bit of buffer overnight. Staining with 1X LabSafe Nucleic Acid Stain™ is an alternative (see the instructions that comes in the packaging).

EtBr Staining

Environmental Health and Safety Officer

For EtBr staining:

Hand the tray with the gel in it to your instructor who will add EtBr solution (for staining) for 20 to 30 minutes. **Remember the safety precautions. Only the instructor should use EtBr. Wear goggles and gloves when in the presence of EtBr.**

The instructor will pour off the EtBr and fill the staining tray with deionized water. Let sit for 2 minutes, then pour off the water.

17. Photograph your gel for a permanent record. Glue the photo in the data section of your notebook. Identify and label the lambda standard fragments. The size of the DNA lambda standard fragments, in base pairs, follows. Estimate the size of the unknowns by comparing them to the known lambda fragments

    23,130 9416 6557 4361 2322 2027 564 (125—difficult to see)

    • You can roughly estimate the lengths of the unknown bands by "eyeballing" the position of the unknown bands versus the known standard bands. Make a better estimate (more quantitative) by plotting the data on semilog graph paper with the standard fragment sizes along the y-axis and the distance they travel from the well along the x-axis. Draw a best-fit straight line through these data to produce a standard curve. To estimate the sizes of the unknowns, look at the intersection of the distance the unknowns traveled.

    • You can make an even better estimate by letting Microsoft® Excel® create the standard curve for you. Open a Microsoft® Excel® spreadsheet. Make a two-column data table with the standard fragment sizes in the first column and the distance the fragments traveled in the second column. Using the Chart menu, plot the data on an XY scatter line graph. Give the graph a title. Label the axis. Double click on the x-axis to view the "Format Axis." Choose "Scale" and "logarithmic scale." Set the minimum on "100." This plots the x-axis logarithmically to straighten the line. Next, click on the line. Choose "Add a Trendline" from the Chart menu. It will give a linear trendline. Click on the trendline. Select "Type" and "Logarithmic." Choose "Options," "Display equation on the chart," and "Display R-squared value on the chart." This gives a best-fit, straight line, standard curve, plus the equation of the line on the graph. To calculate a size for an unknown fragment, measure the distance traveled on the gel "y," and solve for ln (x). When you get ln (x), use f_x to determine "exp (x)" for the ln (x) value, and it will give the size of the unknown fragment. See the example on the next page.

If an unknown fragment travels 1.8 cm, then y = 1.8.
1.8 = -0.5393 ln (x) + 6.2701
ln (x) = 8.2887
exp (8.2887)
x = 3979 bp

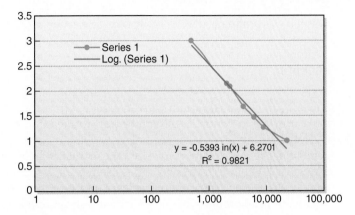

18. Place a label at the well of each lane, identifying the sample that was loaded into the well.
19. In a data table in your notebook, record the size of all of the DNA bands. On the photographs, label the length of each DNA fragment on the bottom of each of their lanes.

Data Analysis/Conclusion

Are the observed bands in the gel what was expected after restriction digestion? Do the digestion fragments indicate that the plasmid sample studied here has the characteristics of the pAmylase2014 plasmid? Give evidence for your statement. Do all groups in the class have similar data? Why or why not? Discuss the possible errors that could lead to varying results from one team to another. If the digestion confirms that the sample is pAmylase2014, why is that information valuable?

Thinking Like a Biotechnician

The pAmylase2014 used in this experiment is added to the tubes at 0.2 µg/µL. After the other reagents for the digestion are added, the final volume is 20 µL.

1. What is the actual concentration of plasmid DNA in Tube A?
2. What mass of plasmid DNA is in Tube A?
3. A restriction map can be drawn showing the relative positions of the *Eco*RI restriction sites to the *Hind*III site. To do this, determine the size of the fragments cut by each enzyme; then try to "fit" the pieces together like a jigsaw puzzle. In the past, restriction digestion mapping helped scientists determine the A, T, C, G sequence on a piece of DNA. Can you explain why?

Laboratory 8c
Transformation of *E. coli* with pAmylase2014

This lab was originally developed by Diane Sweeney, Crystal Springs Uplands School and Punahou School. It was modified by Simon Holdaway, The Loomis Chaffee School, and Ellyn Daugherty.

Background

In the 1970s, scientists wanted to develop an economical method of producing large quantities of amylase. *E. coli* is a bacterium with an excellent transformation "track record." While it does not make amylase in nature, *E. coli* can be transformed in the laboratory to produce amylase.

Transforming *E. coli* takes several steps. First, the gene of interest (in this case, the amylase gene) must be inserted into a plasmid that contains an additional selection gene. In this activity, a pAmylase2014 plasmid (pAmy2014) is used. pAmylase2014 contains both the amylase production gene (from *Geobacillus stearothermophilus*) and the ampicillin resistance gene (Amp^R) from pUC57. The Amp^R gene produces an enzyme that destroys ampicillin in the media on which the bacteria grow. Ampicillin would normally delay the growth of *E. coli* cells, but if the cells acquire the Amp^R gene, they can survive in its presence.

To transform *E. coli* cells, researchers first grow them in broth culture and then make them competent, or more likely to take up pieces of foreign DNA. Scientists are not sure what happens when cells are made competent, but it is thought that the competency enlarges channels in the cells' membranes, making it easier for plasmids to get into the cells (see Figure 8.3). Competency may be induced by treatment with divalent cations such as $CaCl_2$ or $MgCl_2$ or electrically using a process called electroporation. Electroporation is not practical for most academic labs due to the cost and special equipment required. In the following protocol, cells may be purchased already competent or cells can be made competent using $CaCl_2$.

The competent cells are mixed with the recombinant pAmylase2014 plasmid. A heat shock, followed by a cold shock, is given to the mixture, and plasmids are drawn in and trapped inside the cells. Next, the cells are grown in recovery broth, which gives them time to repair their damaged membranes and express their new genes. The culture, containing a mix of transformed and nontransformed cells, is plated on selection media containing ampicillin and starch. Only transformed cells will be able to grow on the ampicillin-containing, starch-agar selection media.

Under the best circumstances, transformation efficiency occurs in only about one in 10,000 cells. The transformed cells are deposited on the selection media, where they grow into colonies. Each cell in the colony is a clone of the original cell deposited in that location. All the cells in the clone contain the new DNA (a new genotype), and they will express the new characteristics (new phenotypes), in this case, ampicillin resistance and amylase production. If the transformation is successful, a colony of cells can be grown in broth and scaled-up into larger volumes for manufacturing purposes.

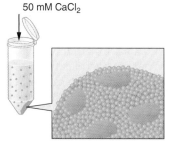

50 mM $CaCl_2$

To make compentent cells, calcium chloride may be added.

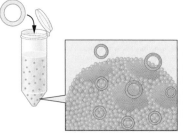

The calcium chloride is thought to make the cell's membrane proteins move apart slightly, widening the pores and allowing easier entry of plasmids.

Figure 8.3. **Making Competent Cells with CaCl2.** When cells are treated with $CaCl_2$, more plasmids enter into cells, increasing transformation efficiency (the number of cells transformed).

Purpose

To transform *E. coli* with a "recombinant" pAmy2014 plasmid, which contains a gene for ampicillin resistance and a gene for amylase production.

To demonstrate that the transformation was successful and that the newly inserted genes are being expressed by the transformed *E. coli* cells.

Materials

Environmental Health and Safety Officer

Hot plate/stirrer
LB broth base, LB agar base
Starch, soluble
Glass beakers, 600mL, 400 mL, 250 mL
Media bottles, 400 mL, 250 mL, 125 mL
Autoclave/sterilizer
Ampicillin, 10mg/mL, filter-sterilized, use 1 mL/100mL of media
Bunsen burner and lighter
Laminar flow hood
Petri plates, 100 × 15-mm
Lysol® disinfectant
Calcium chloride, anhydrous
Aluminum foil
Pipets, 10 mL, 5 mL, 1 mL, sterile, and pumps
Tubes, 50 mL, sterile, and racks
Inoculating loop, Ni/Cr wire or sterile plastic
Tubes, 15 mL, capped, and racks
Centrifuge for 15-mL tubes

Micropipets, P-1000, P-100, P-10 and sterile tips
Bleach, 10%
Reaction tubes, 1.7 mL, sterile, and rack
pAmylase2014 plasmid, 0.005 µg/µL
Water bath, 42°C
Heat block or shaking incubator, 37°C
Incubator oven, 37°C

Additional Materials Option 1:
E. coli DH5alpha, available from G-Biosciences, #BTNM-0093

Additional Materials Option 2:
Z-Competent™ *E. coli* Transformation kit, G-Biosciences # GZ-4 used with *E. coli* DH5alpha, available from G-Biosciences, #BTNM-0093

Additional Materials Option 3:
NEB Express Competent *E. coli*, in glycerol, NEB #C2523I

Procedure

Environmental Health and Safety Officer

Pre-Lab: Reagent/Media/Supply Preparation (2 days prior to Procedure Part II)

1. Prepare and sterilize growth media, selection media, CaCl$_2$, tubes, and micropipet tips. Amounts given are for 16 lab groups. Adjust amounts and replicates as needed.

Item	Amount Needed for 16 replications	Comments
LB agar	Two 400 mLs batches in 600-mL media bottle	1 bottle for 1 sleeve of LB agar plates 1 bottle for 1 sleeve of LB/amp agar plates (add ampicillin after sterile agar has cooled to 60°C just prior to pouring)
LB/2% starch agar	One 400 mL batch in 600-mL media bottle	1 bottle for 1 sleeve of LB/amp/2% starch agar plates (add ampicillin after sterile agar has cooled to 60°C just prior to pouring)
LB broth	One 400 mL batch in 600-mL media bottle and two 50-mL batches in 125-mL media bottles	1 bottle (use in broth cultures of starting non-transformed cells—Option 1 Procedure) 2 bottles for cell recovery after transformation protocol (Option 1 Procedure). Determine what broth is needed for Option 2 Procedure and prepare it, if necessary. For some cells, it is included with the shipment.
1.7-mL reaction tubes	Each team needs only 2 reaction tubes but sterilize several dozen at a time	All tips, tubes, and pipets must be sterile. Sterilize in wide-mouth bottle with jiggly cap, then place in overnight in a 43°C oven to dry.
Micropipet tips	One of each size for each pipetting station	Purchase sterile tips or sterilize and then place in overnight in a 43°C oven to dry.
50 m*M* CaCl$_2$	Two 50-mL volumes in 125 mL bottles	Only needed for Option 1 Procedure

2. Pour plates the same day the media is prepared or reliquify the media in a microwave (set at 50% power). Leave the plates closed, covered with bleach-disinfected aluminum foil, overnight since the media in the plates must "dry out" a bit before use. Plates remain usable for up to 1 week if stored in the dark.

3. If conducting Option 1 Procedure, using non-competent *E. coli* DH5alpha, streak several plate cultures of these cells to produce "stock" plates for the class, and incubate upside-down overnight at 37°C.

General Procedure

Environmental Health and Safety Officer

- Use sterile technique throughout the procedure. Use a laminar flow hood, if available.
- Keep cells on ice unless otherwise directed.
- Dispose of all biohazards appropriately.

Procedure Part I, Option 1: Transformation Using CaCl2 Competent Cells

(This is a method that was developed in the 1980s, using non-competent cells made competent through $CaCl_2$ exposure. This method takes more time and the transformed cells don't grow quite as fast or express as much amylase as those in Option 2, but it will still produce transformants and is less expensive and the timing is more flexible.)

Preparing Competent Cells

1. Place 10 mL of sterile LB broth in a sterile 50-mL capped, conical, centrifuge tube.

2. Inoculate the broth with a small amount of bacteria from one colony of *E. coli* DH5alpha AMY-bacteria, from the overnight, stock plate. Cap the tube and finger-flick the broth to distribute the cells. Be sure the bacteria are well suspended.

3. Incubate the cultures at 37°C for 18–20 hours in a shaking (250 rpm) hot water bath. The cultures should be cloudy. If measured on a spectrophotometer, the cell culture should have an OD_{600nm} of approximately 0.6 au.

4. Transfer all 10 mL of overnight culture to a sterile 15-mL centrifuge tube. Spin the broth culture in a tabletop centrifuge at moderate speed for 8 minutes. The cells will pellet at the bottom. Carefully pour off and discard the supernatant into a trash container containing 10% bleach. **Save the cell pellet.**

5. Using a sterile pipet, add 0.5 mL of **cold** 50 mM $CaCl_2$ to the cell pellet. Resuspend the cells by repeatedly pipeting them up and down. **Be gentle.** These cells are stressed.

6. Tightly cap the tube and keep on ice for at least 20 minutes, or store overnight in the refrigerator.

37°C

Transforming the Competent Bacteria

7. Obtain two sterile 1.7-mL microtest tubes. Label one "C" (for control, no DNA added) and the other "D" (for DNA). Do not touch the inside of the tube or cap.

8. Check to make sure that the competent cell mixture is very cloudy with bacteria. Gently finger-flick the tube to ensure that no bacteria are lying on the bottom of the tube. Be gentle with these cells; they are fragile and can burst and die easily. Using sterile tips, add 150 µL of competent *E. coli* cells to each tube.

9. Place both tubes on ice and keep very cold until Step 13.

10. Add 10 µL of sterile distilled water to Tube C. Mix by finger-flicking. Wrist-flick the sample to pool the reagents. Return Tube C to ice.

4°C

11. Add 10 µL of 0.005 µg/µL pAmylase2014 to Tube D. Pipet the plasmid **directly** into the cell suspension. Mix by finger-flicking. Wrist-flick the sample to pool the reagents. Return Tube D to ice.

12. Leave the cells on ice for a minimum of 15 minutes.

13. After 15 minutes, move your ice bath containing Tubes C and D next to the hot water bath. As quickly as possible, transfer both tubes from the ice to the hot water bath (42°C for DH5alpha) for a "heat shock" of **exactly** 20 sec. **Move the tubes as quickly as possible since the more distinct the heat shock, the greater the transformation efficiency.**

42°C

4°C

14. After 20 seconds, quickly return the tubes to the ice bath for 3 minutes. Move the tubes as quickly as possible from the heat to the cold. **The more distinct the cold shock, the greater the transformation efficiency.**

15. Using a sterile 1-mL pipet, add 250 µL of sterile LB broth to each tube. Mix by finger flicking. Wrist-flick the sample to pool the reagents.

37°C 16. Incubate the tubes at 37°C for 10 to 15 minutes before plating (Procedure Part II).
Note: You may stop at this point and store the tubes in the refrigerator overnight.

Procedure Part I, Option 2: Transformation Using Commercially Available Kit to Prepare Competent Cells

Many vendors sell kits to produce competent cells. These competency kits are inexpensive and produce cells that result in a high transformation efficiency). One such kit is G-Bioscience's Z-Competent™ E. coli Transformation Kit, G-Biosciences # GZ-4. The kit contains a competency buffer (CaCl$_2$ plus other ingredients) to make competent E. coli DH5alpha cells that are ready for transformation (Procedure Part I, step 7), instead of completing Procedure Part I, steps 5 and 6. See the protocol for the Z-Competent™ E. coli Transformation Kit atwww.gbiosciences.com/PDF/Protocol/Z-Competent_Ecoli_Transformation.pdf.

Procedure Part I, Option 3: Transformation Using Commercially Available Competent Cells

(Many vendors sell specially designed, proprietary strains of competent cells (most made competent through electroporation). These competent cells are expensive but transform easily (have a high transformation efficiency) and express higher levels of protein (in this case, recombinant amylase).

1. These competent cells are shipped overnight on dry ice and must be kept frozen (on dry ice or -80°C) until used, within 1 to 2 days of arrival. Excellent planning is required to be ready to use the cells on arrival. Plan on doing the entire transformation in one day.
2. The protocol for the transformation of commercially available competent cells is either included in the cell shipment or is available on the vendor's Web site. There will be differences in media, volumes, and incubations from a transformation using CaCl$_2$ transformed cells. The protocol that is specific to each competent cell line should be used and followed exactly (not the protocol in Option 1 or 2).

Procedure Part II: Plating the Bacteria on Selection Media

1. Disinfect the countertop by cleaning with disinfectant. Disinfect hands by thorough washing with hand soap or by using a hand disinfectant/sanitizer. Use a laminar flow hood, if available.
2. Obtain one plate each of 2% starch LB agar/ampicillin (selection plates), amp/LB agar (control), and LB agar (control). Draw a line down the center on the bottom of each plate. Label one side "C" and one side "D." Also, add your initials and the date to each plate.
3. Finger-flick Tube C to resuspend the cells. Transfer 50 µL of the cell suspension to the center of each of the C sections on the three plates.
4. Finger-flick Tube D to resuspend the cells. Transfer 50 µL of the cell suspension to the center of each of the D sections on the three plates.
5. Spread cells over the surfaces of each section using a new, sterile, plastic inoculating for each section.
6. Leave the plates on the countertop, undisturbed, flat, and right side up for 5 minutes so the suspension will be absorbed by the agar.
7. In your notebook, record your predictions about where colonies should grow on your plates. Consider which samples were spread on what type of agar. Think about and record the numbers of colonies you expect to see.

37°C 8. Invert the plates, stack them together, and place them **upside down,** in a 37°C incubator for 24 hours. After 24 hours check for colonies growing on the "D" sides of the plates. If the colonies are less than 2 mm in diameter, allow them to grow for another 12–24 hours (up to 48 total). Then wrap each plate in parafilm and incubate, upside-down at 4°C for 24 hours.
9. Disinfect countertop, and wash your hands.

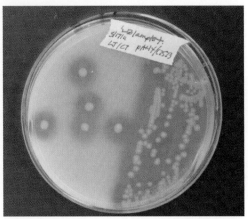

Figure 8.4. These starch/amp LB agar plates show starch digestion, in halos, around pAmylase-transformed colonies. The ampicillin delays the growth of nontransformed cells.
Photo by author.

Procedure Part III: Observing and Recording Your Transformation Results

1. Retrieve the Petri plates from the incubator or refrigerator. Look very closely for bacterial growth. Hold your plates up to the light or against a dark background to help visualize the transformed colonies. Look for "halos," areas of clearing around colonies. Halos result when transformed bacteria produce amylase, because the amylase diffuses out and breaks down the starch in the agar around the colony. By placing the Petri plates in the refrigerator overnight, the halos become much more visible (see Figure 8.4). Also, if the cells will not be used after transformation, a diluted iodine solution (1:10 Lugol's Iodine solution) may be added to the agar surface. The iodine stains starch-containing surfaces black, leaving halos golden-brown and more visible.
2. Observe, draw, and label the plates showing **all** colonies and any halos. Measure so the drawing is accurate.
3. Count the number of colonies (or do sampling and then multiply) on each plate. Record these data.

Data Analysis/Conclusion

Was the transformation protocol successful in creating amylase-producing, ampicillin-resistant *E. coli* cells? Give evidence and explanations about what happened on each selection plate.

Compare your plates with others in the class. What does your transformation efficiency look like compared with that of other groups? Identify three techniques that could have resulted in poor transformation efficiency. If any plate produced any colonies of transformed cells, describe what should be done next with those cells.

Thinking Like a Biotechnician

1. Explain how a D plate could have absolutely nothing growing on it.
2. Sometimes, smaller nontransformed satellite colonies are seen around a central transformed colony. Are there any satellite colonies on your plates? Record the satellite colonies' morphology (size, shape, and color) compared with the transformed colonies and reasons for any difference. Give reasons why the satellite company may be present and exhibit a different growth rate than the transformed cells.
3. Not all the cells in the original culture are transformed. What evidence do you have to support this statement? Determine the transformation efficiency (number of colonies/µg of DNA) of your protocol. Cells from the transformed broth culture can be plated out as a 1:10, 1:100, 1:1000, or 1:10,000 serial dilutions on starch/amp LB agar. The number of colonies per unit volume in the original transformed culture can be calculated by multiplying the number of colonies counted in one of the dilutions by the dilution factor. This will give the number of cells/mg of DNA. This gives the transformation efficiency. A ratio of 1:10,000 transformed cells (0.01%) is considered a good result.

Laboratory 8d
Growing and Monitoring Bacterial Cultures

Background

After cells have been transformed, they must be grown in ever-increasing volumes. During this scale-up process, the clones must be monitored. The culture's growth rate is of critical importance. Cells must be healthy, growing, and multiplying to produce as much product as possible. The goal is to have the cell numbers doubling every 20 minutes, which is called "exponential growth." While a culture grows, the absorbance or OD at 600nm is measured to get an idea of the cell count or culture density. An OD_{600} of between 0.4–0.7au ensures that the cells are not stressed in their environment due to overcrowding. "Stationary phase" is when a culture slows its growth rate to near zero because of a lack of nutrients or space, or because there are too many waste products.

To ensure the maximum growth rate, there must be sufficient food nutrients, space, and oxygen. Also, the temperature and pH must be optimal. Technicians regularly take samples and measurements to ensure that the cell cultures are growing and producing product at the maximum rate.

Purpose

To start, maintain, and monitor broth and plate cultures of nontransformed cells.
To document whether or not the culture exhibits exponential growth.

Materials

Balance, tabletop milligram
Weigh boat, 3.5" × 3.5"
Lab scoops
LB agar base
Beakers, 250 mL
Glass rods
Magnetic stir bars
Hot plate stirrer
Hot hands protector
Media bottle, 250 mL
LB broth base
Media bottle, 125 mL
Sterilizer/autoclave
Laminar flow hood

Lysol® disinfectant
Glasses, safety, plastic
Bunsen burner
Lab gas lighter
Petri dishes, 100 × 15 mm, sterile
E. coli DH5alpha, overnight plate culture
Inoculating loop, Ni/Cr wire or sterile plastic
Incubator oven, 37°C
Tubes, 50-mL, sterile
Tube racks for 50-mL tubes
Shaking incubator, 37°C

Pipets, 5 mL, sterile
Pipet pump, green
VIS Spectrophotometer
Cuvettes for the spectrophotometer
Peg racks for 13 × 100-mm tubes
pH paper, wide-range pH 0–14
pH paper, narrow-range pH 0–6
pH paper, narrow-range pH 5–10

Procedure

- Review sterile technique, media prep, plating, and safe handling of bacteria.
- Work in pairs to prepare the media. Each pair of students should make their own batch of agar, start their own plate cultures, and make their own broth and broth cultures.

Part I: Preparing Media

1. Prepare 125 mL of LB agar in a 250-mL beaker. Do not forget to add the dH$_2$O slowly, mixing the media into a paste. In your notebook, set up a ratio to determine the amount of agar media to mix for the volume you desire, based on the recipe on the media bottle.

$$\frac{\text{mass of media (g) on the bottle}}{1000 \text{ ml of dH}_2\text{O}} = \frac{\text{mass of media (g) for the volume to be made}}{\text{volume of the media to be made (mL)}}$$

Remember to heat the media, while stirring, to just below boiling to suspend the media. Using "hot hands" to hold the hot beaker, transfer the media to a 250-mL media bottle. **Loosely attach the cap.** Label the bottle. Autoclave at 15 to 20 psi for 15 to 20 minutes.

2. Prepare enough media for three batches of 50 mL of LB broth. That will be 150 mL in a 250-mL beaker. Do not forget to add the dH_2O slowly, mixing the media into a paste. In your notebook, set up a ratio to determine the amount of broth media to mix for the volume you desire, based on the recipe on the media bottle.

$$\frac{\text{mass of media (g) on the bottle}}{1000 \text{ ml of } dH_2O} = \frac{\text{mass of media (g) for the volume to be made}}{\text{volume of the media to be made (mL)}}$$

Remember to heat the media, while stirring, to just below boiling to dissolve the media. Transfer approximately 50 mL of the broth to three 125-mL media bottles. **Loosely attach the caps.** Label the bottles. Autoclave at 15 to 20 psi for 15 to 20 minutes. Cool before using.

3. After the agar media has been sterilized and cooled to 65°C, pour the agar into labeled (on the bottom edge), sterile, Petri plates (in a sterile laminar flow hood, if available). Pour the plates about 1/2 full (approximately 20 mL). If a flow hood is not available, clean and disinfect a lab bench in an area of the lab with very little air circulation. Allow the plates to cool undisturbed for 24 hours before using. There should be enough agar for approximately six plates.
Note: The agar and broth media made in steps 1 through 3 will be used during the next few lab sessions.

Part II: Starting the Cultures

1. Streak two plates with stock *E. coli* DH5alpha. Use sterile technique and the "triple-Z " streaking method (see Lab 4g).
2. Place the plates, upside down, in the incubation oven, at 37°C, for 24 hours.
3. After the incubation period, photograph each plate culture. Count the number of isolated colonies in the second "Z" and third "Z" on each plate. Report this value in your notebook.
4. From an isolated colony, start a 50-mL broth culture in a sterile laminar flow hood. This is Broth Culture 1.
5. Pick an isolated colony, and circle it on the bottom of the Petri plate.
6. Use a sterile inoculating loop to sample the colony on the plate, and transfer it to one of the media bottles. Label the culture tube, and include the culture start time. Place the broth culture in a shaking incubator set at 250 rpm and 37°C.
7. After 24 hours, the broth culture should be cloudy with suspended bacteria cells.

Part III: Monitoring the Cell Cultures

1. In a sterile laminar flow hood, four hours before class begins, seed a fresh batch of 50 mL of LB broth with 2 mL of Broth Culture 1. Swirl to thoroughly suspend the cells throughout the new media. Place the culture in a 37°C shaking incubator for 6 hours.
2. **After** the initial 6-hour growth period, using excellent sterile technique, take a sample (the volume depends on the cuvette to be used) and place it in a cuvette. Using pH paper, measure its pH. Using the VIS spectrophotometer, read both its absorbance and transmittance at 600 nm. Use sterile LB broth as a blank solution. Discard all culture samples into a container holding 10% bleach or some other appropriate disinfectant. Do this every hour for the next 6–8 hours returning to the lab as needed.

Data Collection

1. Make a data table and graph showing the change in the broth culture's pH over time.
2. Make a data table, and record the culture's absorbance and the transmittance data over the same time period.

Data Analysis

Produce a growth-curve line graph of the absorbance data The graph reflects the change in cell concentration over time. Label the three growth phases, on the graph, as follows: the initial, slow growth period as the "lag phase," the period of rapid cell multiplication as "exponential growth," and the period when cell multiplication slows, as the culture becomes crowded, as "stationary phase." Place an "*" at 0.4–0.6 au on the growth curve line. This is the best time to use the culture to seed another volume or to do a transformation.

Conclusion

Describe and explain the changes in the pH, absorbance, and transmittance in the broth culture over time. Does it appear that the culture exhibited exponential growth? Explain. Does it appear that the culture exhibited the stationary phase? Explain. Give reasons why the culture may not have grown as expected. How long did it take for the culture to reach the "seeding" OD? Describe what would happen to the culture next if it were, or were not, growing properly.

Thinking Like a Biotechnician

1. How can a technician be confident that a culture is not contaminated with unwanted bacteria?
2. How can you tell when a culture has reached the stationary phase?
3. How can you tell if a culture has sufficient aeration?

Laboratory 8e

Scaling-Up *E. coli* Cultures for Amylase Production

Background

When pAmylase2014-transformed bacteria produce starch-cleared halos on starch/ampicillin agar, it demonstrates amylase production. Although this is quite an accomplishment, growing transformed cells on Petri plates does not produce enough amylase for the marketplace. For manufacturing, bacteria must be grown, in liquid media, in increasingly larger volumes. This is called "scale-up."

During "scale-up," a colony of interest is inoculated into broth media. The broth is placed in a shaker and aerated at a particular temperature. Under optimum conditions, the cells of bacteria divide rapidly, using up the nutrients in the broth and producing new molecules, including amylase. The culture is assayed periodically to determine cell culture density, and checked for amylase production and activity.

As the cells grow and divide, nutrients in the broth decrease, waste products increase, cells become crowded, and culture growth slows. At this point, the cells must be transferred to larger volumes of broth in larger containers: the culture is scaled-up to the next volume. When the volume and concentration of amylase in the culture are sufficient, the culture is "harvested." During harvesting, the cells are separated from the broth by filtration or centrifugation. Then, depending on where the protein is found, the protein is purified from either the broth or from the cells. Purification of proteins from broth culture is presented in later lab activities.

Purpose

What are the characteristics of a transformed *E. coli* broth culture during "scale-up"?
Is there evidence of amylase activity from the transformed cells in the broth culture?
At what time should a 100-mL culture be "scaled-up"?

Materials

Environmental Health and Safety Officer

Balance, tabletop milligram	Laminar flow hood	Petri dishes, 100 × 15 mm,
Weigh boat and lab scoops	Lysol® disinfectant	sterile
LB broth base	Glasses, safety, plastic	Inoculating loop, Ni/Cr wire or
Starch, soluble	Bunsen burner and gas lighter	sterile plastic
Beakers, 250 mL	Ampicillin, 10 mg/mL, sterile	Shaking incubator, 37°C
Glass rods	Pipets, 1 mL, sterile	Pipets, 5 mL, sterile
Magnetic stir bars	Pipet pump, blue	Pipet pump, green
Hot plate stirrer	pAmylase2014-Transformed	VIS Spectrophotometer
Hot hands protector	*E. coli* (plate culture from	Cuvettes for the
Media bottle, 250 mL	Lab 8c)	spectrophotometer
Sterilizer/autoclave		

Procedure

1. Prepare and sterilize 50 mL of 1% soluble starch/LB broth (from premixed LB broth base) in a 250-mL media bottle. Record the calculations you used to plan the recipes.
2. After the media has cooled to room temperature, under sterile conditions, add 0.5 mL of the 10 mg/mL ampicillin solution to each bottle.
3. Select a transformed colony with a large halo.
4. Using sterile technique, inoculate the 50 mL of broth with the colony from the selection plate that shows both the fastest growth and the greatest amylase production.
5. Place the inoculated broth in a rapidly shaking incubator, at 250 rpm at 37°C for 4 hours.
6. Hourly, for 8–10 hours after the first 6 hours, begin taking sterile samples (volume dependent on the cuvette) of the broth culture. Put the samples into cuvette tubes.

37°C

7. Using 300 µL, test all samples of the broth culture for amylase activity using the assays developed in Lab 6d. Measure the amount of starch breakdown compared with a control and measure the amount of sugar production.
8. Also, as in Lab 8d, use the spectrophotometer to determine the OD_{600} absorbance (and, indirectly, the concentration) of the broth every hour. Use sterile, uninoculated broth as a blank. After taking the readings, discard all culture samples into a container holding 10% bleach or some other appropriate disinfectant.
9. In a data table in your notebook, record the absorbance of the culture for the time periods (hours 4–10) studied.

Data Analysis

Graph the absorbance of the cell culture for the time period studied. This represents the growth curve for the culture. Look for "exponential growth" of the culture, the phase in which the number of cells is doubling with every cell cycle, or, for these data, the time period in which the absorbance is doubling.

Conclusion

What is the apparent growth rate of this culture compared with the growth rate of the nontransformed cells in the last activity? Did this culture reach stationary phase during the time period it was monitored? Is there evidence of amylase activity from these transformed cells? Determine and report the time at which the culture should be "scaled-up" to the next volume, when the OD_{600} is between 0.4–0.7 au.

Thinking Like a Biotechnician

1. What was done in this cell culture to decrease the chance of nontransformed cells growing or contaminating the culture?
2. Propose methods to increase a culture's growth rate and to determine the actual concentration of cells in a culture.
3. Propose methods to increase a culture's amylase production.

Laboratory 8f

Alkaline Cell Lysis Minipreparation of pAmylase2014

Background

To confirm that the genetically engineered *E. coli* cells have been transformed with the "correct" DNA, we will attempt to extract the plasmids and analyze them through restriction digestion. In this miniprep procedure, the extraction of the plasmid occurs when the cells are treated with sodium dodecyl sulfate (SDS) and sodium hydroxide (NaOH) at a high pH. The SDS dissolves the cell membrane and precipitates proteins. The NaOH destroys the cell wall and also precipitates proteins. A series of alcohol washes isolates the plasmid from other cell constituents. This method is similar to genomic DNA isolation but the high pH and centrifugation steps separate the plasmid from genomic DNA.

Purpose

How well is pAmylase2014 extracted from transformed *E. coli* cells using the alkaline-cell-lysis method?

Materials

Note: Recipes for preparing the STE, lysozyme, and TE buffer solutions appear at the end of the Procedure section.

50 mL pAmylase2014-transformed *E. coli* culture at 0.6–1.0 au (LB/amp/1% starch in a 250-mL bottle)	Micropipet tips for P-1000
	SDS/NaOH solution (see recipe)
	Potassium acetate/acetic acid solution (see recipe)
Tubes, 15-mL, and racks	Tube rack for 1.7-mL tubes
Centrifuge for 15-mL tubes	Reaction tubes, 1.7 mL
Permanent lab marker pens	Pipet, 2 mL, sterile
Pipet, 10 mL, sterile	Pipet pump, blue
Pipet pump, green	Isopropanol, ice cold
Microcentrifuge, high speed (~14,000 xg)	Ethanol, 95%, ice cold
Plastic beaker, 1L	Dry block heater/heat block, 60°C
Bleach, 10%	TE buffer (see recipe)
Micropipet, P-100	UV-VIS spectrophotometer
Micropipet tips for P-100	UV-cuvettes
GTE buffer (see recipe)	Pasteur pipets, 9"
Micropipet, P-1000	Pasteur pipet bulbs

Environmental Health and Safety Officer

Procedure

Read all of the steps before starting. Determine which solutions need to be prepared, and prepare them before starting. Store all the solutions, except the SDS/NaOH, at 4°C.

1. Obtain 50 mL of *E. coli*/pAmylase2014 overnight (~18 hr, at 0.6–1.0 au) culture (in a 250 mL bottle) in LB/1% starch/amp broth.
2. Finger-flick the culture bottle to resuspend the *E. coli* cells before taking a sample.
3. Label a sterile 15-mL tube with your initials. Use a sterile 10-mL pipet to transfer 1.5 mL of *E. coli*/pAmy2014 overnight suspension to the tube.
4. Close the cap, and place the tube (along with another sample tube) in a **balanced** configuration in a tabletop centrifuge. Spin at 3000–6000 xg for 8 minutes to pellet the cells.
5. Pour off the supernatant (broth) from the tube, into either a waste beaker with 10% bleach solution, or another sterile tube for later amylase purification. **Be careful to not disturb the cell pellets.** Invert the tube, and gently tap on the surface of a clean paper towel to thoroughly drain the supernatant.

**Environmental Health
and Safety Officer**

6. Add 100 µL (0.1 mL) of the GTE buffer solution to the tube. Resuspend the pellet by pipeting the solution in and out several times. Hold the tube up to the light to check that the suspension is homogeneous and that no visible cell clumps remain.

7. Add 200 µL (0.2 mL) of the SDS/NaOH solution to the tube. Close the cap, and mix the solutions by rapidly inverting the tube five times.

8. Place the tube on ice for 5 minutes. The suspension will become relatively clear.

9. Add 150 µL (0.15 mL) of ice-cold potassium acetate/acetic acid solution to the tube. Close the cap, and mix the solution by rapidly inverting the tube five times. A white precipitate will immediately appear.

10. Place the tube on ice for 5 minutes.

11. Using a sterile 2-mL pipet, transfer all of the cell suspension to a sterile 1.7-mL tube. Let the tube stand on ice for 5 minutes.

12. Place the microcentrifuge tube in a **balanced** configuration in a centrifuge, and spin at ~6000 xg for 5 minutes to pellet the precipitate along the side of tube.

13. Transfer 400 µL of supernatant (plasmid DNA in solution) from the 1.7-mL tube into another sterile 1.7-mL tube. **Avoid pipeting the precipitate,** and wipe off any precipitate clinging to the outside of the tip prior to expelling the supernatant.

14. Add 400 µL of isopropanol to each tube of supernatant. Close the cap, and mix vigorously by rapidly inverting the tube five times. Let the tube stand at room temperature for **only** 2 minutes. (Isopropanol preferentially precipitates nucleic acids rapidly; however, proteins remaining in solution also begin to precipitate with time.)

15. Place the tubes in a **balanced** configuration in a high-speed microcentrifuge, and spin for 5 minutes at the highest speed (~14,000 xg) to pellet the nucleic acids. Align the tubes in the rotor so that cap hinges point outward. The nucleic acid residue, visible or not, will collect under the hinge during centrifugation.

16. Pour off the supernatant from the tube. **Be careful not to disturb the nucleic acid pellets** containing the plasmid. Invert the tube and tap gently on the surface of a clean paper towel to thoroughly drain.

17. Add 200 µL of ice cold 95% ethanol to the tube, and close the cap tightly. Flick the tube several times to wash the pellet. Wrist-flick the sample to pool the plasmid and ethanol on the bottom of the tube.

-20°C

Stop Point: Store the plasmid DNA in ethanol at –20°C until ready to continue.

18. Place the tube in a **balanced** configuration in a microcentrifuge, and spin at ~14,000 xg for 3 minutes.

19. Pour off the supernatant from the tube. **Be careful not to disturb the nucleic acid pellet.** Invert the tube, and tap gently on surface of a clean paper towel to drain thoroughly.

60°C 20. Dry the nucleic acid pellets by placing the tubes, with the cap open, in a 60°C heat block for about 5 minutes.

21. At the end of the drying period, hold each tube up to check that no ethanol droplets remain. If ethanol is still evaporating, an alcohol odor can be detected by sniffing the mouth of tube. All of the ethanol must evaporate before proceeding to Step 22. Repeat Step 19, if necessary.

22. Add 50 µL of TE buffer to each tube. Resuspend the pellets by smashing them with the pipet tip, and vigorously pipeting in and out. Rinse down the side of tube several times, concentrating on the area where the pellet should have formed during centrifugation (beneath the cap hinge). Ensure that all of the DNA has dissolved and that no particles remain in the pipet tip or on the side of tube.

-20°C 23. Pool all of the DNA/TE solutions prepared into one tube. Freeze at –20°C until ready to use. Thaw before use.

24. Use the UV spec and a 50-µL adaptor or a 50 µL cuvette, set at 260 nm, to determine the concentration of plasmid DNA, as explained in the text. To calculate the concentration of DNA in a sample, use a simple ratio. It is known that 50 µg/mL of pure, double-stranded DNA absorbs approximately 1 au of light at 260 nm. One can determine the concentration of an unknown DNA sample using the following equation:

$$\frac{50\mu\,g/mL}{1\ \text{au at 260nm}} = \frac{X\mu\,g/mL}{\text{the absorbance of sample at 260 nm}}$$

Environmental Health
and Safety Officer

Pool the samples, if the volume is less than 50 μL.

25. If available, use a G-Biosciences Nucleic dotMETRIC Assay kit (Geno Technology, Inc.) to determine the yield of plasmid in the mini-prep sample (See Lab 8g, Part II, step 1.)

26. Conduct a restriction digestion to confirm that the plasmid is indeed pAmylase2014. Use the procedures in the restriction digestion run in Lab 8b. Run restriction digestion fragments on a 0.8% agarose gel. Stain the gel with EtBr or 1X LabSafe Nucleic Acid Stain™, and photograph it. **Remember to follow the safety precautions. If using EtBr as the DNA stain, only the instructor should use EtBr. Wear goggles and gloves when in the presence of EtBr.**

Good Manufacturing Practices

- Use centrifuge tubes with the hinge on the "up" side so that the pellets will always be on the "hinge" side. This is helpful if pellets are hard to see (as in step 13).
- Good pipeting is critical for the correct change in pH.
- Do step 12 quickly, and make sure that the centrifuge is immediately available for Step 13.
- Do not be concerned if the pellet at step 15 is small or "invisible." Pure DNA in solution is clear.
- Large pellets often indicate contamination.

Recipes for Plasmid Miniprep

GTE + RNase. Make 100 mL.
Store at 4°C or room temperature.
Mix together the following:

> 0.9 g of glucose
> 2.5 mL of 1 *M* TRIS, pH 8.0
> 2 mL of 0.5 *M* EDTA
> 94.5 mL of deionized water plus 10 mg RNase A/100 mL

SDS/NaOH Cell Lysis Solution. Make 100 mL.
Store at room temperature.
Mix together the following:

> 0.8 g of NaOH pellets into 80 mL of deionized water

Gently, mix in 10 mL of 10% SDS.
Add deionized water until a total volume of 100 mL is reached.

Environmental Health
and Safety Officer

TE Buffer. Make 100 mL.
Store at 4°C.
Mix together the following:

> 1 mL of 1 *M* TRIS, pH 8.0
> 200 μL of 0.5 *M* EDTA
> 99 mL of deionized water

6 *M* Potassium Acetate/Acetic Acid Neutralization Solution, pH 5.5. Make 100 mL.
Store at 4°C or room temperature.
29.4 g of potassium acetate in 50 mL of H_2O, pH to 5.5 with acetic acid (approximately 11 mL), bring to a final volume of 100 mL with deionized water

Data Analysis/Conclusion

Do any of the DNA assays (steps 24, 25 and 26) give data that support that the samples contain DNA? Give evidence. Do the digestion fragments indicate that the plasmid extracted during the miniprep has the characteristics of the pAmylase2014 plasmid? Do the observed bands in the gel, after restriction digestion, show what was expected? Give evidence for your statement. Do all groups in the class have similar data? Why or why not? Discuss the possible errors that could lead to varying results from one team to another. If the digestion confirms that the sample is pAmylase2014, why is that information valuable? If you retrieved pAmylase2014, what might it be used for in the future?

Thinking Like a Biotechnician

1. In biotechnology, "time is money." If one procedure works as well as another, and costs less, that is the procedure which will be used. Which of the miniprep procedures (the miniprep kit in Lab 8g or the alkaline lysis) appeared to take longer to conduct? Explain.
2. A concentration of 0.005 µg/µL is usually required for a transformation. Did your miniprep yield enough (50 µL) of a sufficient concentration (0.005 µg/µL) of plasmid for another transformation?
3. Which miniprep procedure, the miniprep kit in Lab 8g or alkaline lysis (this lab), worked better to produce the largest yield of a relatively pure plasmid? Give evidence.

Laboratory 8g
Using a Miniprep Kit for Plasmid Isolation

Background

Plasmid DNA that is suitable for recombinant DNA work and PCR can be recovered from transformed cells using a minipreparation (miniprep) procedure. The goal of a miniprep is to isolate 10 to 25 µg of plasmid in a volume of 25 to 50 µL of buffer or sterile, deionized water. The plasmid DNA should be fairly pure with an Abs_{260}/Abs_{280} value at about 1.8.

Technicians can produce all the reagents needed for a miniprep, such as in the alkaline lysis miniprep (Lab 8f). But to decrease the amount of time and increase the yield, companies have developed commercial miniprep kits.

Several companies have developed easy to use kits that make a miniprep faster, easier, and fairly economic. These vary slightly from one manufacturer to another, but the basic steps are the same. Using a broth culture of transformed cells, explode the cells using detergent (lysis solution). Then precipitate protein and genomic DNA contaminants using alkaline buffer and centrifugation. Bind plasmid DNA to a spin column and use alcohol washes with RNase to clean the plasmid sample. Then, elute the plasmid sample using an elution buffer (usually TE buffer).

A technician who conducts minipreps regularly should compare the time involved and the yield of plasmid isolated using various miniprep kits and protocols. In this activity, a commercially available miniprep kit is used to isolate pAmylase2014 plasmid from transformed *E. coli* cells grown in LB/amp/1% starch broth. The plasmid yield is compared to the plasmid yield from an alkaline lysis miniprep (Lab 8f).

Purpose

How well does the GET™ Plasmid DNA Miniprep Kit isolate pAmylase2014 plasmid DNA from transformed *E.coli* cells as compared to the alkaline lysis method (Lab 8f)?

Hypothesis

The expected result reported in the protocol of the GET™ Plasmid DNA Miniprep Kit, by G-Biosciences, is a plasmid DNA yield of up to 20 µg per minipreparation, depending on the plasmid copy number, culture growth conditions, and strain of *E. coli* utilized.

Materials

GET™ Plasmid DNA Miniprep Kit (G-Biosciences #786-362)
1.5-mL tubes
Overnight culture of pAmylase2014-transformed *E. coli* in LB/amp/1% starch broth
   OD_{600} of 0.4 to 0.7 au
Microcentrifuge, high speed (~14,000 xg)
Ethanol, 95%, ice cold
Dry block heater/heat block, 60°C
G-Biosciences Nucleic dotMETRIC™ Basic kit, Geno Technology Inc. #86-60

Procedure

Follow the GET™ Plasmid DNA Miniprep Kit laboratory protocol found at www.gbiosciences.com/PDF/Protocol/GET_Plasmid_MiniPrep.pdf.

Pre-Lab Notes
1. Prepare 50 mL of *E. coli*/pAmylase2014 overnight (~18 hr) culture (in a 250 mL bottle) in LB/1% starch/amp broth.
2. Finger-flick the culture to resuspend the *E. coli* cells before taking a sample.
3. Ensure that RNase has been added to the Cell Suspension Solution and that ethanol has been added to the concentrated DNA Wash Buffer prior to starting the protocol. Store these at 4°C
4. Warm the TE (elution) Buffer to 60°C before using.

5. Make sure that all centrifugation steps are performed between 12,000 and 16,000 × g.
6. All lab procedure steps are done at room temperature.

Part I: Miniprep

1. Read through the entire protocol for how to use the GET™ Plasmid DNA Miniprep Kit laboratory protocol (found at www.gbiosciences.com/PDF/Protocol/GET_Plasmid_MiniPrep.pdf).
2. Get all of the reagents and supplies ready and label tubes as needed.
3. Perform the GET™ Plasmid DNA Miniprep Kit laboratory protocol following the steps exactly, found at www.gbiosciences.com/PDF/Protocol/GET_Plasmid_MiniPrep.pdf).

Part II: Plasmid Yield Assay

1. Use a G-Biosciences Nucleic dotMETRIC™ Assay kit (Geno Technology, Inc.) to quantify the amount of DNA in the plasmid sample (see Figure 8.5). Read the instructions in the kit to learn how to take a 1 µL sample and blot it on the test strip. Then using their DNA nucleic acid indicator and washes, stain the DNA sample proportional to the mass present.
2. Use the Nucleic dotMETRIC™ Assay kit to test the plasmid sample obtained through the alkaline lysis miniprep (Lab 8f).
3. Use the UV spec and a 50-µL adaptor or a 50 µL cuvette, set at 260 nm, to determine the concentration of plasmid DNA, as explained in the text. Determine the concentration of an unknown DNA sample using the DNA concentration equation found in Lab 8f.

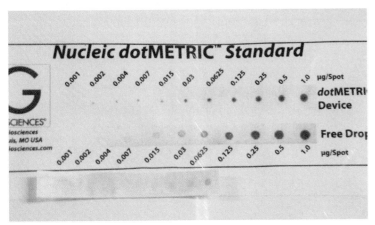

Figure 8.5.   **G-Biosciences Nucleic dotMETRIC™ Assay kit**

Environmental Health and Safety Officer

4. Conduct a restriction digestion to confirm that the plasmid is indeed pAmylase2014 and to compare the yield to the mini-prep samples from Lab 8f. Use the procedures in the restriction digestion found in Lab 8b. Run restriction digestion fragments on a 0.8% agarose gel. Stain the gel with EtBr or 1X LabSafe Nucleic Acid Stain™, and photograph it. **Remember to follow the safety precautions. If using EtBr as the DNA stain, only the instructor should use EtBr. Wear goggles and gloves when in the presence of EtBr.**

Data Analysis/Conclusion

What is the mass (µg) and concentration of (µg/µL) of plasmid in the GET™ Plasmid DNA Miniprep Kit-produced plasmid sample? How close did the sample come to the expected yield? If you conducted the Lab 8f alkaline lysis miniprep, what is the mass (µg) and concentration (µg/µL) of plasmid in that sample? Considering these yields and the time it took to produce each sample, which method gave the highest yield in the shortest time?

Discuss steps in each protocol that may have negatively affected the yield of plasmid in the final samples. What may have been done to mitigate these effects?

Thinking Like a Biotechnician

Often, a variety of kits to accomplish some standard lab task are available from science materials vendors. Several kits for DNA and protein analysis are available from Promega, New England BioLabs, and Qiagen to name a few.

For this activity, evaluate for potential future use a commercial miniprep kit from a different vendor, such as the E.Z.N.A.® Plasmid Mini Kit I from Omega Bio-Tek, Inc. Complete a systematic analysis (Kit Analysis Report) that includes a background section, the objectives of the kit, the expected results, a summary of the procedures, and a cost and value analysis.

Miniprep Kit Analysis Report

Create a word-processed Kit Analysis Report with the following:

Kit Name/Title   _____

Kit Manufacturer/Vendor   _____

Kit Catalog Number   _____

Kit Web site (for ordering)   _____

Kit Use—Number of Trials _____   Kit Cost (total) _____   Kit Cost (per trial) _____

Background:

     4–5 sentences summarizing the science behind the kit procedures.

Objective/Expected Results:

     A description or diagram that describes what should happen if the kit procedures are used and work as directed.

Procedure:

     Summarize the procedural steps (8–10 steps).

     Expected time to complete the entire procedure _____

     Summary of how this kit compares to the GET™ Plasmid DNA Miniprep Kit (time, cost, and yield).

9 Protein Product Purification and Analysis

During biomanufacturing, techniques developed in research and development (R&D) are applied to large volumes (large scale) of broth, with the goal of producing large amounts of pure protein to sell. Biomanufacturing includes growing and monitoring transformed cells in progressively larger volumes of broth. At each step, dozens of assays confirm the health and productivity of each culture.

To harvest large volumes of protein from the cell cultures that produced them, the cells are spun down and separated from the broth media. The protein of interest is purified (separated) from the other proteins in the sample using centrifugation, filtration and column chromatography.

In the following lab activities, you will learn how to scale-up cultures of transformed cells and harvest a recombinant protein of interest from a culture. The skills on which to focus include the following:

A researcher in the Fuel Synthesis Division at the Joint BioEnergy Institute examines high performance liquid chromatography (HPLC) fractions collected by an automated fraction collector. HPLC uses a column, packed with microscopic beads, to separate molecules in a process called column chromatography. Different kinds of column chromatography may be used to separate molecules based on their physical characteristics.
Photo by Roy Kaltschmidt, Lawrence Berkeley National Lab, The Regents of the University of California, 2010.

- harvesting broth containing a recombinant protein of interest by spinning down cells in a centrifuge and removing them from a culture
- using dialysis to move the target recombinant proteins in a broth sample into a different, or more appropriate buffered solution for purification from other contaminant molecules
- separating and documenting proteins to isolate a target recombinant protein using column chromatography
- verifying the presence and activity of a recombinant protein of interest using assays and polyacrylamide gel electrophoresis (PAGE)

The goal of recombinant protein manufacturing is to produce a product in large enough volumes to generate revenue for the company. If a company cannot develop a product for manufacturing in 10 to 15 years, it will probably not survive. Considering the obstacles faced during R&D and manufacturing, it is impressive that so many biotechnology products are on the market. According to FDA CenterWatch, by 2015 the FDA had approved over 1600 pharmaceuticals for the US market with approximately 60 approved each year this decade. Pharma.org reports that in 2015 over 5400 drugs were in clinical trials. Additionally, there are dozens of environmental, industrial, and agricultural biotechnology products on the market and many more in development. With over 2500 biotech companies in the United States, there are considerable opportunities for employment in biotechnology research, biomanufacturing, sales, and marketing.

Laboratory 9a
Harvesting Amylase from Bacterial Cultures

Background

As transformed bacteria cells grow in culture, they produce the recombinant protein of interest along with other proteins and molecules of all kinds. Recombinant amylase, our target protein, is an extracellular protein, meaning that it is made in the cell but it is transported out of the cell to where it functions to breakdown starch in plant materials to sugar. To harvest it, the cells that made it must be removed from the broth culture and then the recombinant amylase must be separated from all other proteins the cell makes.

When a culture has a sufficient volume and concentration of cells, it is "harvested" by separating and purifying the protein of interest from the cells and other molecules in the broth. Harvesting an extracellular protein begins by centrifuging or filtering the broth. These processes separate the transformed cells from the broth that contains the recombinant protein. When amylase isolation is the goal, the cells are discarded, and the scale-up broth, containing a large number of proteins secreted by the cells, is run through chromatographic columns. These columns separate proteins from the mixture, based on their size, shape, and charge.

During the separation and purification process, assays are performed, and gels are run to ensure the presence, concentration, and activity of the protein.

Purpose

To determine whether broth that contains amylase can be separated from bacterial cultures.

Materials

Environmental Health and Safety Officer

Poured LB/amp/2% starch plates
Laminar flow hood
pAmylase2014-Transformed *E. coli* DH5alpha
  (plate culture from Lab 8c with colonies
  showing large, clear halos of starch digestion)
Glasses, safety, plastic
Bunsen burner
Lab gas lighter
Inoculating loop, Ni/Cr wire
Incubator oven, 37°C

LB/amp/1% starch broth, 50 mL,
  sterile, in 250 mL media bottle
Shaking incubator, 37°C
Pipet, 10 mL, sterile
Pipet pump, green
Tubes, 15 mL, sterile, conical
Tube racks for 15 mL tubes
Centrifuge for 15 mL tubes
Lysol® disinfectant

*Optional: At Step 2, 150 µL of 20 mg/mL IPTG in deionized water, filter-sterilized, may be added to increase protein production (see note in *Instructor's Course Planner*).

Procedure

37°C

1. Using sterile technique, streak transformed cells onto LB/2% starch/amp agar plates. Let the cells grow for 24–48 hours, upside down, in a 37°C incubation oven. Look for halos around the colonies to confirm the presence and activity of amylase in the colonies on the selection plates.
2. Obtain 50 mL of sterile LB/1% starch/amp broth. Using sterile technique, inoculate the broth with a colony of transformed cells* and allow them to grow overnight (24–36 hours) in a 37°C shaking incubator set at 250 rpm. Check the OD_{600} for the culture to ensure it is at least 0.6 au. A 50-mL culture is enough for 5 groups.
3. Finger-flick the bottle to resuspend cells that are on the bottom of the bottle. Using sterile technique, transfer 10 mL of the broth culture into 15-mL sterile, capped, centrifuge tubes.
4. Spin in a labtop centrifuge at about 3000–6000 xg for 8 minutes. Use another group's tube as a balance tube. A pellet of cells should form at the bottom of the tube.

5. Pour the supernatant (the broth) into another sterile centrifuge tube. Label all tubes with the culture name, your initials, and the date. Discard the pellet of cells or use for a plasmid preparation (see Lab 8f or Lab 8g).
6. Using several samples of the broth, conduct amylase activity assays (starch breakdown or sugar production) using the procedures outlined in earlier lab activities (see Lab 6d).
7. Create a data table in your notebook, and record the results of the assay(s) in a quantitative fashion. Determine the average results.
8. Refrigerate the remainder of the broth in the sample tube until ready to use. If the sample is to be stored for more than a few days, use a 0.2 μm filter to filter-sterilize it to prevent degradation, aliquot it into 5 mL sample, and freeze it until ready to use. The samples may be used in the PAGE analysis in Lab 9e.
9. If the proteins in the broth are to be purified using column chromatography, conduct a buffer-exchange dialysis to get the proteins into the appropriate chromatographic buffer (see Lab 9b).

Data Analysis/Conclusion

Use the bacterial and human amylase assays from earlier lab activities as standards for comparison. What amount of amylase activity appears to be present in the broth? Give evidence for your statement. Explain why the broth shows more or less activity than the standards. Describe the next steps in the use of the broth. Describe what would happen next in an amylase purification process.

Thinking Like a Biotechnician

1. If the assays for amylase activity do not show much activity, does that mean there is no amylase in the broth? What may be done to remedy the problem?
2. Without using an activity assay, how could a technician confirm that amylase, and not some other carbohydrate-interacting enzyme, is in the broth?
3. What key ingredient would be needed to design an ELISA to recognize and measure the amylase in the broth?

Laboratory 9b
Dialysis of Proteins into Different Buffers

Background

Often, protein molecules, such as in the Chapter 5 seafood-muscle-tissue protein study, or the Chapter 8 rAmylase production, are in solutions or media that interferes with further processing. For example, a buffer may work well for extraction or PAGE, but SDS or other ingredients may interfere with most column chromatography. Therefore, a dialysis of a sample into a new buffer is often conducted.

Figure 9.1. **Dialysis should take place at 4°C to decrease protein degradation. If a stir plate is available, add a stir bar, and set the stir plate to the lowest speed.**
Photo by author.

The new buffer must be one suited for the given chromatography. In an ion-exchange chromatography, such as the one in the following lab activity, the chromatography buffer might be a sodium phosphate buffer. The sample extraction buffer must be exchanged out of the sample solution and replaced with the chromatography buffer without losing the molecule of interest.

For volumes of more than a few milliliters, buffer exchanges are done using a process called "dialysis." A dialysis is done by placing the sample in dialysis tubing (a porous membrane) and tying off the ends to produce a dialysis bag. The dialysis bag is placed in a beaker of buffer for many hours to allow molecules small enough to move in and out of the pores of the dialysis tubing to reach equilibrium. There should be a minimum of 10 volumes of the new buffer to sample volume in a buffer exchange (see Figure 9.1).

Purpose

To exchange the buffer in a protein solution for a different buffer that is suitable for chromatography.

Materials

Equilibration Buffer (1.9 mM NaH$_2$PO$_4$•H$_2$O, 8.1 mM Na$_2$HPO$_4$ (anhydrous), pH 7.35)
Bucket or Beaker, 2L
Dialysis tubing, 1", 18 kDa MW cut-off
Scissors
Pipet, 5 mL, sterile
Pipet pump, green
Plastic beaker, 1L
Tubes, 15 mL, sterile, conical
24-well microtiter plate
Micropipet, P-1000 and tips

Micropipet, P-100 and tips
Lugol's Iodine Solution, 1:2
Glass rods
Glucose test strips
Reaction tubes, 1.7 mL and rack
Lid locks for 1.7-mL tubes
Benedict's solution
Dry block heater/heat block, 100°C
Deionized water
10-kDa or 30-kDa centrifuge filter tubes

Procedure

Note: Prepare the 2 L of Equilibration Buffer (1.9 mM NaH$_2$PO$_4$•H$_2$O, 8.1 mM Na$_2$HPO$_4$ (anhydrous), pH 7.35), prior to starting the activity.

1. Cut a piece of 18,000-Da dialysis tubing. The tubing must be at least 2 times as long as the length necessary to hold the volume of sample to be dialyzed. The volume to be dialyzed will be determined by the supervisor or instructor.
2. Soak the tubing in deionized water until it is thoroughly wetted.

3. Gently, rub the end of the tube with your thumb and finger until it opens.
4. Tie a snug knot in one end of the tube. Be careful to not rip or tear the dialysis tubing.
5. Using a pipet, transfer the entire sample to be dialyzed to the inside of the bag (see Figure 9.2). It should fill the bottom third of the bag. Be careful to not spill any of the sample.
6. Press any remaining air out of the bag.
7. Tie the other end of the bag, about 2 cm from the end, with a snug knot. Be careful to not tear the tubing.
8. Rinse the outside of the bag.
9. Place the bag in dialysis buffer Equilibration Buffer (1.9 mM $NaH_2PO_4 \bullet H_2O$, 8.1 mM Na_2HPO_4 (anhydrous), pH 7.35). The minimum volume required is 10 times the volume inside the dialysis bag. Place the dialysis set-up in the refrigerator at 4°C and leave it for 10 to 24 hours.

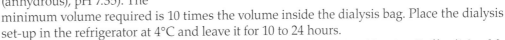

Figure 9.2. Over a large, clean beaker, transfer sample to a prepared dialysis tube. This way, if any of the sample spills, it can be retrieved.
Photo by author.

10. Discard the outer buffer. Refill with an equal volume of fresh Equilibration Buffer (1.9 mM $NaH_2PO_4 \bullet H_2O$, 8.1 mM Na_2HPO_4 (anhydrous), pH 7.35). Leave at 4°C for 3–24 hours.
11. Remove the bag from the dialysis bucket. Pat dry.
12. Carefully cut open the bag (place it in a clean beaker, in case it spills), and pipet the contents into a sterile storage tube.
13. Conduct an amylase/concentration assay on the dialyzed sample using Bradford reagent (see Lab 7d). Report the concentration data in a data table. If the concentration of amylase in the dialyzed sample is substantially less than 1 mg/mL, concentrate the sample using either a 10-kDa or a 30-kDa centrifuge filter (see Figure 9.3). Report how much of the sample was concentrated and the estimated final concentration.

Data Analysis/Conclusion

Describe the appearance of the bag before and after the dialysis period. Describe what has happened during the dialysis procedure to the solutes and solvents that were inside or outside of the bag at the start of the dialysis process. Draw a diagram that illustrates the movement of substances during the dialysis. Does the dialyzed sample show amylase activity? Explain. Whether the sample shows activity or not, propose what should be done next with the dialyzed sample.

Thinking Like a Biotechnician

1. How can you be certain that amylase has not diffused or leaked out of the dialysis bag during dialysis?
2. Before dialysis, on inspection of the broth, cloudy areas are visible. What is the most likely cause of the cloudiness and what, if anything, should be done about it?

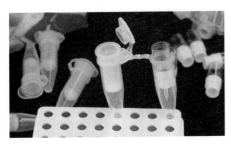

Figure 9.3. These are two types of 10-kDa microtest tube centrifuge filters. They may be used to concentrate a protein sample or to replace one protein buffer with another. Add sample to be concentrated to the top chamber. Spin, for the time recommended in the concentrator literature, in a centrifuge. Buffer will be pulled down, but the proteins that are larger than 10 kDa remain in the top chamber and are concentrated. The longer the spinning time, the more concentrated the sample becomes. If a replacement buffer is desired, it can be added to the concentrated protein sample. Check the technical manual that comes with the filters for recommended spinning times and conditions.
Photo by author.

Laboratory 9c

Using Ion-Exchange Chromatography to Separate Proteins

This lab was developed by with the assistance of David Peers, Genentech, Inc., South San Francisco, CA.

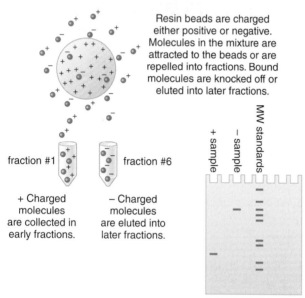

Resin beads are charged either positive or negative. Molecules in the mixture are attracted to the beads or are repelled into fractions. Bound molecules are knocked off or eluted into later fractions.

fraction #1   fraction #6

+ Charged molecules are collected in early fractions.

– Charged molecules are eluted into later fractions.

+ sample   – sample   MW standards

Figure 9.4. Ion Exchange Resin. Resins are manufactured with ions attached. The ions present a certain degree of positive or negative charge, depending on the buffer pH.

Background

In ion-exchange chromatography, resin beads of a certain charge (positive [+] or negative [-]) are used in the column. A mixture of proteins is added to the column, and if the pH and column capacity are correct, everything passes through the column except the protein of interest. This is because the column resin and pH are chosen to produce the "most opposite charge" of the protein of interest on the beads. If the charge on a bead is positive, it will bind and release negatively charged molecules. This technique is called anion exchange. If the beads are negatively charged, they bind and release positively charged molecules (cation exchange). A scientist picks a resin to use based on the properties of the protein of interest. Under ideal conditions, during ion-exchange chromatography, the protein binds to the oppositely charged beads. Buffers are used to flush contaminant proteins out of the column. Finally, a buffer containing an ion with a greater attraction to the bead than the protein of interest knocks (elutes) the protein off the bead (this is the ion exchange). Often, a high-salt buffer is used to elute the desired protein from the column (see Figure 9.4).

Purpose

Using ion-exchange chromatography, how well can lysozyme (positive [+] charge at pH 7.35) be separated from amylase (negative [-] charge at pH 7.35)?

Materials

Equilibration Buffer (1.9 mM NaH$_2$PO$_4 \bullet$H$_2$O, 8.1 mM Na$_2$HPO$_4$ (anhydrous), pH 7.35)

Elution Buffer (1.9 mM NaH$_2$PO$_4 \bullet$H$_2$O, 8.1 mM Na$_2$HPO$_4$ (anhydrous), 0.5 M KCl, pH 7.35)

Alpha-amylase, 7.5 mg/mL in equilibration buffer

Lysozyme, 2.0 mg/mL in equilibration buffer

Tubes, 15 mL, sterile, conical, and racks

Chromatography columns with frit, 8 mL, tops and bottoms

Chromatography pump (see Course Planner)

DEAE Sepharose™ resin

Pipets, 10 mL, 5 mL, and 2 mL, and pumps

Tubes, glass, 13 × 100 mm, caps, and peg racks

Micropipet, P-1000 and tips

Bradford reagent

VIS Spectrophotometer

Procedure

- Prepare the equilibration (100 mL) and elution (50 mL) buffers prior to starting the activity.
- Prepare each of the protein samples.
- Each group will run one of the protein samples (amylase alone, lysozyme alone, or the mixture) and share results.

Figure 9.5. **This small polyprep column is used early in R&D to determine whether a particular molecule can be separated from others by one method or another. A small amount (ie, 2 mL) of an ion-exchange resin is added to the column. If you look closely, you can see the white resin in the bottom one-third of the column. Molecules either bind to or are repelled by the charges on the resin beads.**
Photo by author.

1. Using a pipet, add enough suspended DEAE Sepharose™ (anion) resin (about 5 mL) to a chromatographic column (see Figure 9.5) to produce a 2 mL resin bed. Let it settle by gravity until there is a distinct flat surface. It is important that the resin bed volume is 2 mL.

2. Take off the stopper, and let the buffer drip through until there remains only a tiny bit on top of the column. Replace the stopper on the bottom of the column.

3. Add 10 mL of equilibration buffer (to wash out the preservative) and let it pass through the column.

4. Number a set of 13×100-mm test tubes 1 through 7.

5. Move the column to over collection test tube No. 1. Gently add (the "load") 0.2 mL of the appropriate sample (without disturbing the top of the bed): lysozyme, amylase, or lysozyme + amylase (add 0.4 mL if you are in the mixture group) to the top of the appropriate column. Remove the column stopper, and allow the sample to "load" into the column. Collect the flow-through in test tube No. 1. Plug the column at the instant the sample loads into the resin bed (to avoid drying out the resin bed).

6. Move collection test tube No. 2 under the column. Add 2 mL of equilibration buffer and let it pass through the column. Collect the flow-through in test tube No. 2.

7. Repeat step 6, three more times, collecting fractions into test tubes No. 3 through 5. Each time, stopper the column just before the column runs dry.

8. When the fourth wash (into test tube No. 5) is complete, move test tube No. 6 under the column. Add 2 mL of elution (high-salt) buffer to the top of the column. Collect the flow-through into test tube No. 6.

9. When the first elution (into test tube No. 6) is complete, move test tube No. 7 under the column. Add 2 mL of elution (high-salt) buffer to the top of the column. Collect the flow-through into test tube No. 7.

10. Add 10 mL of equilibration buffer to the columns and let it pass through to clean them.

11. Test each fraction in "your" run with Bradford reagent to determine the presence of protein. The steps below are for a Spectronic 20D+ VIS Spectrophotometer. Adjust the volumes as necessary for the cuvettes being used in the VIS spec available.

- Turn on the Spec 20 D and let it warm up for at least 15 minutes.
- Add 3.0 mL of Bradford reagent to each of the test tubes No. 2 through 7.
- Cover each of the tubes with a 13×100-mm tube cap.
- Invert each tube three times to mix. Be gentle. Do not allow the solution to foam up. Do not mix up the test tube caps. Look at the colors of the solutions in the tubes. Are they the colors you expected? Yes or no? Why or why not? Record your observations.
- Make up a blank with 2.0 mL of equilibration buffer and 3.0 mL of Bradford reagent. Mix. Label this tube "B" for blank.
- Set the Spec to 595 nm. Do you know why a wavelength of 595 nm is used? Zero the transmittance (left-hand knob) with **nothing** in the sample holder. Wipe off the blank. Insert it into the sample holder. Set the transmittance to 100% (using the right-hand knob) with the blank in the sample holder.
- Wipe the outside of each tube, and read the absorbance of each sample.

12. In your notebook, create a data table similar to Table 9.1 to record the absorbance of fractions 2 to 7. Collect data from two other groups so that you have absorbance data for amylase alone through the column, lysozyme alone through the column, and the mixture of lysozyme and amylase through the column.

Table 9.1. **Absorbance of Ion-Exchange Fractions at 595 nm.**

Sample	Fraction No. 2	Fraction No. 3	Fraction No. 4	Fraction No. 5	Fraction No. 6	Fraction No. 7
lysozyme						
amylase						
both						

Data Analysis

Examine the absorbance data. Considering that the minimum absorbance reading on a Spec 20 D is 0.02 au, and the maximum is 2.0 au, do the numbers make sense for what was expected? Explain. Plot your data on a three-line, line graph. Let each line represent the absorbance of ion-exchange fractions from one of the three protein samples.

Conclusion

Does your data show that the column actually separated lysozyme from amylase? Consider the peaks and valleys of each line. Explain why the shape of each line looks the way it does. If the results are not what you expected, discuss errors that might lead to fallacious data. Explain how the ability to separate molecules, such as amylase and lysozyme, on a column is utilized at a biotechnology company. If the separation of amylase and lysozyme was not complete on the column, propose a modification of the protocol that might improve the separation.

Thinking Like a Biotechnician

1. A technician checks the column bed volume on a column that is supposed to be 2 mL. If the bed volume is not 2 mL, is this a problem? Why or why not?
2. The column drips very slowly. Suggest a method to increase the rate of flow through the column. How can you check to ensure that this method does not compromise the separation?
3. A scientist would like to know the charge of a certain protein at pH 7.2. How could this column be used to help determine the overall charge of the protein at pH 7.2? What problems might occur using the proposed approach and how might they be addressed?

Laboratory 9d

Using Ion-Exchange Chromatography to Purify Amylase from Scale-up Broth

Background

Recombinant amylase is produced in pAmylase2014-transformed cells and secreted into the extracellular broth. To purify it from the other extracellular proteins, column chromatography may be used.

Amylase has a distinct overall negative charge at a pH of 7.35. Using ion-exchange resin, such as DEAE Sepharose™, which has an overall positive charge at pH 7.35, amylase may be pulled out of a solution and bound onto the resin beads. Other proteins with a positive charge (or a weak negative charge) do not bind to the DEAE Sepharose resin beads at pH 7.35 and flow through the column. Adding a high salt buffer after other proteins have washed through the column will knock the amylase off the column (elute it), and it can be recovered in the elution fractions. Testing fractions with Bradford reagent and then running fraction samples on PAGE gels lets the technician know if the amylase was isolated from other proteins in the column load.

Purpose

Can amylase be recovered from scale-up broth using ion-exchange chromatography?

Materials

Equilibration buffer (1.9 mM NaH$_2$PO$_4$•H$_2$O, 8.1 mM Na$_2$HPO$_4$ (anhydrous), pH 7.35)
Elution buffer (1.9 mM NaH$_2$PO$_4$•H$_2$O, 8.1 mM Na$_2$HPO$_4$ (anhydrous), 0.5 M KCl, pH 7.35)
Dialyzed scale-up broth containing amylase, concentrated to between 5–10 mg/mL of protein, in equilibration buffer from Lab 9b
Pipets (10 mL, 5 mL, 2mL) and pumps
Chromatography columns, 8 mL, tops and bottoms
DEAE Sepharose™ resin
Tubes, glass, 13 × 100 mm, caps, and peg racks
Micropipet (P-1000) and tips
Chromatography pump (see Course Planner)
Bradford reagent
VIS Spectrophotometer

Procedure

- Prepare the equilibration (100 mL) and elution (50 mL) buffers prior to starting the activity.
- Amylase-containing broth culture is used for this chromatography. The sample must be buffer-exchanged into the equilibration buffer prior to running the column. This may be done one of two ways. The sample may be dialyzed and then concentrated (Lab 9b), or the sample may be concentrated in a centrifuge using the equilibration buffer to resuspend and wash the protein. Bradford tests may be used to estimate the approximate concentration of protein in the final concentrate.

1. Using a pipet, add enough suspended DEAE Sepharose™ (anion) resin to a chromatographic column to produce a 2 mL resin bed. Let it settle by gravity until there is a distinct flat surface.
2. Remove the stopper, and let the storage buffer drip through until there remains only a tiny bit on top of the column. Replace the stopper on the bottom of the column.
3. Add 10 mL of equilibration buffer (to wash out the preservative) and let it pass through the column. Discard the flow-through.

4. Label a set of test tubes No. 1 through 7.
5. Move test tube No. 1 under the column. Gently add 200 µL of concentrated, dialyzed scale-up broth containing amylase to the top of the column (try not to disturb the resin). Remove the stopper and allow the sample to "load" into the column. Collect the flow-through in tube No. 1. This tube is called the "load." Stopper the bottom of the column before the resin top dries.
6. Move collection test tube No. 2 under the column. Add 2 mL of equilibration buffer and let it pass through each column. Collect the flow-through in test tube No. 2. This fraction is called "Wash No. 1."
7. Repeat step 6, three more times, collecting fractions into test tubes No. 3 through 5. Stopper the column just before the column runs dry. These are Washes No. 2 through 4.
8. When the fourth wash (into test tube No. 5) is complete, move test tube No. 6 under the column. Add 2 mL of elution (high-salt) buffer to the top of the column. Collect the flow-through into test tube No. 6. This fraction is called the "Elution 1."
9. Repeat step 8 another time to collect "Elution 2" into tube No. 7.
10. Add 10 mL of equilibration buffer to the columns and let it pass through to clean them.
11. Take a 200 µL sample of each fraction and store it at 4°C or –20°C until a PAGE gel can be run (Lab 9e).
12. Conduct a Bradford assay on the remaining volume of each fraction by mixing 3 mL of Bradford reagent to each of the fractions, inverting gently to mix, and reading the absorbance of each sample at 595 nm. Don't forget to calibrate the spec with a buffer/Bradford blank.
13. In your notebook, create a data table to record the absorbance data for your ion-exchange column fractions.

    If you do not have a spectrophotometer or enough time, the color change of the Bradford reagent is striking enough to see that protein is present. Create a numerical key (5 " 0) to represent the amount of color in the samples.

Data Analysis

Plot the absorbance of the fractions for the column on a line graph. Does the line look the way you expected? Consider where the peaks and valleys on the line should be. Why might the results look different than you expected?

Conclusion

Does it appear that amylase molecules were bound to the column, and then released by the elution buffer? If so, what does that say about their charge? If not, what does that tell you about the charge on the amylase molecules? Did molecules in the broth behave similarly to molecules in the amylase sample run in Lab 9c? If so, what does that mean in terms of the ability to use this technique to purify amylase from broth cultures? If not, what does this mean? Explain the value of a biotechnology company running broth samples on an ion-exchange column and what product is expected.

Thinking Like a Biotechnician

1. The load for the column was 0.2 mL of sample. If the dialyzed broth was concentrated to 5 mg/mL of amylase, how much amylase, in milligrams, was loaded onto the column?
2. If a measurable amount of protein is found in the wash fractions and not much is found in the elution, what should be done to check that the column conditions are correct for binding amylase?
3. If the amylase does not appear to bind to the column, what might the technician try next?

Laboratory 9e

Identifying Amylase after Column Chromatography—Using SDS-PAGE

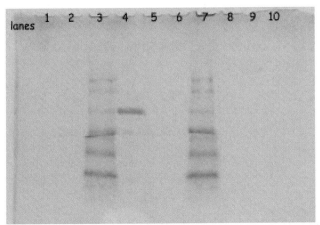

Figure 9.6. This PAGE gel has protein molecular weight sizing standards in lanes 3 and 7. A band, suspected to be amylase, is seen in lane 4.
Photo by author.

Background

The recombinant amylase produced in the transformation lab (Lab 8c) has a molecular weight of approximately 55,000 Da (55 kDa). Using this information, you can visualize amylase in the concentrated dialyzed broth or in dialyzed elution fractions from ion-exchange purification, on an SDS-PAGE gel (see Figure 9.6). If the amylase is present in sufficient concentration, it will appear as a band at a specific location. Its size can be estimated by comparing the location of the band with the proteins of known molecular weights (standards) run at the same time. Using PAGE, a technician can determine whether amylase was indeed separated from other proteins found in the transformed cell-culture broth.

Purpose

Using an SDS-PAGE gel, can amylase be detected in the fractions from the ion-exchange chromatography?
To what degree did the ion-exchange chromatography purify amylase from the broth sample?

Materials

Samples of concentrated
  dialyzed broth (Lab 9b)
Ion exchange fractions, in
  equilibration buffer (Lab 9d)
Amylase, 5 mg/mL in
  equilibration buffer (Lab 9d)
Micropipet, P-100
Micropipet tips for P-100
Reaction tubes, 1.7 mL
Tube rack for 1.7-mL tubes
Microcentrifuge
Heat block, 90°C

Gel box, vertical, for PAGE
PAGE gel, 10% TG, 10 well
Transfer pipets, 3 mL
PAGE gel loading dye with
  BME (see Lab 5e)
PAGE gel loading tips
Protein sizing markers, 15–150
  kDa
Power supply
Petri dishes, square, 100 × 15
  mm, sterile
Coomassie® Blue R-250 stain

Coomassie® Blue R-250 destain
Lab rotator, 12" × 12"
Photo-imaging system, white
  light
Paper, thermal
Printer, thermal
Gloves, large
Glasses, safety, plastic
Lid locks, 1.7-mL tubes

Procedure

- Prepare all gel running buffers, loading dye, stains, and destains prior to starting the activity. Recipes for these are found in Lab 5e.
- Each group runs the fractions from their own group's column chromatography.
- Samples must be concentrated using centrifuge concentrators prior to use. Conduct a Bradford assay to determine when samples are about 5 mg/mL.

1. Place 20 µL of each sample (preload sample, load, four washes, and each elution) into five microtest tubes.
2. Place 20 µL of the 5 mg/mL amylase solution standard sample into a microtest tube.
3. Add 20 µL of PAGE loading dye with BME into each tube. Gently mix.
4. Set up the gel box with a labeled, 10-well gel. Fill chambers with SDS-PAGE electrophoresis running buffer.

90°C

5. Add a locking cap onto each tube. Heat the samples to 90°C for 3 minutes. While the samples are heating, rinse the wells of the gel with buffer.

6. Load 25 µL of each sample into Wells 1 through 9. Load 5 µL of molecular-weight protein standards into Lane 5. In your notebook, record exactly what you loaded into Well 10.

7. Run the gel for 1 hour at 35–60 mA or until the loading dye is about 0.5 cm from the end of the gel.

   Note: New buffers, gel preparations, and stains allow for faster running times at higher currents and faster staining. See manufacturer's recommendations for gel running conditions and staining.

8. Stain with Coomassie® Blue stain for 3 to 7 hours.

9. Destain the gel using the method in Lab 5f and 5g.

10. Photograph the gel, and glue the photo into your notebook. Label the contents of each well, the sizes of the standard bands, and the sizes of the sample bands. If your instructor wants the gel saved, dry the gel on a drying rack for 2 weeks.

Data Analysis/Conclusion

Observe the bands in the sample lanes. Is a 55-kDa band (amylase) visible in any of the lanes? If so, in which lanes is it found? Do the number and the darkness of the bands make sense to you? If not, why? Is there evidence that the ion-exchange column has purified the sample? Explain. How do the results of this gel impact the fate of any purified amylase in the column fractions? If these results were achieved in a manufacturing facility after harvesting and purifying a fermentation batch, what would happen to the fractions containing amylase?

Thinking Like a Biotechnician

1. A technician runs a gel from an ion-exchange chromatography. He or she sees six bands in the wash samples and three bands in the elution, including a band at 55 kDa. Has amylase been purified from other proteins in the broth? Explain.

2. What should the technician in question 1 do next?

3. A PAGE gel with ion-exchange fractions is run. If the only bands visible on the gel are the standards, what might be done to the column fraction samples to try to see any protein present in them?

10 Plant Biotechnology

Here, a plant biotechnician collects seeds from an *Arabidopsis* plant breeding experiment. Seeds represent the next generation of plants. When planted, the seedlings will be studied in an attempt to identify plants that exhibit some desired characteristic.
Photo by author.

Plant biotechnology is a vast field that includes the long-standing practices of plant breeding, asexual plant propagation, and the isolation and manufacturing of plant compounds. It also includes the newly developed techniques of plant tissue culture, plant genetic engineering, and modification of plant compounds for medical and industrial purposes. Plant biotechnologists have many exciting opportunities to work in R&D and manufacturing positions in agricultural, pharmaceutical, and industrial settings within companies, government agencies, and educational institutions.

In this chapter's lab activities, you will learn about growing and observing plants as well as conducting plant breeding experiments. The skills you will develop include:

- documenting plant growth and development over time
- identifying plants parts and using them in breeding experiments
- measuring seed germination, shoot growth, and floral development
- setting up and monitoring a dihybrid, heterozygous plant breeding experiment
- analyzing the results of a breeding experiment using statistical tests
- starting and monitoring leaf and stem cuttings (clones)
- testing the impact of plant hormones on plant growth and plant processes
- setting up and gauging the success of plant tissue cultures

Plant breeding can result in variations in offspring, for example, the great range of types of roses. On the other hand, to produce offspring that are identical to the parents, such as thousands of identical orchid plants, researchers use asexual propagation methods.

Laboratory 10a
Sweet Potato – I Only Have Eyes for You

Background

Everyone is familiar with the common potato, a staple in the American diet. The potato is a member of the nightshade family along with tomatoes, eggplant, chili and bell peppers but differs from those plants in that potatoes produce a large, starchy, edible underground stem.

A sweet potato looks like a potato since they also have a starchy, edible, underground stem, but sweet potatoes are not closely related to the common potato. In the U.S., all sweet potatoes (and that includes U.S. grown yams) are varieties of the species, *Ipomoea batatas*. *Ipomoea sp* are classified in the plant family, Convolvulaceae (the morning glory family). There are several varieties of sweet potatoes and these differ in their skin color and the color of their flesh (starchy inside).

Most people think that sweet potato and yams are different species because there are African yams (genus Dioscorea) that look similar to American sweet potatoes. However, African yams are not safe to eat unless cooked properly. On the other hand, all U.S. grown yams are in the species, *Ipomoea batatas*, are sweet and delicious, and are technically, sweet potatoes. The term "yam" is used to describe sweet potatoes that become soft and moist when cooked.

Sweet potatoes are easy to grow and reproduce asexually (cloning). Sweet potato eyes (buds) contain meristematic tissue and it is easy to coax these to grow roots or branches when given moisture and light (see Figure 10.1). As branches grow and mature they may be cut off (they are then called "slips") and placed in water to root. Once rooted, slips may be planted in soil resulting in an independent offspring plant. Since each sweet potato can produce several slips, it is possible to clone several copies of a parent sweet potato for very low cost.

A list of common sweet potatoes can be found at **www.sweetpotatoes.com/About/ VarietiesandBotanicalInformation.aspx.** When purchasing sweet potatoes they should be labeled with a name and product number that helps describe them. In this experiment, the growth and ability to reproduce selected sweet potato varieties will be studied.

Figure 10.1. Sweet Potato Growth A sweet potato stem, called a tuber, can be induced to grow roots and branches when given water and light. This 16-week sweet potato has an abundance of roots and several branches that may be separated from the plant and grown into genetically identical offspring, or clones. Photo by SooHee Han.

Purpose

What is the difference in growth and behavior of two different varieties of sweet potato over a 3-month period?

Materials

2 varieties of sweet potato, 1 per student lab technician
Aged water (tap water that has set in an open container for at least 48 hours) or spring water
Glass jars, glasses, or beakers (height equal to the sweet potato length)
Barbeque skewers, wooden
Permanent marker
Digital camera

Procedure

Note: The Supervisor will provide two different varieties of sweet potatoes for the class to study. Each student lab technician will be responsible for measuring, monitoring, and documenting the growth and behavior of a single sample of one variety of sweet potato over a 3-month period. The technician's lab partner will study the other variety.

1. Obtain a healthy looking sweet potato or a "yam" with several "eyes" (or buds) and record the variety.
2. Study the sweet potato closely noticing the difference between the buds (eyes) and other marks or creases. Buds are where meristematic tissue can grow into branches and leaves or differentiate into tissue that will become roots. Make a dot with a permanent marker on the equator of the potato. Count and record the number of eyes (buds) above the equator and the number of buds below the equator.

3. Set up the sweet potato into a rooting jar following these directions:
   A. Take 2 skewers and pass each through the center of the potato at right angles to each other, at the equator so that a cross results that will support the potato over the rim of a glass container.
   B. Place the potato suspended over the glass and add aged water up to the a few millimeters from the rim of the glass.
   C. Set the sweet potato rooting unit under light, preferably grow lights or near a south-facing window. Sweet potatoes prefer warmth (70°C) and do not light cold drafty windows. Keep the water level constant and clear. If the water gets cloudy with bacteria or algae dump the water, rinse the container and refill it.
4. Using a digital camera, take a photo of the sweet potato rooting setup on this "Day 0." Print a copy of the photo (5 × 7" – black and white or color). Record observations weekly, starting Day 0, see below.
5. Prepare a data table, starting at Week 0, to record data for 12 weeks (through Week 11). Each week, record:
   • The number of unopened "eyes" above the water line
   • The number of "eyes" that have produced branches/leaves
   • The average length of branches
   • The number of unopened "eyes" below the water line
   • The number of "eyes" that have produced roots
   • Changes in the color or texture of the sweet potato
   • Other observations/comments
6. Each week, take a digital photograph of the potato showing the differences in growth of branches and roots. Make sure the image is clear enough to see rooting. Set aside 12 pages in your notebook as a photo journal to document the growth of the sweet potato. Each week, glue the image of the sweet potato in the rooting setup. Date and label the photograph and write a short summary, under the image, of your observations and thoughts about the growth of your sample versus your partner's.
7. After 12 weeks (Week 11), prepare a data table that summarizes the growth and behavior of your sample as compared to your partner's for each sweet potato, including:
   • The date when branches first appeared
   • The total number of branches growing from buds after 12 weeks
   • The average length of branches after 12 weeks.
   • The date when roots first appeared
   • The total number of roots growing from eyes after 12 weeks
8. Prepare a data table that shows the averages for multiple replications of the data in #7. Find data, from other student groups, for 5 different sweet potatoes variety #1 and 5 replications of sweet potatoes variety #2. How do the results for a single replication of the experiment (your partner and your sweet potatoes) compare to the average results from several replications?
9. Prepare a single bar graph that compares the growth results comparing the average number of branches and roots at 12 weeks in the two varieties of sweet potato.
10. Prepare a single bar graph that compares the growth results comparing the average number of weeks until branches and roots were visible in the two varieties of sweet potato.

Data Analysis and Conclusion

Since branches (slips) can be excised, placed in water where they will root, and then be planted, how many potential clones did your sweet potato produce? How about your partner's sweet potato? Based on the multiple replications, what is the average number of clones that could be yielded from each variety of sweet potato? How reliable do you think this data is? Explain your answer. Are there things that you would have done differently to minimize technician error? Give examples. How is this cloning data of economic importance?

Thinking Like a Biotechnician

1. Using the Internet, learn more about the two varieties of sweet potato being tested. Find something that might explain why one variety might grow faster or produce more branches or roots than the other. Describe what that might be and the effect it might have. Record the URL of the reference you used.
2. Suggest a method encouraging faster and more abundant growth in the sweet potatoes.

Laboratory 10b
Flower Morphology/Dissection

Background

Although plant breeding is one of the oldest forms of biotechnology, it remains one of the most common methods of improving plant products, including crops, ornamental plants, and plants for industrial purposes. Breeding involves sexual reproduction and, for most commercial plants, that means crossing flowering plants.

The function of a flower is to produce the next generation of seeds. Plant breeders must be able to recognize and manipulate flowers and their parts to produce new varieties. Breeders select pollen from plants with specific characteristics and transfer their pollen to other plants with specific characteristics, with the goal of generating offspring with particular characteristics.

Most flowers contain both male and female parts; these are called complete flowers (see Figure 10.2). The male portion of a flower is the stamen. The stamen produces pollen grains that house the sperm nuclei. The female portion of the flower is the pistil, which contains one or more ovules that hold an egg cell. When fertilized, the ovules develop into the seeds. Surrounding the reproductive structures of the flower are the petal and sepals. The petals and sepals protect the developing flower bud and aid in pollinator attraction. Some flowers lack one or more of these structures and, therefore, are called "incomplete."

Pollination occurs when pollen is transferred from a stamen to a pistil. Some flowers are self-pollinators, while others are cross-pollinated (with other flowers) by wind, insects, or animals. Once pollination occurs, eggs are fertilized by the sperm nuclei of the pollen grains. Fertilized eggs develop into seeds of the next generation. Selected breeding occurs when scientists control which plant's pollen reaches and fertilizes selected plants. In order for scientists to control breeding in a floral variety, the ability to access and purposefully transfer the selected pollen to selected pistils is essential.

Purpose

What is the variation that can be seen in the structure of different flowers?
What inferences can be made about the ease scientists may have in breeding the different flowers?

Materials

Magnifying hand lens, 2×
Forceps, fine-tipped
Scalpel handles, #4 and blades, #22
flowers (lily, iris, *Kalanchoe, Fuchsia*, pea, *Azalea*, jasmine, *Campanula*, etc)

Figure 10.2. **Parts of a Flower.** Knowledge of flower parts (left) is helpful in classifying plants, breeding experiments, and understanding a plant species' genetics and evolution. Wisconsin Fast Plants, or *Brassica rapa*, (right) have "perfect flowers" with all four flower parts (sepals, petals, stamen, and pistil). At 15 days, the flowers are open and the pistil is visible in the center with the stamen surrounding it.

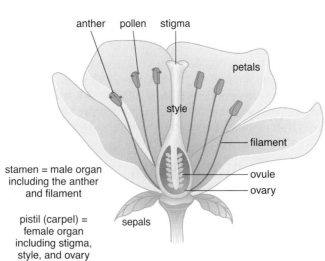

stamen = male organ including the anther and filament

pistil (carpel) = female organ including stigma, style, and ovary

Photo by Timothy Wong.

Procedure

1. Obtain a lily flower and examine its parts. In most lily flowers, the sepals and the petals are the same color. You can tell them apart by where they are attached to the floral stem. Sepals are to the outside of the petals.
2. Dissect the lily flower parts from the flower slowly, from the outside to the inside of the flower. In your notebook, make a data table to record the number and color of the floral parts, and the location of the ovary and petal attachment (ovary above the petal-superior, ovary below the petals-inferior), and other observed characteristics of the lily (see Table 10.1).
3. Repeat your dissection and observations of four other flowers.
4. Propose hypotheses for the type of pollination that occurs in each flower. Use the Internet to find examples of plants pollinated by the wind, insects, animals, or self-pollination. Record the information in a different data table in your notebook (see Table 10.2). Cite the Web sites you used.

Table 10.1. Anatomical Differences in Flowers

Flower	Sepal Number and Color	Petal Number and Color	Stamen Number and Color	Pistil Number and Color	Position of Ovary to Petals	Other Characteristics

Table 10.2. Modes of Flower Pollination

Flower	Predicted Mode of Pollination and Why (Hypothesis)	Actual Mode of Pollination (Referenced)

Data Analysis/Conclusion

Consider the actual mode of pollination in the flowers studied, discuss how easy it might be for scientists to control pollination and breeding outcomes in reproducing the studied flowers.

Thinking Like a Biotechnician

1. "Monocot" and "dicot" are two terms that describe the types of seeds, flower, and leaves of a flowering plant. Monocot plants are more closely related to each other than they are to dicots, and vice versa. Among other characteristics, most of the flower parts of monocots are in threes or multiples of threes, and their leaves have parallel veins. The flower parts of dicots are in fours or fives, or multiples of fours or fives, and their leaf veins are net-like. Identify which of the flowers you have dissected and studied are probably monocots and which are probably dicots.
2. A flower is yellow and has long, dark lines running from the tip of a petal to the base, near the pistil attachment. What type of pollination might this plant use?
3. The petals of some flowers are fused into a long tube, with the pistil and stamen deep inside it. Suggest a reason that, over time, a flower of this type has evolved. What challenges might this floral structure have for plant breeders?

Laboratory 10c
Seed Morphology/Dissection

Background

Like all organisms, plants must reproduce, passing genetic information from parent to offspring. In flowering plants, seeds are the result of sexual reproduction.

Every seed contains a tiny "baby" plant, called an embryo. The embryo has a root, called the radicle, on one end and the first set of true leaves on the other end (see Figure 10.3). Under the right conditions, the rest of the seed will protect and nourish the embryo until it is established as an independent seedling.

Anatomically, the seed is constructed for the purpose of ensuring that the embryo survives until it can grow above ground and photosynthesize. The embryo has a section, the hypocotyl, that bends to push the epicotyl (the embryonic stem portion directly below the first set of true leaves) and true leaves out of the soil. Surrounding the embryo is a food source called the endosperm. The endosperm is packaged in a leaf-like structure called a cotyledon. When a peanut is split apart, the two pieces are each a cotyledon. Some seeds have one cotyledon, while other seeds have two cotyledons.

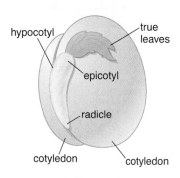

The endosperm in each cotyledon contains protein, sugar, starch, and fat molecules. This is the reason many other organisms eat seeds. The embryo produces enzymes that digest the endosperm. This produces food energy for the embryo until it is above ground and able to photosynthesize.

Surrounding the endosperm is a seed coat. The seed coat protects the seed from mechanical damage and dehydration. Sometimes the seed coat is thick and woody, such as that of a Brazil nut, to give the seed additional protection. Since each plant grows in a unique environment, a seed's size, shape, and structure are a consequence of evolution. Plant species with seeds that function best in their environment survive until the reproductive age and pass the "good-seed genes" to the next generation. The large diversity of seed types is due to the "selection pressure" from each unique environment.

Figure 10.3. Structure of a Seed. A seed protects and nourishes the next generation of a plant. The radicle, or embryonic root, is the first structure to emerge from a germinating seed. The two cotyledons, or seed leaves, full of endosperm, are visible in this germinating seed.

Purpose

What is the difference in the structure of different seeds?
What inferences can be made about how the seeds may have to be planted and grown for successful germination and survival?

Materials

Magnifying hand lens, 2×	Ruler, metric, clear	Various seeds (peanut, corn,
Forceps, fine-tipped	Balance, tabletop milligram	pinto bean, pea, almond,
Scalpel handles, #4 and	Weigh paper, 7.6 × 7.6 cm	filbert nuts, Brazil nuts, rice,
blades, #22		grass, etc)

Procedure

1. Gather the seeds to be observed. Some seeds may need to be soaked overnight to make them easier to dissect.
2. Dissect the peanut seed from the outside inward. Carefully separate the two cotyledons.
3. Observe the size, shape, color, and other characteristics of the seed and seed structures (see Figure 10.3). In your notebook, construct a data table to record the seed data (see Table 10.3).
4. Repeat your dissection and observations for the other seeds.

Table 10.3.   **Anatomical Differences in Seeds**

Seed	Seed Dimensions (mm)	Seed Mass (g)	Seed Coat Color/ Characteristics	Endosperm Color/ Characteristics	Dimensions (mm)	Embryo Other Characteristics

Data Analysis/Conclusion

Summarize the similarities and differences you have observed in the seeds that you dissected. Suggest evolutionary reasons why a plant might produce seeds that exhibit their specific characteristics. Discuss how the seeds' structure may impact how it is planted and grown for successful germination and survival.

Thinking Like a Biotechnician

1. Discuss the advantages and disadvantages of larger seeds versus smaller seeds; more endosperm versus less endosperm; thick seed coats versus thinner seed coats; and any other differences you observe.
2. Go online and find four common methods of seed distribution or dissemination for seeds other than those dissected in this lab activity. Describe these in your notebook and record the Web site of each reference you used.
3. Dicots have two cotyledons (seed sections) and monocots have only one. Can you tell which of the seeds that you dissected are monocots and which are dicots? Does the venation (vein pattern) in the "true" leaves confirm this?

Laboratory 10d
Seed Germination: How Fast Is a Fast Plant?

Background

Seeds contain an embryo, the tiny plant that resulted from combining genetic information from the parents' sex cells. The embryo is the next generation of the plant. Germination, or seed sprouting, occurs when a seed's dormancy (resting state) is broken, and the embryo inside the seed starts to grow and becomes visible. An appropriate temperature, an appropriate amount of water, and oxygen trigger germination. Depending on the seed, germination can take a few days to several weeks.

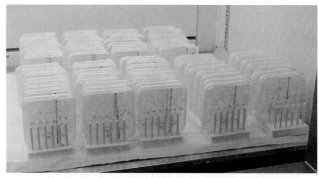

Figure 10.4. **Seed germination chambers allow seeds to be studied while they germinate.**
Photo by author.

When placed under favorable conditions, rapid-cycling *Brassica rapa* (*B. rapa*) seeds, also designated as Rbr seeds or Wisconsin Fast Plants (WFP), will germinate quickly (see Figure 10.4). They have been bred for rapid germination, growth, and seed production. They are ideal for genetic experiments because of these characteristics, in addition to their variety of interesting phenotypes. Many characteristics of WFPs can be manipulated and monitored through selective breeding experiments.

Purpose

What is the germination rate of *B. rapa* seeds compared with other plant seeds?

Materials

Filter paper, 18.5 cm	F1 GgAa *Brassica rapa* seeds	Aged tap water, left out
Petri dishes, square,	Seeds, carrot and cabbage (or	overnight
100 × 15 mm, sterile	other *Brassica* sp.)	Forceps, fine-tipped
Reaction tubes, 1.7 mL	Permanent lab marker pens	Transfer pipets, 3 mL
Tube rack for 1.7-mL tubes	Cotton, absorbent	Ruler, metric, clear
Bleach, 10%	Gauze squares, 6" × 6"	

Procedure

Note: Sterilize instruments and materials prior to use.

1. Cut a piece of filter paper so that it is the same width as the Petri dish, but 5 cm longer. Draw a pencil line on the filter paper 1 cm down from the "top." This is where the seeds to be germinated will be placed.
2. Obtain a total of six (two *B. rapa*, two cabbage (or other *Brassica* sp.), and two carrot) seeds (see Figure 10.5).
3. Soak the seeds and the filter paper in 5% bleach solution for 5 minutes. Rinse with tap water.

Figure 10.5. **Cabbage and broccoli, like *Brassica rapa*, are members of the cabbage family (Brassicaceae) and are closely related to each other.**
Photo by author.

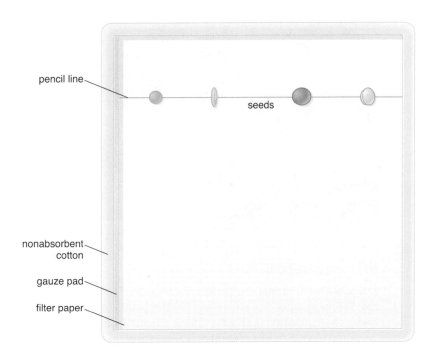

Figure 10.6. **Germination Chamber Setup.** Gently place the germination chamber in an almost upright position. This helps ensure that the roots will grow straight and downward for easy measuring.

4. Set up the Petri dish germination chamber as follows:

   a. Label the top edge of the Petri dish with your name and the date, using a permanent marker.
   b. Add absorbent cotton that has been soaked in aged tap water (squeeze out excess water) to the dish.
   c. Add a gauze pad on top of the layer of absorbent cotton.
   d. Place the filter paper on the cotton so that the pencil line is at the top, and the bottom of the filter paper is folded down and around, underneath the wet, absorbent cotton.

5. Using sterile forceps, place the seeds on the filter paper, equally spaced on the pencil line (see Figure 10.6).
6. Using a transfer pipet, place 4 to 5 mL of aged water under the absorbent cotton, so that the filter-paper strip has plenty of water to absorb. Water will rise up the filter paper by capillary action and provide the seeds with the moisture they need to germinate.
7. Put the lid back on the dish. Keep the seeds in the dark until the first one germinates. Then, move the dish to a spot with indirect light (not in a window). Do not let the chamber become too hot. Keep the filter paper moist, but not soaking wet, by adding water to the cotton reservoir when necessary. Keep the chamber vertical, so that the seeds will grow in response to gravity.
8. Every 12 hours, for 1 week, observe each seed. In a data table that you construct in your notebook, record the changes that occur to each seed over time. Look for seed swelling, color changes, cracking, etc. In a second data table, record the number of hours until each seed germinates. Create a bar graph that compares the germination time of each seed.
9. As the embryonic root (radicle) emerges, record the length of each seedling's root over time (growth rate) in a third data table. Consider the hour zero as the time the germination chamber is set up, and measure every 12 hours for 168 hours (7 days). Measure from the base of the cotyledons to the main root meristem, in millimeters (mm).
10. Graph the length of *each* seed's root over time. The data for all six seeds should be shown on a six-color line graph. Determine the average growth rate in centimeters (cm) per day for each seedling. Report this value in your notebook, along with the calculations.

Figure 10.7. Some seeds, such as those of *Arabidopsis thaliana*, are so tiny that they cannot be easily counted or planted. Here, Elizabeth Kohl, a Research Associate at Mendel Biological Solutions, weighs a specific mass of seeds prior to planting for a hydroponic experiment. The seeds she is working with are transgenic, meaning that selected genes have been added to the plants that produced the seeds. In this case, genes have been added that are thought to help plants better tolerate certain environmental conditions, such as drought, high salt, or high or low mineral content. Photo by author.

Data Analysis/Conclusion

Discuss the differences in germination rates in the different species. Do the observed germination rates support what was expected? Do the plants more closely related to *B. rapa* germinate any faster than the others? Did the fastest germinators also grow at the fastest rate once they had sprouted? Explain. List several possible errors in experimental technique that could affect the quality of data collected. Give an example of how a seed company might use an assay like the one conducted here (see Figure 10.7).

Thinking Like a Biotechnician

1. Of what value is a shorter germination time to a particular species and to a lab researcher studying plant genetics?
2. What other factors besides genetics may affect the expected germination rates? Explain how some of those factors might affect the germination rate.
3. What would happen if a tiny seed with only a small amount of endosperm were planted too deeply in the soil?

Laboratory 10e

Wisconsin Fast Plants: Model Organisms for Plant Breeding

Based on information from the *Wisconsin Fast Plants Manual,* published by Carolina Biological Supply Company © 1989 by Wisconsin Alumni Research Foundation.

Background

If you asked a scientist to name a specific type of bacterium, it is likely that *E. coli* would be the response. *E. coli* is well known as a genetic research organism because it is usually used in basic research. Scientists have conducted so many studies on this bacterium that they understand its life cycle as well as its environmental and nutritional requirements.

Like *E. coli, Drosophila melanogaster* (fruit flies), tobacco plants, *Arabidopsis thaliana* plants, mice, and the fungus, *Neurospora,* are often called "model" organisms. For research purposes, a model organism is a species that is used repeatedly and extensively for experimentation. Eventually, so much is known about the model organisms that scientists prefer to conduct experiments with them because they can more easily control these organisms.

A model organism often serves as a representative of other similar species. For example, scientists test mice and often apply the results to other mammals. To ensure safety and efficacy, tests are frequently conducted on chimpanzees before they are conducted on humans. The more closely related organisms are to each other, the better a model organism represents other organisms.

After more than 15 years of selective breeding, Dr. Paul H. Williams, of the University of Wisconsin at Madison, produced a variety of *B. rapa,* known as Wisconsin Fast Plants, with many characteristics desired in model organisms. These WFPs are excellent for research since they have the following characteristics:

- a short generation time (approximately 5 weeks from seeds to flowers to seeds)
- a relatively compact size, and they can be grown in a small space
- grow well in the laboratory (at room temperature, with continuous watering and fluorescent lighting)
- produce relatively large amounts of seeds that mature rapidly

Under optimum conditions, WFPs grow rapidly, producing flowers about 14 days after the seeds are planted (see Figure 10.8). Scientists selectively cross-pollinate WFPs using bee sticks. Fertilization occurs within a day of pollination. Seed pods develop and are visible 3 to 5 days after pollination. Twenty days after the final pollination, the plants are pulled and dried. Within a week, seeds can be harvested and a new generation planted.

In this activity, specific WFPs are cross-pollinated in a selective breeding experiment. Predictions of the possible offspring outcomes are made and analyzed.

Figure 10.8. **Wisconsin Fast Plants at approximately 16 days.**
Photo by author.

To make predictions and evaluate the inheritance of specific traits, breeders use a chart called a Punnett Square. A Punnett Square analysis shows the possible gene (allele) combinations that could result when crossing specific genotypes. Preparing this analysis allows breeders to determine the probability of producing offspring with certain genotypes and phenotypes.

When considering the possible outcomes for the cross, follow the four steps shown below.

1. List the parents' genotypes. For example: TtGG   ×   ttgg
2. List the possible combinations of alleles in the gametes: TG or tG   tg
3. In a Punnett Square, show the possible combinations of genes that could occur in a random fertilization.

Punnett Square of the Cross

Genotypes of Male/Female Gametes	tg
TG	TtGg ← offspring possibility No. 1
tG	ttGg ← offspring possibility No. 2

4. Show expected genotypic and phenotypic results of the crossing of these gametes:

1/2 of offspring are expected to be TtGg
1/2 of offspring are expected to be ttGg

Expected phenotype(s) of offspring:

If T = tall and G = green, then
1/2 of offspring are expected to be tall and green
1/2 of offspring are expected to be short and green

In the following activity, you will set up a cross and analyze the results, taking into consideration what is expected to happen according to a Punnett Square.

Purpose

How closely do the data collected from an intended dihybrid, heterozygous cross of F1 green-leafed, anthocyanin-containing (purple) plants match what is expected?

Materials

WFP watering system, with reservoir, mat, wicks, and anti-algal squares
Liquid dishwashing soap
Planting quads (or pots or film tubes)
Bleach, 10%
Quad water wick strips
Plastic beaker, 1000 mL

Potting soil
Fertilizer pellets
F1 heterozygous non-purple stem, yellow-green leaf (GgAa) seeds
Forceps, fine-tipped
Pipets, transfer, 3 mL
Plant labels, sticks or tape
WFP light bank system

Plant support stakes
Dried bees
White glue
Toothpicks
Cups, Styrofoam™
Petri dishes, square, 100 × 15 mm, sterile

Note: When the GGAA seeds grow into plants, they have green leaves and purple in their stems (see Figure 10.9a and 10.9b). The recessive mutants, "ggaa," have yellow-green leaves and no purple in the stems. The F1 seeds used in this cross were produced by crossing "GGAA" parent plants (green leaves, purple stems) with "ggaa" parent plants (yellow-green leaves, green stems).

Procedure

Part I: Planting WFP Seeds

1. In your notebook, show the entire problem, including the Punnett Square for the proposed cross. Calculate the expected percent of F2 offspring from each phenotype resulting from crossing F1 parent plants, which are heterozygous for green leaf color, and for purple color, anthocyanin, in the stems.

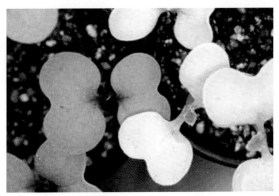

Figure 10.9a. **Green Leaf and Yellow-Green Mutant**
© Wisconsin Fast Plants Program, University of Wisconsin-Madison.

Figure 10.9b. **Purple Wild Type and Nonpurple Mutant**
© Wisconsin Fast Plants Program, University of Wisconsin-Madison.

2. Plant and grow the F1 (GgAa) seeds. See the planting instructions below. Start on a Monday or Tuesday to ensure daily watering until the seeds have germinated.

a. Prepare the water reservoir (see Figure 10.10). Fill the reservoir 2/3 full with tap water. Add 3 mL of liquid detergent. Soak the mat in the soapy water for 1 minute. Squeeze the soapy water out of the mat. Repeat this process for a total of three times. After the last soaking, do not squeeze out the mat. Lay the soapy mat on the cover of the water reservoir so that the long mat tip will hang into the water reservoir. Make sure that the mat makes good contact with the cover and that no air bubbles are under the mat. If you are reusing a reservoir and mat, scrub it with soapy water, dunk it in 10% bleach for 15 minutes, and rinse it well with water before use.

b. Fill the water reservoir with tap water.

c. Place one copper sulfate anti-algae square in the reservoir water.

d. Place the reservoir cover, with the mat, on the reservoir so that the mat is in the water.

e. Prepare the potting soil mixture by moistening it in a plastic beaker until it is slightly damp.

f. Locate a Styrofoam™ quad (or a Styrofoam™ pot with a hole punched in the bottom) and label it with a label stick or labeling tape. Use a permanent marker. If you are reusing a quad, scrub it with soapy water, dunk it in 10% bleach for 15 minutes, and rinse it well with water before using.

g. Obtain 4 wicks, and push one wick into each cell until the wick tip extends 1 cm through the hole in the bottom of the quad. When a wet wick touches a wet mat, capillary action will draw the water into the quad (see Figure 10.11).

h. Fill each cell of the quad or pot 1/2 full with moistened potting-soil mix (see Figure 10.12).

i. Obtain 12 fertilizer pellets and add three to each cell/pot or quad.

j. Fill each cell to the top with more potting mix. The soil should be loose, not packed down. Use a pencil to make a 4-mm depression in the soil surface of each cell.

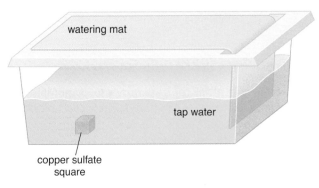

Figure 10.10. **Setting Up the Water Reservoir.** The water reservoir ensures a constant amount of water. It is critical that it is wetted thoroughly, and the air is squeezed out, so water will move via capillary action through the matting and up the wicks to the soil.

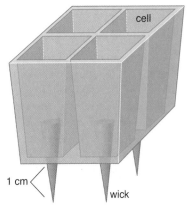

Figure 10.11. **Setting Up the Quad.** Each wick must be in contact with both the soil in the cell and the water on the mat.

Plant Biotechnology **219**

k. Place three seeds into each depression, close but not touching.

l. Add just enough of the moistened potting soil to each cell to barely cover the seeds.

m. Using a pipet, water each quad thoroughly, but gently, until water drips out of the bottom of each cell. The soil and wick must be thoroughly wetted.

Part II: Growing Wisconsin Fast Plant Seeds and Plants

3. Place the quad on the water mat. Make sure that the wetted wick is in contact with the wetted mat. As other quads are added to the mat, make sure that all wicks are still in contact with the mat. Water each cell from the top before leaving the lab.

4. Place the water reservoir under the light bank. The top of the quad should always be 5 to 8 cm from the bulbs of the light bank. WFPs are very sensitive to insufficient light (six fluorescent light bulbs, in a light bank, are required). As the plants grow, raise the light bank to keep an average distance of about 6 cm between the bulbs and the plants (see Figure 10.13). Directions for a "homemade" light bank are on the Carolina Biological Supply Co. Web site.

5. Once the WFP seedlings are showing the first set of true leaves, thin them out to maintain one plant per cell by pinching the unwanted plants off with your fingernails. Create a data table in your notebook to monitor stem growth over 2 weeks, measuring from the attachment of the first set of true leaves to the growing tip (see Figure 10.14).

6. If necessary, use small wooden stakes and plastic rings to support the plants as they grow. When flower buds appear, make bee sticks as directed below (see Figure 10.15).

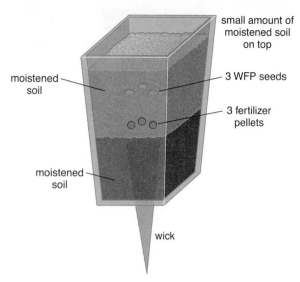

Figure 10.12. **Planting WFP Seeds.** The seeds are planted close to the top to allow plenty of room for the roots to develop.

labels: small amount of moistened soil on top; 3 WFP seeds; 3 fertilizer pellets; moistened soil; moistened soil; wick

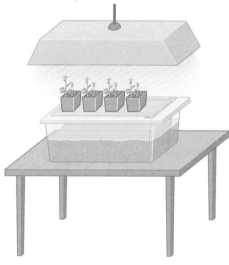

The equivalent of six flourescent bulbs should be kept at a distance of 6 cm from the growing plants at all times.

Figure 10.13. **Setting Up the Light Bank.** Adjust the height of the light or reservoir as often as necessary to keep it an average distance of approximately 6 cm above the plants.

Part III: Pollination of Plants and Harvesting F2 Seeds

7. Cross-pollinate F1 plants using the premade bee sticks (see Figure 10.12).

a. Make the bee sticks at least 24 hours in advance to allow the glue fumes to evaporate. Using white glue, glue a honeybee thorax (excised from a bee's body) onto a toothpick (see Figures 10.15 and 10.16).

b. Holding the toothpick end of the bee stick, rotate the bee-thorax end over the stamen of the flowers to pick up pollen.

c. Cross-pollinate other flowers by rotating the bee stick on other flower pistils. Continue to pollinate in this way for 2 to 3 days.

d. After 3 days of cross-pollination, remove all unopened flower buds. Record the date of the last cross-pollination in your notebook. Continue to remove all new flower buds, being careful not to disturb the developing seed pods.

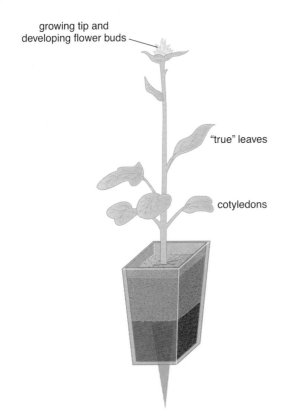

Figure 10.14. **The Growing Fast Plant.** As each plant grows, the cotyledons shrivel and may fall off. The soil level may compact with watering. Measuring should be done from the attachment of the first set of true leaves to the growing tip (left). Evaluate your plants' growth compared with other plants around the class. Plants that are growing more slowly than the others may need more light or an adjustment in watering. Since germination rates are approximately 80%, sprouted seedlings must be thinned to one plant per cell quad. The cotyledons are short-lived and present only until the true leaves are healthy. The cotyledons are round with smooth edges. The true leaves arise above them and are long and narrow with serrated edges.

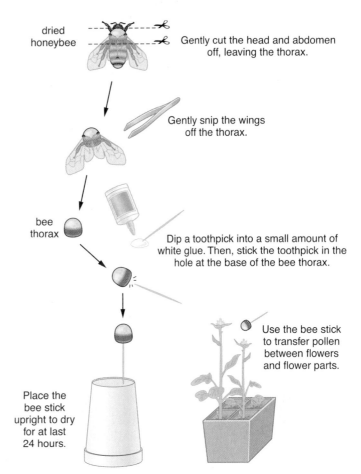

Figure 10.15. **Making and Using Bee Sticks.** White glue contains chemicals (fumes) that can sterilize bee pollen. Make the sticks early enough (at least 24 hours in advance) so that the fumes diffuse before use.

Figure 10.16. **Do all work with WFP, including planting, making bee sticks, and harvesting seeds, over a lab mat. This work is messy, and cleanup is easier when lab mats are used.**
Photo by author.

8. Harvest the F2 seeds from their pods following the directions below:
   a. Remove the quads from the water reservoirs 20 days after the last pollination. Allow them to dry for at least 5 days.
   b. Using a Petri dish as a collection plate, harvest the seeds by gently rolling the dry seed pods between your hands. Seeds can be used immediately or stored in a cool, dry place for several months or more, if they are kept dry and in an airtight container.

Troubleshooting and Growing Hints (see Figure 10.17)

Dried plants: If the plants or soil in the quads dry out, water them from the top down and place them in a beaker of water for about 24 hours. Sometimes this will revive the plants.

Insect infestation: If insects or insect damage is apparent, try one of the two of the following methods:

- Pick the insects from your plants and squish them with your hand.
- Spray the plants with a solution of commercial insecticidal soap.
- Make sure to clean and, if necessary, spray the growing area before the next planting.

Bee sticks: Prepare the bee sticks by holding the bee and pinching off the abdomen, head, legs, and, finally, the wings. Dip a toothpick into a tiny amount of white glue. Stick the glue end of the toothpick into the hole of the thorax. Stick the bee sticks into the bottom of an inverted Styrofoam™ cup to dry for at least 24 hours.

9. Observe the results of the dihybrid, heterozygous cross by planting the F2 seeds (offspring of the F1 starting seeds). Grow them until the pigments in the stem and the cotyledons are visible and obvious (within the first 3 days of germination). Follow the same planting instructions used for the F1 generation, except that before the next planting, soak the water reservoirs, platforms, water mat, quads, and wicks in a 10% bleach solution for at least 15 minutes. Then, scrub the quads with a brush and rinse all materials thoroughly with water. Let all materials dry completely before reusing. Also, if there is a shortage of quads, plant five seeds per cell. The more seeds available to count give a larger sample size, which increases the validity of the results and multiple plantings are suggested.

10. Once the F2 plants have sprouted enough for you to recognize their phenotypes (second or third day), count the number of plants in each of the four expected phenotypes: 1) green with anthocyanin, 2) green with no anthocyanin, 3) yellow-green with anthocyanin, and 4) yellow-green with no anthocyanin. Record these data (for the plants in your quad) in a data table in your notebook. If you are not sure of the phenotype of a certain plant, ask a colleague or two for their opinions.

11. Determine the expected number of offspring in each phenotype group and compare that number to the observed number of offspring in each phenotypic group. Remember that the percentage of each expected phenotypic group was calculated at the beginning of the procedures. Record this information in the data table. Determine whether the observed data are within 10% of the expected values. Add this information to the data table.

12. In your notebook, create a data table to show all the phenotypic data for the class. Record each group's observed and expected values, and the observed and expected totals for the class. Make a bar graph of the observed and expected values (totals) for the class.

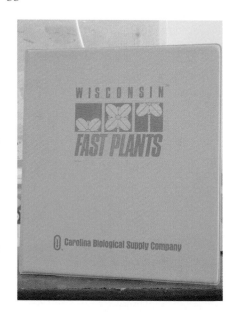

Figure 10.17. **A WFP Instruction Manual is available through Carolina Biological Supply Company at biotech.emcp.net/Carolina.** Photo by author.

Data Analysis/Conclusion

Analyze the data by determining whether the actual results are close enough to the expected results to support a valid dihybrid, heterozygous cross. Use the Chi Square analysis method to analyze the data (see the next activity). Give evidence for your statements. If your data do not come close to the expected values, give reasons for the poor results.

Thinking Like a Biotechnician

1. Use Microsoft® Excel® to determine the standard deviation (SD) for the average stem growth of your WFPs. If you do not know how to do this, access the Help feature from the Menu bar of Excel® and search for the topic.
2. For the F2 phenotypic counts, list at least three reasons why these counts might be inaccurate.

Laboratory 10f

How Can You Determine If the WFP Data Are Good Enough?

Background

In the WFP experiment, a known F_1 generation of WFP was grown. These F_1 plants were dihybrid, heterozygous for green leaves, and anthocyanin in the stems. Do you remember the genotypes of these plants?

When these F_1 plants flowered, they were cross-pollinated with other F_1 plants of the same genotype. Based on a large sample size and random breeding, the Punnett Square of this cross predicted a 9:3:3:1 ratio of offspring in each phenotypic group. Thus, in any population of F_2 offspring:

9/16 are expected to show the dominant/dominant traits of green with anthocyanin
3/16 are expected to show the dominant/recessive traits of green, with no anthocyanin
3/16 are expected to show the recessive/dominant traits of yellow, with anthocyanin
1/16 are expected to show the recessive/recessive traits of yellow, with no anthocyanin

We rarely get only 16 offspring, so it is more useful to consider the percentage of the offspring in each phenotypic group. Therefore, in any given population of offspring we expect the following:

56% (9/16) to show the dominant/dominant traits = green, with anthocyanin
19% (3/16) to show the dominant/recessive traits = green, with no anthocyanin
19% (3/16) to show the recessive/dominant traits = yellow, with anthocyanin
6% (1/16) to show the recessive/recessive traits = yellow, with no anthocyanin

Thus, in a population of 200 offspring, the following are expected:

112 are expected to be green, with anthocyanin (200 × .56)
38 are expected to be green, with no anthocyanin (200 × .19)
38 are expected be yellow, with anthocyanin (200 × .19)
12 are expected to be yellow, with no anthocyanin (200 × .06)

You may have more or fewer seeds than you expect as F_2 offspring in each phenotypic group from your F_1 plants. Through a Chi Square (χ^2) analysis of the phenotypic results of the F_2 offspring, the validity of the data collected from the dihybrid, heterozygous cross can be evaluated.

How to Calculate the Chi Square Value (χ^2)

Use the equation below to calculate the χ^2 value for a set of data.

$$\chi^2 = \Sigma \left[\frac{(O-E)^2}{E} \right]$$

The terms represent the following:

O = observed number for a phenotypic group
E = expected number for a phenotypic group
Σ = the Greek letter, sigma, which represents the "sum of"

The χ^2 equation examines and compares each phenotypic group's observed data to the expected results. The difference is the deviation between the actual and the expected results. Then, Σ sums up all of the phenotypic group's deviations.

The final χ^2 value represents the sum of all of the deviations in the experiment. By looking on the Chi Square probability table (Table 10.4), one can see if the observed deviation from the expected results is small enough that it supports the experimental hypothesis and that there is no significant difference between observed and expected data. In this case, the hypothesis is that the data are similar enough to be considered a valid dihybrid, heterozygous cross (see Table 10.4). If the χ^2 value is too large (greater than the $P = 0.05$ value), the deviation from what is expected is so large that the data do not support a valid dihybrid, heterozygous cross.

Purpose

Does the χ^2 value for the WFP cross support the hypothesis that a dihybrid, heterozygous cross was conducted in the WFP breeding experiment by showing that there is no significant difference between observed and expected results.

Procedure

1. Determine the degrees of freedom (df) for the WFP dihybrid, heterozygous cross. The df is one less than the number of phenotypic groups.
2. Using the data collected in the WFP cross, determine an χ^2 value for each of the following. Show all calculations for each χ^2 determination in your notebook.

   - your own F2 seeds from your own F1 plants
   - the F2 seeds from the entire class' F1 plants
   - the F2 seeds from multiple classes' F1 plants

3. For each determination, report the spot where the χ^2 value falls on the Chi Square Probability Table and the meaning of that value.

Table 10.4. Chi Square Probability Table. To use the table, find the χ^2 value for the degrees of freedom (phenotypic groups –1) in the experiment. If the χ^2 value falls to the left of the 0.05 column value, then the hypothesis is accepted (the data are good enough).

df*	0.95	0.90	0.70	0.50	0.30	0.20	0.10	0.05*	0.01	0.01 Probability
1	0.004	0.016	0.15	0.46	1.07	1.64	2.71	3.84	6.64	10.83
2	0.10	0.21	0.71	1.39	2.41	3.22	4.61	5.99	9.21	13.82
3	0.35	0.58	1.42	2.37	3.67	4.64	6.25	7.82	11.35	16.27
4	0.71	1.06	2.20	3.36	4.88	5.99	7.78	9.49	13.28	18.47
5	1.15	1.61	3.00	4.35	6.06	7.29	9.24	11.07	15.09	20.52
6	1.64	2.20	3.83	5.35	7.23	8.56	10.65	12.59	16.81	22.46
7	2.17	2.83	4.67	6.35	8.38	9.80	12.02	14.07	18.48	24.32
8	2.73	3.49	5.53	7.34	9.52	11.03	13.36	15.51	20.09	26.13
9	3.33	4.17	6.39	8.34	10.66	12.24	14.68	16.92	21.67	27.88
10	3.94	4.87	7.27	9.34	11.78	13.44	15.99	18.31	23.21	29.59

← Accept the experimental hypothesis | *Reject the experimental hypothesis →

*df = degree of freedom

Data are close enough to the expected results | Data are not close enough to the expected results

Data Analysis/Conclusion

Describe the significance of each χ^2 value. How well does each set of data fit expectations for a dihybrid, heterozygous cross? Are any of the experimental results close enough to what was expected to occur during a dihybrid, heterozygous cross to show a valid experiment? Explain how results might not show a dihybrid, heterozygous cross even though all the seeds were thought to be GgAa. Did the χ^2 value improve as the sample size increased? Explain.

Thinking Like a Biotechnician

1. For each of the following cross pollinations for *B. rapa* plant characteristics, give the genotypes of the parents, gametes, and offspring, and the offsprings' phenotypes, as well as the expected results for a cross between parents that have 50 offspring.

   a. Cross a homozygous-dominant, green-leafed (G) plant with a homozygous-recessive, yellow/green-leafed plant.

      Parents' genotypes:
      Alleles possible in the gametes:
      Punnett Square of the cross:
      Genotypic results of crossing these gametes:
      Phenotype(s) of offspring:

   b. Cross a heterozygous, purple-stemmed plant with a homozygous-recessive one (pp).

      Parents' genotypes:
      Alleles possible in the gametes:
      Punnett Square of the cross:
      Genotypic results of crossing these gametes:
      Phenotype(s) of the offspring:

   c. Cross a plant, heterozygous for both green leaf color and purple stems, with a plant that is homozygous recessive for leaf color and heterozygous for stem color.

      Parents' genotypes:
      Alleles possible in the gametes:
      Punnett Square of the cross:
      Genotypic results of crossing these gametes:
      Phenotype(s) of the offspring:

2. For the cross in problem 1c, calculate the χ^2 value and explain its significance if the breeding experiment resulted in 33 green-leafed purple plants; 15 green-leafed, not purple plants; 11 yellow-leafed purple plants; and seven yellow-leafed, not purple plants.

Laboratory 10g

Asexual Plant Propagation through Leaf and Stem Cuttings

Background

When plant growers want all the offspring of a particular plant to be identical to the parent plant, they do not want the plant to reproduce sexually. Instead, they want to make identical copies of the plant. These copies are called clones. Clones are made through asexual reproduction. One parent gives rise to several identical offspring. Clones can be produced by taking pieces of a plant (one cell, many cells, or even a whole plant organ), and growing them in the right environment.

The oldest form of asexual plant propagation is the use of pieces of leaves or stems. These are called cuttings. Many plants grow well from cuttings (see Figure 10.18). Cuttings are grown in water or in sterile potting media. There are several types of media including perlite, vermiculite, soil, peat moss, and agar. Under suitable conditions, leaf cuttings may be induced to produce roots and stems, while stem cuttings may be induced to produce leaves and roots.

Figure 10.18. **Coleus plants are commonly cloned through stem cuttings in water.**
Photo by author.

Purpose

What is the difference in root production in *Kalanchoe* leaf and stem cuttings?

Materials

Environmental Health
and Safety Officer

Plastic beaker, 1 L
Potting soil
Vermiculite
Sand
Cups, Styrofoam™, 6 oz
Permanent lab marker pens

Bleach, 5%
Several large *Kalanchoe* plants
Scalpel handles, #4
Scalpel blades, #22, for #4
   handles
Liquid detergent

Pipets, transfer, 3 mL
Lab scoops
Beakers, 250 mL

Procedure

- The instructor will assign an experimental treatment to the lab team, either leaf cuttings or stem cuttings.
- Each student is responsible for one experimental setup with three replications.
- All media should be sterilized before use.
- A setup is a pot containing some medium and three cuttings.

1. In a 1 L container, moisten the medium (soil, vermiculite, and sand in a 2:1:1 ratio) with water until it is thoroughly wetted.
2. Punch four holes in the bottom of a labeled Styrofoam™ cup.
3. Fill the cup loosely with the selected moistened medium. Tap the soil down gently to 0.5 cm from the top.
4. Sterilize the work area with 5% bleach solution before making any cuttings.
5. For leaf cuttings, use a sterile scalpel to remove some young leaves from one of the parent plants. Use a small- to medium-size leaf (3 to 5 cm²). To sterilize the leaves, immerse them in a 5% commercial bleach/liquid detergent (1 drop detergent:1 L bleach) solution for 10 seconds, then dunk them three times in sterile distilled water. Use sterile forceps to move them.

6. Use a sterile scalpel to cut the leaf petiole (leaf stem) to 0.5 cm from the leaf base. Cut the leaf petiole at a 45° angle to increase the amount of exposed meristematic tissue. Use a pencil wiped with 5% bleach to make an indentation in the potting medium, wide and deep enough to insert your cutting. Place the leaf cutting in the medium so that its base is submerged at least 2 cm or 1/3 of the way. Gently pat the medium around the cutting.

7. For stem cuttings, take a stem or stem piece that has at least three nodes (nodes are where leaves attach). Remove the leaves from at least the two bottom nodes. Trim off large leaves, leaving one or two small leaves at the top. To sterilize the stem cutting, immerse it in a 5% commercial bleach/liquid detergent solution for 10 seconds, and then dunk it three times in sterile distilled water. Use sterile forceps to move it.

8. Use a sterile scalpel to cut the stem base back to 0.5 cm from the bottom node. Cut the stem at a 45° angle to increase the amount of exposed meristematic tissue. Use a pencil to make a hole in the potting medium and place the stem cutting in the medium so that at least one node is submerged. Pat down the medium around the cutting.

9. Use a large transfer pipet to water the cutting medium with aged tap water from the top down until water drips from the bottom holes.

10. Place the labeled pots in a spot with indirect light for 3 to 4 days before moving the pots to a plant light stand. Check daily to make sure that the medium is damp but not soaked.

11. Look for evidence of new growth. Record changes in each cutting over time in three separate data tables. The day the cuttings are started is "Day 0." The title of the data tables should be:

    a. Changes in color in *Kalanchoe* _____ cuttings over 28 days
    b. Changes in turgidity in *Kalanchoe* _____ cuttings over 28 days
    c. Changes in number of leaves in *Kalanchoe* _____ cuttings over 28 days

    Record the data in a quantitative fashion, converting qualitative data to numerical data. For example, use a 5 to 0 system. For color, 5 = green and 0 = white or brown. For turgidity, 5 = firm and completely turgid and 0 = limp and not turgid at all. Remember to include three replications, averages, and comments.

12. After 28 days, gently scoop up each cutting from the medium. Gently remove the medium from the roots by carefully dunking each in a beaker of water and rinsing with a transfer pipet. Be careful not to rinse soil down the sinks or break any roots!

13. Count the number of roots present on each cutting. Create a new data table for these data and their averages. Share your averaged data with the class.

Data Analysis

Using class averages, graph the average number of roots produced by each type of cutting (leaf vs. stem). Does it appear, overall, that the leaf or stem cuttings rooted better? Give evidence and explain why these results support or refute your expectations.

Conclusion

Discuss the results of the class' cuttings experiment. How successfully were the plants cloned? Give your answers as percentages of the total number of cuttings attempted, and explain any findings that indicate the rooting medium affected root production. Discuss possible reasons for the results obtained. Propose variations in the experiment to improve the results. Discuss how these results might impact a company that produces these plants for market.

Thinking Like a Biotechnician

1. The procedures suggest smaller leaf sizes for leaf cuttings. What is a possible disadvantage of a large leaf cutting?
2. Discuss the advantages and disadvantages of sterilizing the media before using it in this experiment.
3. Suggest a method of encouraging more root development in cuttings that are slow to root.

Laboratory 10h
The Effect of Hormone Concentration on Plant Propagation

Background

When applied at the "right" concentration, a plant hormone, or plant growth regulator, can speed root and/or shoot development in cuttings. Powdered commercial rooting hormones, available for home use, contain a synthetic auxin, present at some concentration (see Figure 10.19). The instructions do not specify use at a particular concentration. The user dips the cutting into the powdered hormone, and a variable amount sticks to the plant tissue.

For use in industry, hormone concentration must be optimized to ensure the maximum amount of root growth in the shortest amount of time. It is challenging to determine the optimum concentration of one hormone versus another. In this activity, the effect of varying the concentration of one hormone on rooting is determined.

Purpose

What is the optimum concentration of 1-naphthaleneacetamide, the auxin commonly found in rooting compound, for stimulation of rooting in stem cuttings?

Materials

Parent plant such as *Epipremnum aureum, Fuchsia,* or *Abutilon megapotamicum*
Balance, weigh boat, lab scoops
Commercial plant rooting compound
Note: Read the package label to determine the type and concentration of auxin and adjust the protocols as needed.
Beakers, 250 mL
Plastic funnels, short-stemmed
Filter paper, 12.5 cm
Graduated cylinder, 25 mL
Bottle, media, 250 mL
Scalpel handles, #4
Scalpel blades, #22 for #4 handles
Tubes, 50 mL, and racks
Parafilm®
Cotton, nonabsorbent
Aluminum foil
Pipet, 10 mL, and pump

Figure 10.19. **Commercial rooting hormone is available at most nurseries. Depending on the brand, it may contain one of a few different kinds of synthetic auxin. This brand contains the auxin indolebutyric acid (IBA) at 0.1%.** Photo by author.

Procedure

1. The auxin, 1-naphthaleneacetamide, is found as 0.20% of the mass of the rooting compound. Prepare 200 mL of a rooting compound solution where the 1-naphthaleneacetamide is represented as 10 mg/mL in the solution. To do this, add 2 g of rooting compound to 200 mL of dH$_2$O. This is the stock solution.

   The math is as follows: 0.20% = 0.2 g/100 g = 200 mg/100 g = 200 mg/100 mL = 2 mg/mL, which is 5 times less than the desired 10 mg/mL. So, multiply the 0.2 g per 100 g by 5, which equals 1 g/100 mL, and add 2 g into the 200 mL of water.

   Note: The rooting compound contains inert materials that are not plant hormones, and they do not dissolve. To ensure a clear solution, filter the stock solution through a Whatman filter paper funnel. The clear filtrate is the 10 mg/mL stock solution used below.

2. Prepare a serial dilution of the 10 mg/mL stock solution to end up with 100 mL each of four solutions of decreasing concentration (5.0, 2.5, 1.25, 0.625 mg/mL 1-naphthaleneacetamide). Use sterile, distilled, aged water. Save all extra stock solution for refilling tubes later in the experiment. Label all vessels completely.
3. Using a sterile scalpel, remove five branches from the "parent" plant of about the same size and nodal arrangement. Remove the leaves from the two bottom nodes of each cutting. Trim off large leaves. Cut the stem base to 1 cm from the bottom node. Cut the stem at a 45° angle to increase the amount of meristematic tissue exposed.
4. Fill five 50-mL sterile, conical centrifuge tubes with 45 mL of one of each of the four 1-naphthaleneacetamide solutions. To the fifth tube, add some plain sterile, aged water as a negative control. **The solution volume must remain at 45 mL throughout the experiment.**

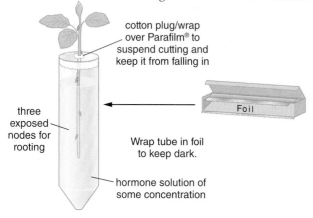

cotton plug/wrap over Parafilm® to suspend cutting and keep it from falling in

three exposed nodes for rooting

Wrap tube in foil to keep dark.

Foil

hormone solution of some concentration

Figure 10.20. **If Parafilm® is available, it can be pulled over the tube opening. Then, a small hole can be punched in the Parafilm®, and the cutting can be inserted through the hole. A small piece of cotton wrapped around the stem provides additional support so that the cutting and cotton do not fall into the solution.**

5. Seal the top of each tube with Parafilm®. Punch a hole in each. Place one of the cuttings to the desired depth, through the Parafilm®, into each tube. Wrap some nonabsorbent cotton around each cutting to keep it upright in the tube. Make sure the cotton does not get wet (see Figure 10.20). Wrap the outside of the tube in aluminum foil to keep the rooting area dark. Place a tape label on the outside of each setup.
6. Check tubes every other day to make sure that there is still 45 mL of solution in each. If the volume is less than 45 mL, add enough of the appropriate solution to bring it back up to 45 mL.
7. Record the date (number of days) when the first root appears on each cutting. Create a data table to record the "days to first root" data. Rewrap the tube in foil to exclude light.
8. At the end of each week, for 4 weeks, count the number of roots present on each cutting. Make a data table to record the data.

Data Analysis

Using your lab group's data, graph the number of roots that each hormone concentration produced by Day 28 of the experiment. On a different graph, show the number of days until the first root appeared in each concentration.

Collect class data (make a class data table) so that there are at least eight replications of the experiment to examine (average). When possible, use averaged data rather than individual trials. Averaged data better represent the impact of the variable than individual values. Prepare graphs showing all of the class data.

Conclusion

In a conclusion statement, discuss the results of your experiment. Does it appear that the hormone concentration affected the rooting of cuttings? How so or how not? Do other results in the class support your lab group's results? Do any data seem odd or fallacious? Why so or why not? Propose applications of these results, as well as further experiments. How might these hormone studies be used by commercial plant produces to increase the amount of product they have for market?

Thinking Like a Biotechnician

1. Does it appear that there is a limit to the amount of hormone that will affect the rooting process? If so, above what concentration is there no additional effect? Sketch a graph showing how such results would look.
2. How can you tell if the concentration of hormones is too high in all of the treatments?
3. On the graph, how would a line appear if there were no relationship between the rooting hormone concentration and rooting?

Laboratory 10i
Cloning African Violets

This lab was inspired by a lab written by Doug Lundberg that appeared in *The Science Teacher* in April 1987. It can be found at **biotech.emcp.net/lundberg**.

Background

Although African violets (*Saintpaulia ionantha*) are native to subtropical areas, they are very popular houseplants throughout the world. One reason that African violets are so popular is because of their showy flowers. Another reason is that they are easy to asexually propagate indoors, in the home or in greenhouses. This is fortunate, since African violets cannot easily be propagated outdoors or by seeds.

Like many herbaceous plants, African violets can be cloned through plant tissue culture (PTC). Leaf tissue may be taken, sterilized, and grown into a complete plantlet in the "right"

Figure 10.21. Under the right conditions, African violets are asexually propagated through leaf cuttings and plant tissue culture.
Photo by author.

type of plant tissue culture (PTC) medium (see Figure 10.21). The PTC medium contains all the nutrients and hormones needed, at the proper concentration, to promote callus (undifferentiated cell division) and cell differentiation. On PTC medium, plantlets can grow and develop until they are able to photosynthesize and can be transplanted into a soil or soil-like medium.

A PTC produces genetically identical offspring in a relatively short time. Growers of ferns, lilies, raspberries, and many other plants also use PTC methods similar to those conducted here on African violet tissue.

Purpose

What different stages in the cloning of African violets are observed by the time explants reach transplantable size?
What percentage of tissue cultures result in viable plantlets?
What is the yield of offspring from a single PTC explant?
What is the average yield of offspring from all the explants in the class?

Materials

Bleach, 10%
Ethanol, 70%
Scalpel handles, #4
Scalpel blades, #22 for #4 handles
Scissors, stainless steel
Forceps, fine-tipped
Sterilizer/autoclave
Murashige-Skoog Multiplication Medium, for African violets
Sucrose
Balance, tabletop milligram
Weigh boat, 3.5" × 3.5"

Lab scoops
pH Meter and electrode
pH Buffer, pH 7.0
Hydrochloric acid, 1 *M*
Potassium hydroxide, 1 *M*
Plant tissue culture agar
Beaker, 2 L
Hot plate stirrer
Beakers, 250 mL
Tissue culture tubes and caps
Laminar flow hood
African violet plants
Tubes, 50 mL, sterile
Tube racks for 50 mL tubes

Petri dishes, 60 × 15 mm, sterile
Pipets, 2 mL, and pump
Parafilm®
Murashige-Skoog Pretransplant Medium, for African violets
Tape, labeling
Cups, Styrofoam™, 6 oz
Plastic beaker, 1 L
Soil, potting
Plastic vegetable bags

Procedure

Part I: Preparing Reagents/Medium

1. Prepare the ethanol and bleach solutions required in the materials list. Sterilize deionized water, forceps, scissors, scalpels, and any other items in an autoclave for 15 to 20 minutes at 15 to 20 psi.

2. Prepare the multiplication medium (for between 50 and 100 tubes) by combining the premixed Murashige-Skoog multiplication medium packet with 800 mL of distilled water and 30 g of sucrose. Bring the pH to 5.7 with 1 M HCl or 1 M KOH. Pour the mixture slowly into a 2-L beaker containing 8 g of plant tissue agar, mixing the agar into the solution while pouring. Bring the final volume to 1 L with deionized water. Heat until *just before* boiling. DO NOT LET IT BOIL.

3. Pour the mixture into test tubes, about 7 to 10 mL into each for small tubes, and 15 to 20 mL each for large tubes. The agar should fill approximately 1/2 of the tube.

4. Cover test tubes with PTC tube caps. The caps allow for gas exchange, but they will still maintain sterility after autoclaving.

5. Autoclave the medium-filled tubes at 15 to 20 psi for 20 minutes (see Figure 10.22). Do not "overautoclave" since some of the hormones are heat-sensitive and could break down, which could affect the hormone concentration.

Figure 10.22. Tissue cultures can be set up in almost any kind of vessel that can be autoclaved and kept sterile. Here, flasks plugged with gauze and covered loosely with aluminum foil are used instead of fancy tissue culture tubes.
Photo by author.

Part II: Preparing the Explants

- African violet tissue culturing is challenging because the leaves are covered with tiny hairs (trichomes). Because the trichomes trap tiny particles, including bacteria and fungi, it is critical to properly wash the leaves to remove any particles without damaging the plant tissue.
- Do all of your work in a sterile laminar flow hood that has been disinfected using 10% bleach and 70% ethanol.
- Unless directed otherwise, wash and rinse in small volumes of solutions in sterile Petri dishes or 50 mL, sterile conical tubes. Setting up a series of washing plates works well. Make sure leaf disks do not go into a solution that contains another explant.

6. Remove a medium-size leaf from a healthy African violet or other test plant. For about 1 minute, gently rinse both sides of the leaf under tap water to remove any large pieces of debris.

7. To disinfect the surface of the leaf and remove any remaining particles, shake it vigorously three times in three consecutive capped, sterile, 50-mL, conical centrifuge tubes containing sterile distilled water.

8. To sterilize the leaf, use sterile forceps to dunk it in 70% ethanol three times.

9. In a sterile Petri plate, use a sterile scalpel or razor blade to cut a leaf disk approximately 1 cm by 1 cm square (or a size that fits well into the PTC tube) from the middle of the leaf near the base. Include some of the center vein (containing meristematic tissue) in the leaf disk.

10. To sterilize the leaf disk, immerse it in a 10% commercial bleach solution for 3 minutes only.

11. Rinse the leaves by dunking them in three separate washes of fresh, sterile distilled water.

12. Place the sterilized leaf disk, bottom side up, on the surface of the multiplication medium in the PTC tubes (see Figure 10.23). The leaf section edges should just break the surface of the medium, but the "bottom" side should still be exposed to air. **Be extremely careful not to introduce contamination into these culture tubes. Use sterile pipets to position the disks.**

13. Cap and label the multiplication-medium culture tube. Use a small piece of Parafilm® to secure the tube top, but allow a tiny slit for air exchange. Place the cultures, in a rack, in "room light." Avoid bright light for the first three days. Then place the cultures under plant grow lights for the remainder of the experiment.

14. Set up a data table to record observations of the changes in the African violet tissue culture over time. Include observations of changes in color, swelling, fuzziness, contamination, etc. Use numerical data wherever possible. Make observations once per week. Include the number of plantlets developing on the explant.

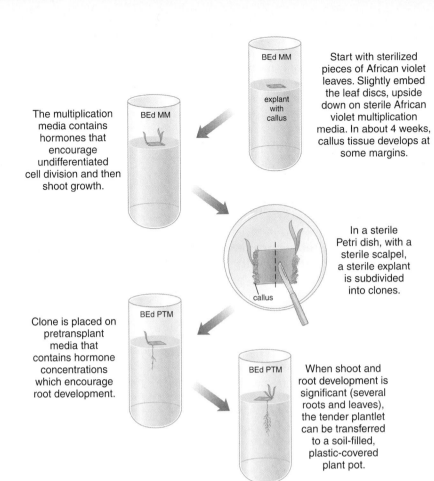

The multiplication media contains hormones that encourage undifferentiated cell division and then shoot growth.

Start with sterilized pieces of African violet leaves. Slightly embed the leaf discs, upside down on sterile African violet multiplication media. In about 4 weeks, callus tissue develops at some margins.

In a sterile Petri dish, with a sterile scalpel, a sterile explant is subdivided into clones.

Clone is placed on pretransplant media that contains hormone concentrations which encourage root development.

When shoot and root development is significant (several roots and leaves), the tender plantlet can be transferred to a soil-filled, plastic-covered plant pot.

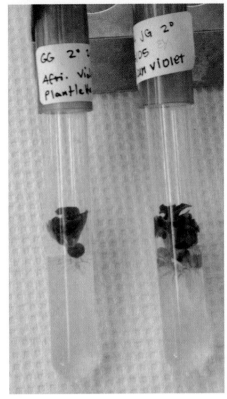

Photo by author.

Figure 10.23. African violet tissue culture.

Part III: Maintenance of Clones

- The clones usually need to be transferred to pretransplant medium, but not always. It depends on the number of plantlets (and whether they are to be subdivided), and the amount of shoots and roots on each plantlet. If an explant has only one plantlet, and if it has a well-developed shoot and root, skip the pretransplant steps. For most cultures, though, continue at step 15.
- Two days before it is needed, make a batch of pretransplant medium, which stimulates root production. Use the same procedures used for the multiplication medium, substituting Murashige-Skoog Pretransplant Medium base for Murashige-Skoog Multiplication Medium base.

15. After 5 to 6 weeks in multiplication medium, the explants should be covered with small plantlets (shoots with no roots).
16. Use sterile technique and sterile forceps to place the leaf pieces inside a sterile Petri dish. Use a sterile scalpel to cut the small plantlets away from each other.
17. Move the plantlets to individual culture tubes of pretransplant medium. Record the number of plantlets transferred. Make sure the explants are in contact with the media with no air gaps. Cap the culture tubes and put them in "room light" for a few days and under grow lights for 4 to 6 weeks.
18. When many roots are visible in the culture tube, set up a labeled Styrofoam™ pot with four holes punched in the bottom for water drainage. Add moistened potting soil to within a centimeter of the top. Make a depression for the roots of the plantlet.

19. Gently, move the plantlets from the pretransplant medium to the soil. Very gently, wash all of the medium from the plantlets' leaves and roots with room-temperature, aged tap water before planting. Place the plantlet in the soil until only the root is submerged in soil and the explant is at the soil surface. Gently, pat it into place. Record the number of plantlets moved to soil.
20. Maintain humidity by putting the small pots in a larger container, which has 1 to 2 cm of water in the bottom. Cover both containers with cellophane wrap or a vegetable bag to produce a tiny greenhouse environment.
21. After 1 week, fold back the bag a little every day for another 1 to 2 weeks, until it is all the way off. This is called "hardening off," and gives the transplant a chance to repair damaged roots and get used to the new humidity. Record the number of plantlets still appearing healthy and viable after 2 weeks.

Data Collection/Analysis

Record the number of successful tissue cultures in the class. Determine what percentage of each tissue culture produced offspring that were still alive after each transfer. Determine the average number of plantlets per explant that survived until the "greenhouse" stage. Make graphs to show these results. Discuss the expected yield versus the actual yield. Make suggestions for improving the number of successful clones.

Thinking Like a Biotechnician

1. Discuss the texture of the PTC media compared with that of LB agar. Propose a reason for any difference.
2. If the explant shows no signs of swelling or callus after 6 weeks, what may be the reason?
3. Suggest a few other herbaceous plants that might be successfully cultured using the same media and protocol.

Laboratory 10j
Lily Cloning

Based on protocols developed by Phytotech Laboratories, **phytotechlab.com**
Modified by Odile Scorso, SMBCP Student Researcher, 2013

Background

There are over 100 species of lilies that grow in nature, and according to the USDA, 35 species of lily (*Lilium sp.*) grow in the U.S. Lilies belong to the plant family, Liliaceae, along with onions, garlic, agapanthus, and trillium. Lilies are monocots with broad, parallel-veined leaves that grow from underground stems (bulbs). Lilies often have showy flowers containing floral parts in threes or multiples of threes. The large beautiful flowers of some lilies make them an important commercial product for indoor or outdoor use. Several lilies have been propagated for home and garden markets.

Figure 10.24. **Lily Bulb Showing Bulb Scales**
© Clive Nichols/Getty Images.

Although most lily flowers are large, some are hard to propagate sexually (from seeds). Some lilies produce small seeds that require special germination conditions such as temperature or dormancy treatments and most lilies take two to six years to grow from seed to flowering plant. Although lilies propagated sexually may produce new varieties, the majority of lilies are produced through asexual propagation or cloning. Cloning assures that virtually all offspring are identical.

The easiest ways to clone lilies is by bulb division or plant tissue culture. In bulb division, lily bulbs, which grow in clusters, are dug up, cleaned and subdivided into smaller groups of one or more bulbs. These bulbs may be replanted. Additionally, bulb leaves (called scales) will grow into small (bulblets) if cleaned, packed in sphagnum moss in a plastic bag and left in a cool, dark area over winter (see Figure 10.24). Bulbs and bulblets may be planted and grow into adult lilies.

For commercial purposes, cloning small pieces of bulb tissue (explants) in sterile tissue culture is gaining popularity. From a single bulb, hundreds of identical lilies may be produced. At the base of each bulb leave scale and along the veins of the bulb leaves there is meristematic tissue that may be induced to grow and differentiate into a new lily plant. Similar, to other plant tissue culture protocols, sterile lily bulb scale samples are place on sterile media that containing the nutrients for cell growth. In addition, plant growth regulators (plant hormones) are added at some specific concentration to encourage cell and tissue differentiation. The plant hormones most associated with lily bulb and shoot formation are auxin and cytokinin.

In this activity, two commercially prepared brands of Murashige and Skoog (MS) plant tissue culture media containing two different types of cytokinin will be tested. The first is kinetin, a naturally occurring cytokinin first isolated from coconut plants. The second is 6-Benzylaminopurine (6-BA or 6-BAP, for short), a synthetic cytokinin, produced in the lab.

Purpose

What is the difference in bulb, shoot, and root formation in lily explants grown on two different multiplication media?

Materials

Beaker, 2 L
Distilled water
Murashige & Skoog Modified
  Basal Medium (w/BA),
  Phytotech #M401, 1 L
Murashige and Skoog
  Modified Multiplication
  Medium (w/ Kinetin),
  Phytotech #M555, 1 L
Plant Tissue Culture (PTC)
  Agar, Phytotech #A296
pH meter and/or pH paper
KOH, 1 M

HCl, 1 M
Plant Tissue Culture (PTC)
  tubes
Sterilization pouches
Laminar flow hood
Isopropyl alcohol, 70%
Bleach, 10% (for sterilizing
  hood)
Forceps, sterile (in sterile
  pouches)
Scalpel and blades, sterile
  (in sterile pouches)
Bunsen burner

Lily bulbs, 1 per group of
  4 students
Beakers, 250 mL
Cheesecloth
Rubber band
50-mL tubes or Petri Dishes,
  for explant sterilizing
Distilled water, sterile
Ethanol, 95%
Bleach solution, 10%, 1 L with
  300 μL Tween-20

Procedure:

Part I: Media Preparation, enough for 1 L of media or eighty 25-mL tissue culture tubes half full

6-BA/MS Modified Basal Media

1. Place the entire contents of the Murashige & Skoog Modified Basal Medium (w/BA), Phytotech #M401 media container into a 2 L beaker.
2. Add 8g of plant tissue culture agar to the beaker.
3. Stirring, slowly add 700 mL of distilled water to the media and agar until it is suspended. It will not go into solution.
4. Measure and then adjust the pH of the mixture to pH 5.6, using 1M KOH and/or 1M HCl.
5. Using deionized water bring the mixture up to a final volume of 1 L.
6. Add a stirring magnet, stir on medium, and heat the media on high until just before boiling. If watched closely, as it approaches boiling, the agar will go into solution and clarify.
7. While the media is heating, label the top of the PTC tubes with the type of media and the date. Be careful to label in a way that won't block observations the cultures as they grow. Don't forget to watch the heating media.
8. Using Hot hands, remove the media before it boils.
9. Fill the labeled PTC tubes about half way full. Line the tubes up in an autoclavable rack.
10. Make sure the tubes are loose enough to jiggle and will release pressure when heating but will stay on to keep the media sterile.
11. Autoclave the media in the tubes for 15-20 minutes (but no more) at 15-20 psi (121°C). The tubes must be at 15-20 psi for a minimum of 15 minutes.
12. Allow the autoclave to cool or vent, then the Supervisor will remove the tube racks with hot hands and place on a sterile counter or in a flow hood, in a dark corner, until ready to set up the cultures.

K/MS Modified Multiplication Media Preparation

13. Follow the directions for preparing the 6-BA/MS Modified Basal Media except substitute the Murashige and Skoog Modified Multiplication Medium (w/ Kinetin), Phytotech #M555 for Murashige & Skoog Modified Basal Medium (w/BA), Phytotech #M401 media.

Part II: Preparing the Clones

Note: Preparing the explant samples require several washes in several vessels. Make sure everything is sterile including instruments, plastics, glassware, solutions, the working surface, and the technician's hands. When moving explant samples from one vessel to the other it is best to perform all procedures inside a working flow hood. Dip forceps in alcohol and flame-sterilize after each use, following the Supervisor's demonstration.

1. Autoclave all instruments (forceps, scalpels, and blades) in sterilization pouches.
2. Turn on the laminar flow hood for 5-10 minutes before using. Wipe down the inside of flow hood with 70% isopropyl alcohol as well as everything that is in the flow hood or will be placed in hood.
3. Outside of the hood, remove the outer layer of damaged scales from lily bulbs and discard. At the sink, under running water, remove the rest of the scales: place scales in a 250-mL beaker containing tap water. Remove scales down to the point in which they become small and narrow, and discard rest of the bulb.
4. Place a single layer of cheesecloth over the beaker. Use a rubber band to hold the cheesecloth in place. For 5 minutes, run tap water through the cheesecloth, into the beaker so that the bud scales (explants) are gently agitated. Once rinsed remove the cheesecloth and transfer the beaker to the flow hood.
5. Pour just enough 95% ethanol over the scale explants to cover them, swirl for 3-4 minutes, and gently decant the ethanol into a trash beaker. Use the sterile forceps to keep the explants from falling out.
6. Pour 10% bleach/Tween-20 over the scale explants and swirl for 15 minutes to sterilize and decant the 10% bleach/Tween-20 solution into a trash beaker.
7. Rinse the scale explants three times, for 1 minute each, in sterilize deionized water.
8. Transfer scales to a sterile Petri dish. Using the sterile scalpel, cut scales into 5-mm wide explant pieces recording where each explant piece came from, either the base of the scale or from the tip.
9. Place explants onto media in each tube as follows. Wipe the outside of the culture tubes to be used with a paper towel soaked with 70% isopropyl alcohol. One lab partner should take two explants cut from the base and place one explant on 6-BA/MS media and one explant on K/MS media. One lab partner should take two explants cut from the tip of the scale and place one explant on 6-BA/MS media and one explant on K/MS media. Make sure the explants are on the media with their cut edges touching the media but not buried in the media. Cap the tubes with their sterile caps.
10. Once all cultures are have been prepared place them in racks, in low light, at room temperature. Each lab partner is responsible for their 2 tubes but will share data with the other partner
11. Check for changes in each explant at least one time per week for 3 months, recording the condition of each explant in a data table similar to Table 10.5. Look for explant swelling and the development of callus, nodules, bulblets, and shoots and use the numerical rating system in the key.

Table 10.5. Observations of Lily Explants, from Scale Base or Tip, on Different Media In the data table, record the following values for what is observed:

Key	
0 = dead	4 = swelling or nodules
1 = dying	5 = bulblets
2 = bleaching of tissues	X = contamination
3 = no change	

Time (Weeks)	Base Explant on 6-BA/MS media	Tip Explant on 6-BA/MS media	Base Explant on K/MS media	Tip Explant on K/MS media	Comments
1					
2					
3					
4					
5					
6					
7					
8					
9					
10					
11					
12					

Data Analysis and Conclusion

Describe the difference in the growth and differentiation in the explants tested. Was there a difference in the explants over time in the two different media? Was there a difference in the explants from the tip of a scale versus the base of the scale? Consider how the explants behaved during the three-month period and at the end. Survey other groups in the class for their data. Look for trends. What can you say, and give support to, about the difference in bulb, shoot, and root formation in lily explants grown on the two different multiplication media?

Did you and your partner have the same results as others groups? Why or why not? List technical errors in setting up the experiment that might lead to erroneous data. Suggest methods for minimizing these technical errors.

Discuss the value of learning how to clone lilies using plant tissue culture. How would this technique be valuable to biotechnologists? Suggest a modification of the procedure to further apply the technology.

Thinking Like a Biotechnician

1. Go to the www.phytotech.com website and find the list of ingredients for each of the MS media. List the differences in the chemical composition of the two media. What is the function of each of the different ingredients? Do the different ingredients appear to have an effect on explant growth?
2. Auxins, such as IAA, are known to have an impact on explant growth and differentiation. Use the Internet to learn more about how IAA might be added to the MS media to promote more explant growth. Suggest a variation to the media preparation to test the effect of IAA on lily explant growth and differentiation.

11 Agricultural Biotechnologies

A plant technician checks the growth of several sets of *Arabidopsis thaliana* plants, some of which are genetically modified plants (GMO) in that they have received genes for drought tolerance (low water conditions). Arabidopsis plants are model laboratory plants and are often the plant of choice for indoor plant studies.
Photo by author.

Agricultural biotechnology is generating new products and having a significant impact on the food industry, fuel production and horticulture industries. Plant biotechnologists in particular are creating new breeds, cloning new traits into crops, and improving the processes for growing and processing plants. Many plant scientists work in facilities focused on plant cloning using asexual plant propagation and integrating recombinant DNA technology with other propagation techniques.

As in all experiments, multiple replications of each experimental setup are conducted. For plant breeding or cloning experimental studies, that could mean many acres of crop plants or hundreds of flats or pots of plants in greenhouses or growth chambers. Good documentation skills are required to manage the typically large number of plant samples and related data.

In the following lab activities, you will learn some new methods of studying and manipulating plant growth and characteristics. Specifically, you will develop and practice the following skills:

- testing plants for the effect of different fertilizers
- growing plants hydroponically
- extracting and quantifying plant DNA
- isolating and quantifying plant and animal proteins
- using molecular biology techniques such as DNA isolation and analysis to confirm a plant genetic engineering procedure

The ability to clone crop plants and to isolate and manipulate a plant's DNA code and protein production is opening up vast new areas for plant or plant-based product development. In the future it is expected that similar advances will propel livestock agriculture.

Laboratory 11a
Testing Fertilizer Content

Background

A fertilizer is any substance or mixture that promotes plant growth. Fertilizers are usually used as amendments to soil with the hope that plant processes such as growth, flowering, or fruiting will be increased. Fertilizers may be composed of organic (compounds made in living things and containing carbon) and/or inorganic compounds (usually minerals such as iron, phosphorus, and potassium).

Common garden fertilizers contain a mixture of plant macro- and micronutrients. Three nutrients found in relatively high concentration in garden fertilizers are nitrogen (which promotes leaf growth), phosphorus (which promotes flower and fruit growth), and potassium (which promotes root growth). The percent of these are printed on the labels of most garden fertilizers (see Figure 11.1).

Fertilizer manufacturing is a large sector of agriculture. The use of fertilizers on the farm and in the home garden has dramatically increased over the last hundred years. Fertilizer manufacturers realize that different plants respond to different combinations and concentrations of fertilizer components. They work to produce special blends of fertilizer components optimized to give specific results for specific applications.

Although maximizing crop growth requires the right amount of nutrients, using too much fertilizer can be expensive and can pollute the environment. Alternatives to excessive fertilizer applications are being researched. Plant genetic engineers are developing crops that need less fertilizers because they have new genes that code for proteins that use nutrients more efficiently.

Figure 11.1. Figure 11.1. The percent of nitrogen, phosphorus, and potassium (N:P:K) is shown on the label of garden fertilizers. The consumer chooses a fertilizer based on the desired product. In the case of promoting additional leaf growth, the middle fertilizer (30-10-10) might be chosen.
Photo by author.

Purpose

Which fertilizer mixture promotes the most flower development in tomato plants?

Environmental Health
and Safety Officer

Materials

Tomato seedlings, in flats or pots, started approximately 4 weeks prior to starting the lab activity or purchased from a nursery.
 *See note in procedure.
Cups, Styrofoam™, 12 oz
Potting soil

Five different brands of commercial garden fertilizer with varying N:P:K content
Several large plant trays (to hold plants in cups)
Lighted growth chamber, greenhouse, or controlled light environment

Procedure

*Notes

- The instructor will assign an experimental treatment (type of fertilizer) to a lab team. Students should predict how the fertilizer they test will affect tomato plant growth.
- Each lab team (six students) is responsible for one experimental setup with three test plants testing a fertilizer and three negative control plants (ie, one plant in a pot per student). For 30 students, five fertilizers may be tested.
- Each student is responsible for one plant in a pot containing potting medium and a tomato seedling. Seedlings in a setup should be matched for size, number of leaves and branches, and general health. Starting seedlings should have no flowers or flower buds. These may be gently excised with dissecting scissors or sharp fingernails.
- The class should set up a few extra pots in case some seedlings die during transplanting.
- All teams' experimental setups must be in the same growth environment and exposed to the same light, temperature, humidity, and air movement.

1. Each team obtains six Styrofoam™ cups. Label each cup with the student's name and treatment (type of fertilizer or negative control). Using a pencil, punch five holes in the bottom of the cup for drainage. Fill each pot one-third full with potting soil.
2. Each team selects six plants of approximately equal size and vigor and gently transplants these into their six Styrofoam™ cups. Care should be taken to minimize damage to the roots. When transplanted, the tomato plants should be at the same soil depth as in the previous container. Gently water the transplants from the top of the cup until water drips from the bottom of the cup.
3. Place the plants from one experimental setup in a plant tray and place the tray in bright but indirect light for 3 days. This allows the seedlings to overcome transplant shock. Move the plants to the experimental growth area for 4 more days.
4. After 7 days, each team determines the application rate for the fertilizer following the package directions and begins applying the assigned fertilizer to their test pots. This begins the experiment and is considered Week 0. In addition to the fertilizer application(s), pots must be watered until water drips from the bottom of the cup every second day. Pots should not be allowed to sit in water. Place the tray with a trial's test pots in bright light where the temperature will not drop below 60°F.
5. Immediately after the first fertilizer application, count the number of leaves, branches, and flowers or flower buds (should be zero) on each plant. Record these numerical data on a data table that monitors all six plants (three test and three control) in an experimental setup and measure them each week for 8 weeks. Add a row to show the average weekly values for the test plants and the control plants. Add an additional column to the data table to record comments about the general health/vigor of each plant.
6. After 8 weeks, determine the difference in the average number of flowers or flower buds, average number of fruits (tomatoes), number of leaves, and numbers of branches for the test and control plants in your experimental setup since Week 0.
7. Share average differences in data for each experimental setup with other groups testing other fertilizers.
8. For each variable measured (number of flowers/flower buds, number of fruits, number of leaves, and number of branches), plot the average difference data for each setup on a large bar graph. It is the average differences in growth that are being analyzed on this summary graph.

Data Analysis/Conclusion

Does it appear that one fertilizer treatment promoted more flower or flower bud development than any other treatment? If so, which one and how much more flower promotion? What about the other factors measured? Does it appear that one fertilizer treatment promoted more leaf or branch growth or improved the general vigor of the tomato plants versus any other treatment? If so, which one and how much more? Do the data support any hypotheses you may have had about the different fertilizer contents and what their effect might be? Can you make any recommendations about use of each fertilizer for other some common vegetable crops such as lettuce, corn, carrots, or watermelon?

Thinking Like a Biotechnician

1. Why is it important that the pots are not standing in excess water?
2. What do you predict would be the effects of doubling the amount of fertilizer applied?
3. Suggest a method of testing the effect of adding additional amounts of phosphorus and only phosphorus to tomato seedlings.
4. For the fertilizer your group tested, find the ingredient list either in the packaging or online. List the macro- and micronutrients in the fertilizer and their relative percentage of the total fertilizer sample.

Laboratory 11b
Using Hydroponics to Develop Fertilizers

How does a company know the "best" concentration for each ingredient in a fertilizer? Propose an experimental procedure to determine the optimum concentration of one fertilizer ingredient (calcium nitrate) on hydroponically grown tomato plants. Use 12 plants (four groups of three). Keep the budget for plants and chemicals below $100. Be sure to include all recipes for any nutrient solutions, as well as all measurements, units, replications, conditions, etc.

Purpose

What are the effects of adding calcium nitrate solutions of various concentrations on the growth and appearance of tomato or green bean plants?
How might changing calcium nitrate concentrations in fertilizers improve plant growth?

Materials

Lab scoops
Plastic bucket
Plastic beaker, 1 L
Balance, weigh boat, lab scoops
CHEM-GRO Tomato Nutrient
  Mix #4-18-38 (5 lbs) from
  hydro-gardens.com
Calcium nitrate, 4-hydrate

Magnesium sulfate
Aluminum foil
Parafilm®
Silent air pump, air stone,
  tubing
Plant light system or
  greenhouse

Young tomato or green bean
  plants (with two sets of leaves),
  seeds available from from
  www.hydro-gardens.com or
  www.fishersci.com
Funnel, plastic
Tape, labeling
Permanent lab marker pens

General Procedure for Creating an Experimental Plan

- Search for articles on the Internet that suggest how to prepare a chemical solution (which the ingredients available) to grow tomatoes hydroponically.
- Plan an experiment including step-by-step procedures of how to set up and monitor the hydroponics experiment on either tomato or green bean plants.
- Determine what solutions you will need for your proposed experiment and how to prepare them.
- Write up your proposal, including all recipes and protocols for solution preparation and data collection. Include references and sources for purchasing reagents, including the source, amount, and price.
- Submit this to the supervisor for evaluation and approval.
- If your experimental plan is selected as most promising, the class will proceed with the procedures.

Procedure

1. Grow tomato or green bean plants in flats until the second set of true leaves is just visible (4 to 6 weeks), or purchase them from a nursery.
2. Prepare solutions as described in the approved experimental plan.
3. Gently, scoop up each plant and gently plunge it into a bucket of water to wash the soil off the roots.
4. Set up hydroponic tanks to hold a total of three plants each, following the directions below:

Hydroponic Tank Design

a. Use 1-L, clear, plastic tri-pour beakers.
b. Fill each to 800 mL with the appropriate solution.
c. Cover each tightly with Parafilm®, which will supply the major support for the plants. Wrap the outside with aluminum foil. Leave a small opening in the foil, on the side, to observe the solution level.
d. Punch five holes in the Parafilm® (one in the middle and four surrounding it).

e. Into three of the holes, gently place three plants (approximately the same size), supported by nonabsorbent cotton.

f. Into a fourth hole, place the tube from an aquarium pump. Secure it so that it will bubble continuous air into the tank.

g. Into the fifth hole, place a 20-cm length of plastic tubing that connects to a funnel (on the other end, for adding more solution) without disturbing the rest of the tank.

h. Secure everything so that it will not fall over during the experiment (a minimum of 4 weeks). Add more aluminum foil to the outside, as necessary, to block light from the roots.

5. On a data table, record the initial appearance of each plant. Number each plant in each tank so that you can keep track of them. Record the number of leaves/plant and the "average" amount of green color/leaf. In another column, record other observations, such as spotting, leaf curling, or insect damage.

6. Check the solution level in the tanks once a week. Using the funnel apparatus, fill the "tank" back up to 800 mL with the appropriate solution.

7. Once a week, record data on plant health as described in step 5.

8. If substantial differences in the experimental groups are apparent at 4 weeks, stop the experiment. If differences are not apparent, continue the experiment for a total of 8 weeks.

9. At the end of the experiment, remove the plants from their tanks (keep track of which is which by putting a 3-cm tape label around each stem).

10. Allow the plants and roots to dry overnight. Weigh each plant. Record the final plant weight data in a data table.

Thinking Like a Biotechnician

Prepare graphs that best demonstrate the effects of varying the concentration of added calcium nitrate solutions to hydroponically grown tomatoes. Write a formal conclusion with the results of the experiment, presenting evidence and explanations for the results. Discuss possible errors in the experimental design that could lead to misleading results. Propose or make recommendations about adding calcium nitrate to fertilizers to improve plant growth.

Laboratory 11c

Developing an Optimal Extraction of Spoolable DNA from Plant Cells

Background

To study or modify the genetic information of a plant, one must be able to extract and manipulate the plant's cellular (genomic) DNA. The procedure is similar to the extraction of DNA from bacterial or mammalian cells, except that the pectin-impregnated, cellulose-containing cell walls make it significantly more difficult to burst open plant cells. Once plant cells are burst open, the rest of the cell's molecules are separated from the cell's DNA through a series of precipitations and centrifugations.

Many plant DNA extractions begin with a cell-grinding step. Using either a blender or a mortar and pestle, plant cells are burst open by grinding the cells in some kind of extraction solution and/or in the presence of liquid nitrogen. Typical extraction solutions contain deionized water plus a buffer, detergents, and/or enzymes. Detergent is needed to dissolve the membrane of the plant cells and burst the cells open. The detergent also precipitates proteins, removing them from solution. Some protocols use 5% of either Dawn® (Procter and Gamble Co.) dishwashing detergent or 10% sodium dodecyl sulfate (SDS) in volumes of 0.5 to 1 mL per 100 mL. Salt is often used in an extraction solution. NaCl precipitates proteins and covers the DNA molecules' negative charge, which results in better DNA isolation. It is common to use 2 M or 5 M NaCl in volumes of 1 to 5 mL of NaCl per 100 mL of extraction solution.

As the cells dump their contents into the extraction solution, cell debris and unwanted molecules settle to the bottom. Centrifuging can facilitate this separation. The supernatant (top layer) containing the DNA can be poured off. To retrieve long strands of DNA, a glass rod can be used to scoop and spool the DNA out of the extraction solution/alcohol interface (see Figure 11.2). Spooling is rarely used in research and development labs and instead DNA is precipitated out of solution using high-speed (10,000 xg or higher) centrifugation. Given the right conditions, relatively pure DNA can be pelleted and the DNA pellet resuspended in TE buffer for analysis.

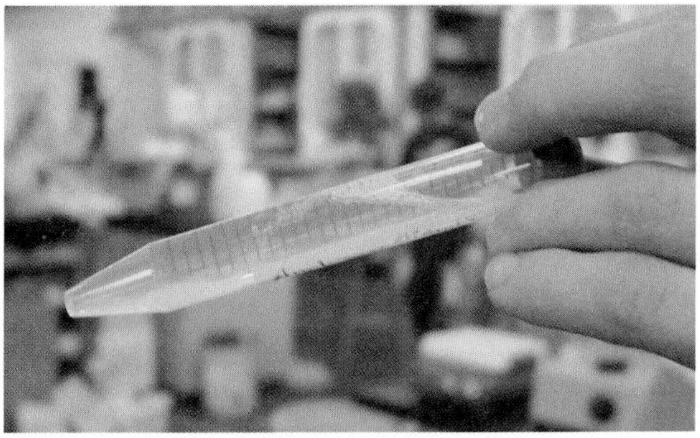

To ascertain the presence, concentration, and purity of DNA, samples are measured in a UV spectrophotometer (Lab 11e). DNA concentration assays may be used to estimate the DNA concentration in a sample such as the G-Biosciences dotMETRIC™ Assay kit by Geno Technology Inc. Running DNA samples on a gel can also give the technician an idea of the amount of gDNA extracted.

Figure 11.2. **DNA strands wrap around each other and may trap air bubbles. This makes it easier to see globs of DNA in solution and to pool them out on a glass rod.**
Photo by author.

Purpose

What are the best procedures for the extraction of measurable amounts of genomic, chromosomal DNA (gDNA) from a target plant sample (eg, spinach)?
Can the yield of DNA extraction be improved with procedural modifications (process development)?

Materials

Note: The materials list is variable depending on the approved protocols used by each group, but may consist of:

Spinach leaves
Balance, weigh boats, lab
  scoops
Pipets and pumps
Mortar and pestle
Liquid nitrogen
Sodium dodecyl sulfate (SDS),
  10%

Liquid dishwashing detergent
Sodium chloride
Protease
RNase
Water bath, 65°C
High-speed microcentrifuge
  (10,000X g or greater)
Ethanol, 95%, ice-cold

TE buffer
Tubes, 15 mL, sterile and racks
Reaction tubes, 1.7 mL and
  rack
Glass rods, 200 mm
Beakers, 50 mL

Safety Precautions

- Gloves and goggles are required when using chemicals.
- Only the instructor should use liquid nitrogen.

Procedure

1. Long strands of spoolable spinach plant DNA will be the target of the extraction process development. If spooling does not retrieve DNA strands then samples will be dehydrated and then rehydrated in buffer to yield DNA samples. Plan to use 5 g of plant tissue for each extraction. Plan to repeat each trial three times, and then average the results.

2. Consider a typical DNA extraction (ie, from *E. coli* cells, from protocols found on the Internet, from Lab 4h in this lab manual, or from discussions in the Background section of this lab manual). Plan how you might conduct a DNA extraction from your plant samples. Write up a proposed set of procedures for your supervisor to review and approve. Limit your group to 1 hour of research time on the Internet, and 1 hour of planning and writing your procedures. Record all bibliographical references.

   Include all of the following in your procedures:

   What ingredients could be in the extraction solution(s) or buffer(s)?
   How many steps are there to the procedure? What are the steps? What equipment should be used?
   What volumes of solutions? At what concentrations? With heat? On ice?
   How will you get rid of contaminants (eg, centrifuging or filtering)?
   How will you spool or separate the DNA out of solution?
   How will you measure your retrieved DNA volume, concentration or purity?

3. Outline the general procedures for the extraction, separation, and spooling or pelleting using Microsoft® Word® on the computer. Record all steps and procedures. Plan to do three replications of the procedure, simultaneously, so that you have results to average. Print copies of these procedures for all members of your group. Save them on the computer for further editing. Title them. Call them the "1ˢᵗ Run_Your Intitials.doc." Submit them to your Supervisor for approval or suggested changes. When approved move to step no. 4.

4. Prepare the extraction solution, and any other solutions or reagents that you plan to use. Label and store them properly.

5. Conduct the extractions and prepare for the DNA spooling. USE ONLY 2 mL of SAMPLE PER SPOOLING or separation. Spool in a 50 mL beaker. If bubbles are visible at the interface between the alcohol layer and the sample, there is probably measurable amounts of DNA whether it is spoolable or not. If spooling does not pull the DNA strands out of solution, place the beaker on a warmed hot plate set at 60°C to dry overnight. The dried sample can be resuspended in TE buffer for analysis.

6. After the spooling, blot the excess ethanol with a lab tissue and scrape the spooled DNA into a sterile, 15-mL, conical centrifuge tube containing 2 mL of TE buffer. For each variation of the process, determine the approximate volume of DNA that was extracted by calculating the amount of displacement of TE buffer by the spooled DNA. Add these data to a data table.

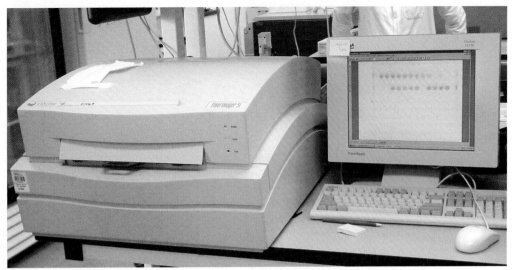

Figure 11.3. A fluorometer is a type of spectrometer that reads the concentration of DNA in 96 wells (seen on monitor) in picogram amounts (considerably smaller amounts than those isolated in this activity). If the protocol tested in this activity is successful, µg amounts should be retrieved and confirmed through UV spectrophotometry.
Photo by author.

7. Store all samples, in clearly labeled tubes, in your own rack at 4°C until the DNA has dissolved into the TE solution (2 to 4 days).
8. Test samples using EtBr Dot testing (Lab 4d), gel electrophoresis (Lab 11e), UV spectrophotometry (Lab 11e), or a G-Biosciences dotMETRIC™ Assay (Lab 11e) (see Figure 11.3).
9. Construct data tables and graphs to report quantitative data for each extraction and spooling.
10. Suggest a variation of your experiment to your supervisor. If approved, repeat steps 3 through 9, but alter just one variable from the first run.

Thinking Like a Biotechnician

Write a formal conclusion of the results of the two versions of your experiment. Present evidence and explanations as to the amount of DNA extracted in your samples versus other groups, as well as data from your first run versus your second run, and the success your group made in extracting genomic spinach DNA. Discuss possible errors in the experimental design that could lead to misleading results. Propose or make recommendations about further DNA extractions.

Laboratory 11d
Using Commercial Kits for DNA Extractions from Cells

Background

Spooling DNA is fun, and often a large amount of long strands of gDNA is recovered. However, for R&D purposes, small volumes of relatively pure DNA is the goal of most extraction protocols. This is because proteins, RNA, and other molecular contaminants may interfere with experimental processes such as DNA sequencing or PCR. Therefore, when scientists want high-quality samples of gDNA or plasmid DNA (pDNA), they may choose to use one of several commercially available DNA extraction kits.

There are several reasons to use commercial DNA extraction kits in addition to their reliability. One is that the buffers used in the extractions are often challenging to prepare. Many are at a very high or very low concentration or require significant amounts of pH adjustment. Sometimes, it is worth the cost to save the technician's buffer prep time.

Another reason to use a kit is that they are relatively cheap. Since they can be used for several extractions, the cost per extraction may be only a few dollars.

Using commercially available kits is especially advantageous when attempting to extract DNA from plant cells. Since plant cells have a large amount of carbohydrates in their cell walls, plant DNA extraction is a bit more challenging than DNA extraction from animal or bacteria cells.

Purpose

How well do two commercial kits extract spinach gDNA as measured by yield and purity of product and cost per extraction?

Materials

Environmental Health and Safety Officer

Spinach leaves
Micropipets and tips
XIT™ Genomic DNA from Plant Tissue, G-Biosciences #786-298
GET™ Genomic Plant DNA, G-Biosciences #BTNM-0090
Balance and weigh boats
Mortar and pestle

Microcentrifuge tubes, 1.5 mL, DNase-free
High speed microcentrifuge (10,000 xg or higher)
Isopropanol, 70%
Ethanol, 90% and 70%
Liquid Nitrogen (recommended) - use appropriate safety apparatus including cryo-gloves

Procedure

1. Get copies of the protocols from each kit for extracting plant DNA. These are downloadable from the www.gbiosciences.com website.
2. Follow the directions to produce three 50 μL samples of gDNA. Use the 1.7-mL tube top to punch the leaf, and use the leaf tissue that results.
3. Pool the three 50 μL samples from each kit, and then determine the amount and purity of DNA in the pooled sample through UV spectrophotometry, indicator assays, or electrophoresis, (Lab 11e). Record all the data in your notebook. Compare the yield of each extraction.
4. Prepare a form (or use your facility's version of a "Purchase Order/Requisition") to order each of the kits above. Include all the necessary information, as if you were ordering it to be delivered to your laboratory/department.
5. Find one other DNA extraction kit online from another manufacturer that would provide approximately the same kind and quantity of DNA as the kits tested above. List the ordering information and explain how this kit differs in reagents, procedures, and products.

Thinking Like a Biotechnician

1. Write a statement that reviews, for your supervisor, the pros and cons of using each kit. Include an assessment of the price, time, equipment, ease of use, and product yield.
2. Suggest a gel electrophoresis method for assessing the type and quality of DNA in each extraction.
3. Explain why using DNA extractions contaminated with proteins could lead to future experimental problems.

Laboratory 11e
Measuring DNA in Samples

Background

DNA is colorless in solution, so its presence in a sample must be determined either indirectly, using an indicator, or with an instrument, such as a spectrophotometer.

A common indicator/stain used to visualize DNA molecules is ethidium bromide (EtBr). In gel electrophoresis, EtBr is usually used to "stain" DNA gels. EtBr intercalates itself between DNA bases, affecting the light-absorbing properties of the molecule. When exposed to UV light, the EtBr-stained DNA molecules show as bands of glowing orange on the gel. As the number of DNA base pairs increase, more EtBr intercalates, so the glowing is brighter.

Companies have developed other indicator systems that quickly quantify small amounts of DNA. One is the G-Biosciences Nucleic dotMETRIC™ Assay (see Figure 11.4). Using a proprietary indicator, this assay measures microgram amounts of DNA in small volume samples.

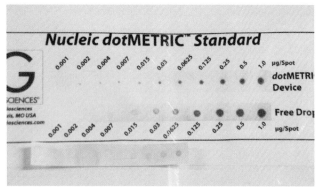

Figure 11.4. **G-Biosciences Nucleic dotMETRIC™ Assay kit.**

A UV spectrophotometer (or a fluorometer) is routinely used to study the concentration and purity of DNA samples in solution. These instruments measure DNA concentration and purity by measuring a sample's absorbance of UV light (the optical density, or OD) at specific wavelengths. Spectrophotometers can detect to microgram per milliliter (μg/mL) units. A fluorometer can measure to nanogram per milliliter (ng/mL) units.

To determine the concentration of a DNA solution, the OD (absorbance) is measured in absorbance units (au) at 260 nm. Since 50 μg/mL of DNA in solution gives an absorbance of 1 au, using the following formula (DNA Concentration Equation) will give an approximate concentration of a sample in μg/mL.

DNA Concentration Equation

$$\frac{50 \ \mu g/mL}{1 \ au} = \frac{X \ \mu g/mL}{OD_{260} \ (au)}$$

For example, a 1-mL sample is placed in a calibrated UV spectrophotometer. The absorbance is read at 260 nm and is determined to be 0.365 au. What is the approximate concentration of DNA in the sample?

$$\frac{50 \ \mu g/mL}{1 \ au} = \frac{X \ \mu g/mL}{0.365 \ au} = 0.365 \times 50 \ \mu g/mL = 18.25 \ \mu g/mL \text{ of DNA in the sample}$$

A simple test can determine DNA purity in a sample. The test determines the ratio of absorbance at 260 nm (the wavelength of DNA absorbance) compared with the absorbance at 280 nm (the wavelength of protein absorbance). This is called an A_{260}/A_{280} reading.

DNA Purity Equation

$$\frac{OD_{260} \ (au)}{OD_{280} \ (au)}$$

If the A_{260}/A_{280} ratio is approximately 1.8, the DNA sample contains a significant amount of DNA and it is considered fairly clean or pure. The closer the 260/280 ratio is to 2.00, the more RNA contamination is suspected. More protein contamination is suspected as the ratio approaches 1.50 or less.

For example, a 1-mL sample is placed in a calibrated UV spectrophotometer. The absorbance is measured at 260 nm and is determined to be 0.365 au. The absorbance is also read at 280 nm and is determined to be 0.203 au. To what degree is the sample contaminated? The A_{260}/A_{280} ratio= 1.798, indicating that there is no significant amount of protein in the DNA sample.

$$\frac{OD_{260} \ (au)}{OD_{280} \ (au)} \ = \ \frac{0.365 \ au}{0.203 \ au} \ = \ 1.798$$

Thus, the sample is relatively pure, with little RNA or protein contamination. Determining an A_{260}/A_{280} value is so common that on some spectrophotometers there is an A_{260}/A_{280} button.

When determining the purity of a sample, the A_{260}/A_{280} reading will not be accurate if the concentration of DNA is too high or too low. A technician must consider this when making inferences about the samples and adjust the concentrations by diluting or concentrating samples, as needed, until absorbance falls between 0.1 to 1.0 au. Likewise, readings will be erroneous if the volume of sample is too small for the spec's cuvette and light path.

Purpose

Using electrophoresis, indicator assays, and spectrophotometry, what is the yield and sample quality of spinach DNA from different extraction methods?

Materials

Environmental Health and Safety Officer

For Procedure Parts I, II, and III

DNA extraction samples from previous lab activities	Micropipets and tips	Pipets, transfer, 3 mL or 1X
Reaction tubes, 1.7 mL and racks	Balance, weigh boats, and lab scoops	Glasses, safety, plastic
Pipets and pumps	Beakers and media bottles, 250 mL	Gloves
		TE buffer

For electrophoresis:

DNA Electrophoresis Buffer concentrate, TAE (40X or 50X) or LB buffer (10X or 20X)	DNA, salmon testes, in TE buffer (100 µg/mL)	Ethidium bromide, 0.5 µg/ mL or LabSafe Nucleic Acid Stain™
Agarose	Lambda/HindIII, DNA standard markers or other DNA sizing standard markers	Gel photo imaging system
Gel box, horizontal, for agarose gels	DNA loading dye, 10X (for TAE gels) or 5X LB Loading Dye (for LB gels)	Weigh boat, 5.5" × 5.5"
Power supply, 300 V		

For G-Biosciences Nucleic dotMETRIC™ Assay

G-Biosciences Nucleic dotMETRIC™ Assay kit	Beakers
Forceps	Reaction tubes, 1.5 mL and rack
	Digital camera

For UV spectrophotometry

UV-VIS spectrophotometer and standard quartz cuvettes	Pasteur pipets, 9"
UV cuvette, 50 µL plastic disposable or a small volume quartz cuvette and adapter	Pasteur pipet bulbs
	Methanol

Safety Precautions

- Gloves and goggles are required when using EtBr or other chemicals.
- Only the instructor should use EtBr.

Procedure

Part I: Electrophoresis

1. Prepare 500 mL of 1X electrophoresis buffer from the concentrate.
2. Prepare a 0.8% agarose gel in electrophoresis buffer with a 6-well comb at one end and a 6-well comb in the middle.
3. Prepare up to eight samples to load into the gel wells from previous DNA extractions. For each sample, mix 20 µL of sample and 2 µL of 10X DNA loading dye (for TAE gels) or 4 µL of 5X LB Loading Dye (for LB gels). Mix thoroughly but gently. Label all tubes.
4. Place 20 µL of (100 µg/mL) of salmon sperm DNA solution (positive control, known) in a 1.7-mL tube and add 2 µL of 10X DNA loading dye (for TAE gels) or 4 µL of 5X LB Loading Dye (for LB gels). Mix thoroughly but gently.
5. Place 20 µL of deionized water (negative control) in a 1.7-mL tube and add 2 µL of 10X DNA loading dye (for TAE gels) or 4 µL of 5X LB Loading Dye (for LB gels). Mix thoroughly but gently.
6. Load 20 µL of each sample into the well. Change tips for each sample.
7. Load the 10 µL of the prepared Lambda/*Hind*III, DNA standard markers into Well 6 and Well 12. Make sure these have been made with the appropriate DNA Loading Dye for the gel you are running.
8. In your notebook, draw a diagram to show which well contains which sample.
9. Run the gel at 110 V (65 mA) for 30 to 40 minutes for a TAE gel or at 300 V (about 100 mA) for about 12 minutes for a LB gel, until the loading dye is about 2/3 of the way down the gel.
10. Transfer the gel to a weigh boat for staining. Add DNA staining solution until the gel is just covered. **Note: Gloves and goggles are required when using DNA stains. If using EtBr stain, the instructor will add the EtBr for you.**
11. Stain for 15 to 20 minutes, and then rinse with deionized water. Place the gel on a transillumination light box. Look for the amount of colorization as compared with the positive and negative controls to ascertain whether or not your sample contains DNA. Photograph the gel for a permanent record.
12. Glue the photo in the middle of a notebook page. Label all the sample wells, standard fragments, and sample bands on the gel photograph.
13. Assign a numerical value to the amount of colorization of your sample compared with the standards. Assume that "5" represents the positive standard and "0" represents the negative standard. Record these values in a data table. Make a rough estimation of the concentration of your extracted samples by comparing them to the 100 µg/mL salmon testes DNA standard sample.

Part II: Indicator Assay

1. Follow the directions in the G-Biosciences Nucleic dotMETRIC™ Assay kit to test 1-µL samples of each extract. Getting reproducible results takes a few practice strips.
2. Determine the approximate mass (µg) of DNA in each 1 µL sample and record the values on a data table.
3. Photograph the indicator test strip key and place it by the test strips in your notebook. These may be taped in.

Part III: Spectrophotometry

Notes

- Some UV spectrophotometers have preprogrammed A_{260}/A_{280} readings. If the spec you are using has this feature, all readings can be taken at one time.
- Determine the minimum volume to get an accurate reading with the cuvettes to be used in your spectrophotometer. Most standard cuvettes must hold at least 500 µL of the sample. Some specs have cuvette adaptors that hold less volume (see Figure 11.5). Some manufacturers offer 50-µL UV quartz or disposable plastic cuvettes.

Figure 11.5. **Spectrophotometer with a 50-μL adaptor and cuvette.**
Photo by author.

Concentration Determinations

1. By pooling replicate samples as necessary, prepare enough volume of each DNA extraction sample to get accurate readings with your spectrophotometer. If possible, avoid diluting the samples. If necessary, perform a dilution (1:2, 1:3, or 1:4) of the sample using TE buffer to ensure enough sample volume. Keep track of the sample's dilution so that the concentration of the undiluted sample can be determined (by multiplication) following the analysis of the diluted samples.

2. Calibrate the UV spectrophotometer at 260 nm by using a TE buffer blank. If using a quartz cuvette, rinse the cuvette with methanol (for cleaning) and deionized water, as directed by the instructor. Then, add 1 mL of TE buffer for blanking.

3. Remove the blank and add enough extraction sample to get an absorbance (OD) reading. If the sample's volume is low, consider using a 50-μL adaptor and cuvette. Read the OD (in au) of each sample and record the values in a data table.

4. Recover each sample and replace it into its tube.

5. Repeat steps 3 and 4 with each extraction sample.

6. Use the DNA Concentration Equation to calculate the concentration of DNA in each sample. Multiply by dilution factor if the sample was diluted. Record the absorbance data, calculations, and your inferences about the data in the data table.

Purity Determinations

Note: On some models of UV spectrophotometers a A_{260}/A_{280} program will give you readings for the OD at 260 nm and 280 nm at the same time, saving the trouble of taking readings for each sample twice.

1. Calibrate the UV spectrophotometer at 280 nm using a TE buffer blank. Rinse the cuvette with deionized water, then add 1 mL of TE buffer to blank the unit.

2. Remove the blank and add enough extraction sample to get an absorbance (OD) reading. If the sample's volume is low, consider using a 50-μL adaptor and cuvette. Read the OD (in au) of each sample and record the values in a data table.

3. Recover each sample and replace it into its tube.

4. Repeat steps 3 and 4 with each extraction sample.

5. Calculate the ratio of ODs (A_{260}/A_{280}) for each sample. Record the purity data, calculations, and your inferences about the data in the data table.

Data Analysis/Conclusion

Evaluate the effectiveness of each extraction method you used in light of the electrophoresis, indicator assay, and spectrophotometer data. Determine which extraction method resulted in the largest amount of the purest DNA. Write a conclusion discussing the extraction method "results with evidence and explanation" (REE), "possible errors" (PE), and "practical applications" (PA) of the experiment.

Thinking Like a Biotechnician

1. If samples float out of gel wells and do not sink when loading, what may be the cause?
2. Why are contaminant proteins not visible on these DNA gels?
3. What happens to the absorbance reading, concentration, and purity calculation if the DNA is too concentrated, for example, at 1 mg/mL? What must be done to solve this problem?
4. If an A_{260}/A_{280} purity reading was calculated to be 2.8, what might be the cause?

Laboratory 11f

Testing Plant and Animal Samples for a Protein of Interest

Developed with the assistance of Tina Doss, Bay Area Biotechnology Education Consortium.

Background

Hydrogen peroxide (H_2O_2) is produced in cells as a byproduct of cellular respiration. Since H_2O_2 is toxic, cells must rid themselves of it rapidly. Within cells there are specific enzymes called peroxidases (hydrogen peroxidase) that are designed to recognize H_2O_2 and break it down into water and oxygen. Hydrogen peroxidase is stored in cells in an organelle called a peroxisome. Hydrogen peroxidase breaks down H_2O_2 to water (H_2O) and oxygen (O_2). The overall equation is as follows:

$$2\ H_2O_2 \xrightarrow{\text{hydrogen peroxidase}} 2H_2O + O_2$$

Purpose

To find animal or plant samples that have hydrogen peroxidase activity.

Materials

Environmental Health and Safety Officer

Scalpel handles, #4	Carrots	Permanent lab marker pens
Scalpel blades, #22 for	Horseradish root	Pipet, 2 mL
#4 handles	Beef liver	Pipet pump, blue
Apples	Chicken thigh meat	Hydrogen peroxide, 3%
Potatoes	Tubes, glass, 13 × 100 mm	Balance and weigh boats
Onions	Peg racks for 13 × 100 mm tubes	Forceps

Procedure

1. Use a numerical scale to represent the amount of reaction when a sample's hydrogen peroxidase acts on hydrogen peroxide. Consider, for example, a scale of 0 to 5, where 5 = enough bubbles to overflow the tube, and 0 = no bubbles.
2. Using Microsoft® Excel®, create a data table to report the amount of bubbling for each of the items being tested. Place the table in your notebook.
3. For each item to be tested, use the same amount of sample (ie, 1 gram or one cm^3) (cut with a knife or scalpel). Place the sample in a 13 × 100 mm centrifuge tube. Set up a negative control tube with 1 mL of dH_2O (1 mL of H_2O = 1 gram).
4. Add 2 mL of 3% H_2O_2 to each 13 × 100 mm tube.
5. Allow the enzymatic reaction to occur for exactly 60 seconds. At 60 seconds, use a permanent marker to draw a line on each tube at the top of the bubbling. Compare the results of each 60-second trial. If there is bubbling, H_2O_2 is being broken down.
6. Test each item three times, and determine the average amount of reaction. Record the data in your data table.

Data Analysis/Conclusion

Discuss the results of testing for peroxidase. Which samples had the greatest amount of peroxidase activity and which had the least? Considering what you know about each item and its use in nature, why do you think some samples had less hydrogen peroxidase activity than others? Discuss at least two reasons why individual results might vary from trial to trial. Propose a better way of assaying peroxidase activity than measuring the amount of bubbling. If you wanted a gene for peroxidase to use to genetically engineer *E. coli*, which sample would be the best source? Give an explanation for your recommendation.

Thinking Like a Biotechnician

1. H_2O and H_2O_2 seem similar in structure and function. Compare and contrast the structure and function of these molecules.
2. Enzymes are protein catalysts that may be used over and over again to speed reactions. They are not used up in the reactions they catalyze. How can you test to see whether the enzymes are used in a reaction?
3. Propose a method of extracting hydrogen peroxidase from liver.

Laboratory 11g
Isolation of HRP from Horseradish Root

Based on labs developed by Theo Leung and Adolfo Vargas, Biotechnology students, with the advice of Paul Bethke, University of California, Berkeley.

Background

Plant proteins are potential biotechnology products. To examine proteins for their commercial or research value, researchers must purify them from their source cells. The protein of interest for this activity is horseradish peroxidase (HRP), an enzyme from horseradish root. In cells, HRP breaks down H_2O_2 into safer water and oxygen molecules. HRP is used in research and industry. The molecular weight of HRP is approximately 43 kilodaltons (kDa), and it may be visualized using PAGE.

Purpose

Can an active form of HRP be isolated from horseradish root and identified on a PAGE gel?

Materials

Environmental Health and Safety Officer

25 mM KH$_2$PO$_4$ (potassium phosphate, monobasic), pH 7.0
Horseradish root
Grater
Balance, weigh boat, lab scoops
Mortar and pestle
Ice
Cheesecloth
15 mL conical tubes and racks
Micropipet, P-100 and tips
Micropipet, P-10 and tips
Plastic beaker, 1 L
Acetone
10-kDa microcentrifuge concentrators (sample reservoir and collection tube)

High-speed microcentrifuge
Sample Prep Loading Dye (SPLD) (see Lab 5f) with beta-mercaptoethanol (BME), 950 µL SPLD + 50 µL BME, prepared in a running chemical fume hood
10-well, 10% Tris-Glycine (TG)/SDS PAGE gel
1X PAGE electrophoresis running buffer (see Lab 5f)
PAGE vertical gel box
Tranfer pipets, 3 mL
PAGE gel loading tips
Power supply, 300 V

Protein standard markers (PAGEmark™ Tri-color protein ladder [G-Bioscience, Inc.])
Locking caps
Dry block heater/heat block, 90°C
Petri dish, 150 × 15 mm
Coomassie Blue stain (see Lab 5f)
Coomassie Blue destain (see Lab 5f)
Photo-imaging system
Lab orbital shaker/rotator
Gloves
Glasses, safety, plastic

Procedure

Part I: Preparation of Horseradish Root Sample

1. Prepare 100 mL of 25 mM KH$_2$PO$_4$ (potassium phosphate, monobasic), pH 7.0 solution, and grate 5 g of horseradish root.
2. Prepare a stock HRP protein sample at approximately 200 mg/mL by mixing 5 g of grated horseradish root with 15 mL of the 25 mM KH$_2$PO$_4$ solution.
3. Homogenize the stock-root protein sample, grinding with a mortar and pestle until the sample appears as a suspension (about 3 minutes).
4. Filter the homogenate through three layers of cheesecloth to remove large cellular debris into one or more 15 mL conical centrifuge tubes, placed on ice.
5. Centrifuge the sample tubes for 5 minutes in a 3000X g centrifuge (or the highest power possible). Make sure the sample tubes have equal volume and the centrifuge is balanced.
6. After centrifuging the tubes, discard the supernatant and save the pellets. The pellets are cell debris that contains a large amount of proteins. Place the tubes containing pellets on ice to chill them for at least 5 minutes.
7. Prechill about 200 mL of acetone in a freezer (-20°C) for at least 30 minutes.

Environmental Health
and Safety Officer

8. Add acetone to the samples that have been on ice (0°C to 4°C) at a concentration of one part extract for every three parts of acetone (a 1:4 ratio). Finger-flick to mix. Invert to mix three times. **Caution: Wear goggles and gloves.**

9. Centrifuge the samples for 15 minutes in a 3000X centrifuge (or the highest power possible). A pellet containing HRP should appear at the bottom of each the tubes.

10. Gently, decant the supernatant into a trash container. The supernatant contains cellular debris.

11. Redissolve the protein-containing pellet in 2 mL of cold 25 mM KH$_2$PO$_4$ solution. The sample is now approximately 10 to 20 times more concentrated than the starting sample. Consider this a 20X stock sample.

Part II: Analyzing Protein Extracts on a PAGE Gel

12. In a 1.7 mL tube, prepare dilutions of the 20X protein samples following the reaction matrix (see Table 11.1).

Table 11.1. **Cell Extract Sample Dilutions**

Tube No., Dilution	Amount of Cell Extract (µL)	Amount of Buffer Diluent (µL)
1:1	20.0	0
1:2	10.0	10.0
1:4	5.0	15.0
1:8	2.5	17.5
1:16	1.25	18.75

13. To prepare samples to load for PAGE, add 20 µL of SPLD/BME to each of the samples. Pipet up and down once to mix. Incubate at room temperature for 40 minutes, then overnight at 4°C.

14. Set up and prepare a 10-well, 10% TRIS-Glycine-SDS PAGE gel for loading. Use 1X PAGE running electrophoresis buffer (see recipe in Lab 5f).

15. Heat all samples for 3 minutes only at 90°C, with locking caps, prior to loading. Load one of each sample (30 µL) into adjacent Wells 3 through 7.

16. Put 10 µL of protein standard markers into Wells 2 and 8.

17. Run the gel following the instructions in the gel packaging, until the loading dye has run into the bottom quadrant of the gel.

18. Stain the gel in PAGE Coomassie Blue stain for 30 minutes to 3 hours depending on the brand used; destain for 1-7 hours or as recommended in the stain packaging.

19. View the gel bands on a white-light box and make a permanent record using a photo-imaging system. Analyze the samples for evidence of horseradish peroxidase at 43 kDa. Label the photo, including sample wells, protein standards, and sample bands.

20. If samples give bands that appear to dilute, use a 10 kDa concentrator to concentrate a sample. Follow the directions with the concentrators. Run several groups' concentrates on a gel.

21. For each of the original samples, conduct a peroxidase activity test following the protocol in the next lab activity.

Data Analysis/Conclusion

Using the PAGE data, describe the variety of peptides found in the samples. What is the likelihood that one or more of the bands is peroxidase? Give evidence. Suggest methods for future peroxidase isolation.

Thinking Like a Biotechnician

1. If large smears of sample appear in some of the lanes, what might be done to improve the resolution of sample in the lanes on the gel?

2. Discuss methods that could be used to determine whether peroxidase is present, and, if so, at what concentration or activity.

3. The samples loaded on the gel are dilutions of the extraction. How can we know the total content of protein in the sample versus the concentration of HRP in the sample?

Laboratory 11h

Colorimetric Assay for Peroxidase Activity
Background

Hydrogen peroxide (H_2O_2) is a product of cellular metabolism. As cells break down food molecules, some of the reactions liberate H_2O_2. Because H_2O_2 is poisonous to the cells, it can kill them if it is not removed or destroyed. Cells produce the enzyme peroxidase to break down H_2O_2 into safer molecules.

Peroxidase splits H_2O_2 into water and oxygen as shown in the following equation:

$$2H_2O_2 \xrightarrow{\text{peroxidase}} 2H_2O + O_2$$

As the peroxidase catalyzes the reaction, oxygen bubbles out of the solution. This is one way that the reaction may be observed and monitored.

Another way to test for peroxidase activity is to use an indicator. The indicator used here to test for peroxidase activity is TMB, which stands for 3,3',5,5'-tetramethylbenzidine. The TMB changes to a blue product with the breakdown of H_2O_2 and the transfer of electrons from H_2O_2 to TMB. This is an oxidation-reduction reaction. If a stop solution containing acid is added, the HRP is denatured, and the reaction stops. In the presence of the acid, TMB turns from blue to yellow. The degree of color change is directly related to the amount of peroxidase activity.

In this activity, the horseradish extracts from the last activity will be tested for peroxidase activity. Of particular interest are extracts that showed suspected bands of peroxidase at approximately 43 kDa on the PAGE gels.

Purpose

Do horseradish root extracts show peroxidase activity?
What is the lowest concentration of horseradish root extract to show activity?

Materials

Horseradish root extracts (from Lab 11g)
25 mM KH_2PO_4 (potassium phosphate, monobasic), pH7

96-well microtiter assay plate
Micropipet, P-100 and tips
TMB solution, diluted 1:2 in deionized water

Micropipet, P-1000 and tips
Hydrochloric acid, 0.5 M

Procedure

1. Prepare samples for the assay by doing a 1:4 serial dilution of the horseradish root extract. Use the potassium phosphate solution as the diluent. Make at least 8 dilutions.
2. Obtain a 96-well, microtiter assay plate. Label the wells to show where the extract samples will be placed. Test at least three replications of each sample following the instructions in steps 3 and 4. Include negative controls containing potassium phosphate solution. Place the microtiter assay plate on a piece of paper towel to absorb any spills.
3. Add 100 µL of the diluted TMB solution to each well. Have the 0.5M HCl ready to use at Step 5.
4. Do this quickly. Add 100 µL of the appropriate horseradish root extract to each well. Mix thoroughly. Test undiluted starting sample first. Then test 1:4, 1:16, and 1:32 dilutions, etc. Let stand for 3 to 5 minutes.
5. Quickly, add 30 µL of 0.5 M HCl (stop solution) to each well and stir with the pipet tip. **Caution: Wear goggles and gloves. Wipe spills immediately.**
6. Look for a color change from blue to yellow (see Figure 11.6). If a digital camera is available, photograph the assay results.
7. Dilute the extracts until there is no evidence of a positive TMB assay. Up to 10 dilutions may be necessary.
8. Design a data table to record all the data, including a rating system for the degree of yellow color visible. Include averaged data.

Environmental Health and Safety Officer

Environmental Health and Safety Officer

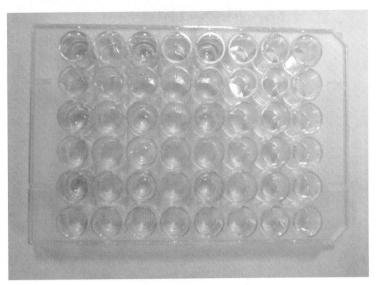

Figure 11.6. **Yellow or yellow-green color indicates that HRP has reacted with TMB.**
Photo by author.

Data Analysis/Conclusion

Compare the results of the unknowns with the negative control. Is there evidence of peroxidase activity in any of the samples? If so, which ones? What is the lowest concentration of extract that shows a positive TMB assay? Explain and give evidence. Discuss the possible errors in this type of experiment. Propose some other applications of this technology and how HRP/TMB might be used.

Thinking Like a Biotechnician

1. If the TMB color change is still occurring even at extremely low concentrations of HRP, what might the technician do to make the assay more usable?
2. The HRP enzyme can be linked (conjugated) to an antibody. How might that allow visualization of molecules of interest?
3. Explain how an antibody conjugated with HRP might be used in an ELISA.

Laboratory 11i
Using an ELISA to Identify Meat Samples

Inspired by a lab activity originally developed by Nancy Lightbody and David Nordstrom, University of Southern Maine, under National Science Foundation Grants #HRD 9628307 and #HRD 9800241. Modified by Dan Segal, Biotechnology student, 2003.

Background

An enzyme-linked immunosorbent assay (ELISA) can be used to recognize and quantify a specific protein in a protein mixture. This is very useful in protein production and purification since technicians must be able to determine the presence and concentration of a protein of interest.

In the meat industry, ELISAs are used to determine if samples are contaminated with other meat products so that a customer can be certain, for example, that ground beef does not contain some less-expensive filler meats, such as pork.

In the ELISA below, a protein from pig blood serum, pig immunoglobulin G (IgG), can be recognized by an anti-pig IgG antibody. Since both IgG (an antigen) and anti-pig IgG (an antibody) are colorless, an enzyme that causes a color change (horseradish peroxidase [HRP]) is bound to the anti-pig IgG. When the anti-pig IgG/HRP binds to IgG in a sample and tetramethylbenzidine (TMB) is added, a blue color change occurs, indicating the antibody-antigen recognition. The more antibody-antigen recognition, the more the color changes. This color change can be measured using a spectrophotometer in an ELISA plate reader.

In the ELISA procedure, a sample thought to contain a protein of interest (pig IgG) is coated onto the bottom of wells in a 96-well ELISA microtiter plate. Protein in the sample that does not stick is washed off with phosphate-buffered saline (PBS). A blocking solution containing milk protein is added to cover any remaining exposed plastic in the wells. Excess blocking solution is washed off with PBS. Anti-pig IgG antibody/HRP is added. It should only bind to pig IgG molecules. In this way, a sample contaminated with pig meat (blue) can be distinguished from the sample free of pig molecules (clear). Adding acid in a final step changes the blue colors to yellow. The more yellow, the higher the concentration of target protein in the sample.

Figure 11.7. **How can one be certain that ground beef does not contain some less-expensive filler meats?**
Photo by author.

Purpose

Do samples of ground beef show evidence of pork contamination?

Materials

Gloves and safety goggles
Balance, weigh boats, scoops
1X PBS:
  $NaH_2PO_4 \cdot H_2O$
  Na_2HPO_4, anhydrous
  Sodium chloride
Nonfat milk powder
Beakers, 250 mL
pH meter, electrode, and
  buffers
Hydrochloric acid, 1 M

Sodium hydroxide, 10%
Tubes, 15 mL sterile, and racks
Permanent lab marker pens
Pipets and pumps
Storage tubes, 5 mL, sterile
Micropipets and tips
Anti-pig IgG/HRP
  (diluted 1:80,000)
TMB solution (diluted 1:2)
Reaction tubes, 1.7 mL
  and rack

Cow (bovine) serum
Pig (porcine) serum
Suspected serum samples
ELISA microtiterplate, 96-well
Hydrochloric acid, 0.5 M
Digital camera
Tween 20, 10% solution

Procedure

Part I: Pre-Lab Preparation of Reagents

1. Prepare 100 mL of 1X PBS wash solution; store at room temperature:

$$1X\ PBS\ Buffer =$$
$$1.9\ \text{m}M\ NaH_2PO_4 \cdot H_2O\ \text{(monohydrate)},\ 8.1\ \text{m}M\ Na_2HPO_4\ \text{(anhydrous)},\ 150\ \text{m}M\ NaCl,\ pH\ 7.3$$

   In your notebook, show the calculations and make a diagram to explain how to make this three-chemical buffer.

2. Prepare 50 mL of blocking solution (50 mL of 5% nonfat milk in 1X PBS solution. Add 500 µL of 10% Tween 20 to the blocking solution. Store at 4°C). In your notebook, show the calculations and make a diagram to explain how to make this solution.

3. Place 3 mL of diluted (1:80,000 dilution) anti-pig IgG antibody conjugated with HRP enzyme in a 5-mL sterile tube. The supervisor will prepare the stock diluted anti-pig IgG solution for all groups (1.25 µL of anti-IgG in 100 mL of 1X PBS).

4. Place 3 mL of 1:2 diluted TMB solution into a 5-mL sterile tube.

5. Place 500 µL of 0.5 M HCl into a 1.7-mL microtube.

6. Place 400 µL of each of the extracts of cow and pig sera (known samples) into separate 1.7-mL microtubes.

7. Place 400 µL of each unknown sample (extract of beef sample suspected to be contaminated with pork) into a separate 1.7-mL microtube.

Part II: Experimental Protocol

8. Obtain a 96-well ELISA microtiter plate.

9. Label five columns of three rows with "C," "P," "-C," "Unk1," and "Unk2." These labels mark where three replications of the cow, pig, negative control, and unknown samples will be placed. Leave an empty column between each test column.

10. Add 125 µL of the appropriate sample to each well. Gently tilt to swirl. Let stand for 5 minutes.

11. Remove **all** of the contents of each well with a micropipet.

12. Add 125 µL of 1X PBS wash solution to each well. Gently swirl to rinse, and remove with a micropipet.

13. Add 250 µL of blocking solution to each well. Gently tilt to swirl. Let stand for 10 minutes.

14. During the blocking waiting period, draw a diagram to show the rows of wells being filled. Label the diagram to show which serum is being added to each well.

15. Remove **all** of the blocking solution from each well.

16. **Rinse 5 times** with 250 µL of blocking solution. Let each rinse sit for 1 minute before removing.
17. Add 125 µL of the diluted HRP-linked pig anti-IgG antibody to each well. Gently tilt to swirl. Let stand for 15 minutes.
18. Remove **all** of the antibody solution. **Rinse 5 times** with 250 µL of 1X PBS. Let each rinse sit for 1 minute before removing.
19. Quickly add 125 µL of diluted TMB solution to each well. Gently tilt to swirl. Look for a color change. Check after 3 minutes for evidence of a change. The HRP oxidizes the TMB molecules (the HRP transfers electrons from hydrogen peroxide to TMB), which causes them to turn blue.
20. After about 10 minutes, before the negative control turns blue, record the degree of blueness in each well (0 = no blue/clear; 5 = medium blue) on a data table. If there are no wells showing blue, check again every 5 minutes until the pig serum samples turn blue; then proceed to step 21.
21. Before the negative control turns blue, add 30 µL of 0.5 *M* HCl to each well. The acid turns the blue TMB to a yellow color and denatures the HRP so that no further reaction occurs. The amount of yellow color, compared with the negative control, is an indication of the amount of protein that the ELISA antibody recognizes. In a data table, record the amount of yellow in each well (0 = no yellow/clear; 5 = "lemon yellow"). Take a digital photo of the plate if possible.
22. In your notebook, record the color results of all the replications of each test in a data table. Present the data in numerical form.

Data Analysis and Conclusion

Study the colors of the known solutions, both positive controls and negative controls. Are they the colors you expected them to be? Why or why not? Compare the results of the known solutions to the unknown(s). Is there evidence of pork contamination in either of the unknowns? Explain and give evidence. Discuss the possible errors in this type of experiment that may result in false positives or false negatives. Propose some other applications of this technology to both the meat industry and the biotechnology industry.

Thinking Like a Biotechnician

1. What is the most likely reason for all of the wells showing color (false-positive results)?
2. Propose a method to decrease the number of false-positive results.
3. How can the data be made more quantitative? Is there an instrument that can quantify the amount of color in each well? Describe how these readings could be taken.
4. In your notebook, draw and label a schematic to show what is attaching to what in the ELISA plate wells during the ELISA and color development.

Laboratory 11j
Using a Western Blot to Identify Actin

Optimized by Matthew Hong, SMBCP student, 2010.

Background

Being able to recognize and source ingredients and contaminants in foods is of significant importance to manufacturers and consumers. The application of several biotechnology assays, including ELISAs and Western blots, makes it possible to recognize the source of several agricultural ingredients used in food and industry, as well as some contaminants in food products.

A Western blot may be used to visualize a specific protein in a sample. Western blots utilize antibodies to recognize specific antigen molecules. Antibodies can be isolated or purchased that recognize the unique amino acid sequence of a molecule and bind to it. Using antibodies that have attached colored markers, enzymes, or other reporter molecules, a technician can visualize a molecule of interest.

A specific protein of interest, actin from chicken muscle, is identified in the Western blot procedure below. Actin is found in all cells with the important function of maintaining cell shape. Actin is also found in high concentrations in muscle cells, where it is involved in cell contraction.

For this blot, a PAGE gel is run with known purified samples of actin and "unknown" samples, thought to contain actin, that are extracted from ground chicken thighs. The gel samples are blotted onto a nitrocellulose membrane using a Western blot transfer unit. The membrane is treated with an anti-actin antibody (1° Ab) that binds only to actin. A secondary (2°) antibody recognizes the constant region of the 1° Ab and binds to it. The 2° antibody has an enzyme (alkaline phosphatase [AP]) attached to it. When nitro blue tetrazolium (NBT) is washed over the blot, the alkaline phosphatase linked to the 2° Ab changes the NBT from yellow to blue. The blue NBT deposits on the actin bands on the blot membrane, making them visible. The degree of blueness is related to the amount of antigen with bound antibody that is present.

Purpose

Is a band on a PAGE gel at 43 kDa the protein actin?

Materials

Note: Several of the buffers used in the procedure will be good for only 2 to 3 days. Prepare fresh buffers for each run of the experiment. *Recipes follow in the Pre-Lab section of the Procedure.

Reaction tubes, 1.7 mL
Micropipets and tips, P-1000, P-100, P-10
Pipets and pumps, 10 mL, 5 mL, 2 mL, 1 mL
6M HCl and 1M HCl for pH adjustment
pH meter and pH paper
1X SDS loading dye buffer/BME*
Actin, MP Biomedical #159848,
Chicken muscle tissue samples suspected to contain actin, extracted as in Lab 5g
Pre-stained protein molecular weight standard markers
PAGE loading tips

10-well, 10% Tris-glycine PAGE gel
PAGE gel box with Western blot module and sponges
10X SDS running buffer, dilute to 1X TBST before using*
1X Transfer buffer*
Nitrocellulose membrane, Protran™
Filter paper
Large petri plates, 150 × 15 mm
Plastic tray, shoebox-size
Orbital shaker/rocker
Graduated cylinders
TBST wash buffer (prepare at 10X TBS-Tween), dilute to 1X TBST before using*

Blocking/Diluent buffer (1% BSA in 1X TBST)*
1° antibody (anti-beta-actin, polyclonal IgG, developed in rabbit), Rockland, 600-401-886
2° antibody (anti-rabbit IgG-alkaline phosphatase, developed in goat), Rockland, 611-1502
Color substrate buffer*
X-phosphate (BCIP)
NBT
Stop solution*
Digital camera

Procedure

Part I: Pre-Lab Buffer and Sample Preparation

Prepare the buffers and samples as directed below. Volumes are for a class of 16 lab groups, each conducting a blot with two gel-membrane transfers per blot module.

1X SDS Loading Dye Buffer/BME (SLDB/BME):
1. To make the 1X SDS loading dye buffer, mix the following in a 50 mL tube:
     2.5 mL 2 M TRIS base, pH 8.9
     0.5 mL 0.2 M EDTA pH 7
     5 mL 20% SDS (The instructor measures the SDS in the flow hood with the fan turned off and the shield down. SDS powder should not be inhaled!)
     10 mL glycerol
     50 mg bromophenol blue powder
     32 mL dH$_2$O
2. Mix gently and thoroughly at room temperature until dissolved.
3. For 10 mL of 1X SDS loading dye buffer/BME, in fume hood, mix 9 mL of 1X SDS loading dye buffer with 1 mL of beta-mercaptoethanol (strong reducing reagent), and mix well. Store at room temperature for several weeks or at 4°C for several months.

Actin Stock Standard
Prepare 1 mL of 1 mg/mL in 1X SDS loading dye buffer/BME. Stored at -20°C in 100 µL aliquots.

10X SDS Running Buffer
1. Measure 30.3 g of TRIS base.
2. Add 144 g of glycine.
3. Suspend the TRIS base and glycine into 700 mL of dH$_2$O.
4. Add 10 g of SDS. (The instructor measures the SDS, in the flow hood with the fan turned off and the shield down. SDS powder should not be inhaled!)
5. Add dH$_2$O to a final volume of 1 L.
6. Dilute to 1X prior to using.

1X Transfer Buffer (10.5 L)
1. Measure 60.9 g of TRIS base.
2. Add 304.5 g of glycine.
3. Fill up to 8.4 L with dH$_2$O.
4. Add 2.1 L of methanol.

TBST Wash Buffer (10X TBS-Tween)
1. Measure 61 g of TRIS base.
2. Add 90 g of NaCl.
3. Fill up to 700 mL with dH$_2$O.
4. Adjust the pH to 7.6 (Have the instructor add 6 M HCl until the pH is close to 7.6, then add 1 M HCl to bring it to exactly pH 7.6).
5. Add 5 mL of 10% Tween 20.
6. Fill up to 1 L with dH$_2$O.
7. Dilute to 1X prior to using.

Blocking/Diluent Buffer (1% BSA in 1X TBST)
1. Measure 20 g of bovine serum albumin.
2. Fill up to 2 L of 1X TBST (wash buffer).

1° Antibody (anti-actin)
Add 160 µL of 1° anti-actin antibody to blocking/diluent buffer up to 480 mL (1:3000 dilution).

2° Antibody (anti-Rabbit IgG-AlkPhos)
Add 192 µL of 1° anti-actin antibody to blocking/diluent buffer up to 480 mL (1:2500 dilution).

Color Substrate Buffer
1. Prepare 250 mL of 100 mM TRIS, pH 9.5 (121.14 g/mol).
2. Add 2.9 g NaCl.
3. Add 5.1 g $MgCl_2$.
4. Add 0.02 g $ZnCl_2$.
5. Add dH_2O to a final volume of 500 mL.

Stop Solution (TE Buffer)
1. Prepare 700 mL of 10 mM TRIS, pH 8.0 (121.14 g/mol).
2. Add 0.29 g EDTA (MW=292.24 g/mol).
3. Add dH_2O to a final volume of 1000 mL.

Part II: Actin Sample Preparation
1. Prepare 100 µL of three known actin samples at the desired concentrations (10 µg/mL, 1 µg/mL, and 0.1 µg/mL) by performing a 1:10 serial dilution of the 1 mg/mL stock actin sample and using the 1X SDS loading dye buffer/BME as the diluent.
2. Prepare chicken muscle tissue samples (suspected to contain actin) following the procedure in Lab 5g. Dilute the extracted chicken muscle sample to prepare three samples that are 1:20, 1:30, and 1:40 of the stock. Prepare 120 µL of each using 1X SDS loading dye buffer/BME as the diluent.
3. Move 30 µL of all samples to be run on the PAGE gel into new 1.7-mL reaction tubes. Five minutes before loading the PAGE gel, place locking caps on each sample tube and heat the samples at 90°C for 5 minutes. Wrist-flick to pool the samples.

Part III: Electrophoresis
1. Set up a 10-well, 10% TRIS-glycine gel, with 1X SDS running buffer in a vertical gel box. Wash the preservative out of each well and pre-run the gel for 5 minutes at 35 mA.
2. Load actin samples and protein standard markers according to the reaction matrix below.
3. Run at 120-135 volts or 35 mA for 1 to 1.5 hours or until the loading dye reaches the bottom of the gel.

Lane	Sample	Load Volume (µL)
1	IX SLDB/BME	25
2	prestained protein standard marker	10
3	actin, 10 µg/mL	25
4	actin, 10 µg/mL	25
5	actin, 0.1 µg/mL	25
6	chicken muscle extract, 1:20	25
7	chicken muscle extract, 1:30	25
8	chicken muscle extract, 1:40	25
9	IX SLDB/BME	25
10	IX SLDB/BME	25

Part IV: Western Blot Transfer
1. Using forceps to hold it, cut a nitrocellulose membrane in a rectangular shape about 8 × 8 cm. Make sure it is smaller than the blot sandwich apparatus, otherwise it will wrinkle during transfer. Make a notch at the top left-hand corner of the membrane. **Never touch the membrane with your fingers.**
2. Near the end of the gel run, prepare two sponge-blotting pads by soaking them in transfer buffer in a shoebox-size plastic tray. Five minutes before the gel is finished, soak the nitrocellulose membrane and two pieces of filter paper in transfer buffer in a large, plastic Petri dish.

Figures 11.8a–d. **Western Blot Sandwich Assembly.**
Photos by author.

3. Assemble the Western blot transfer sandwich (steps a–i) in the large plastic tray, about the size of a shoebox (see Figures 11.8a through 11.8d).
   a. With the sandwich locked closed, place the black side down. Then open the sandwich so the clear or white side is farthest from you. This ensures that the sandwich is oriented correctly and so that it may be locked closed after it is assembled.
   b. Place a sponge on the black side. Then place one of the pieces of filter paper down on top of the sponge. Pour transfer buffer into the tray as needed so that both the sponge and filter paper are covered but not floating.
   c. Loosen the gel from the plastic cassette using a gel knife. Cut off the foot and wells. Rinse the gel box with dH_2O.
   d. Place the gel atop the wet filter paper. Do not let the gel rip or touch the sponge.
   e. Using tweezers, put the wet nitrocellulose membrane on top of the gel such that the notch is on the same side as your standards. Try to get the membrane on the gel positioned correctly the first time; you should not move it once it is placed.
   f. Place the other piece of wet filter paper on top of the membrane. Put another wet blotting sponge on the filter paper.
   g. All the components of the sandwich should be wet with transfer buffer. If not, pour some more transfer buffer atop the sandwich.
   h. Using a 15-mL conical tube, gently roll the tube across the top of the sponge several times to remove any air bubbles.
   i. After removing any bubbles, grab the other side of the transfer sandwich unit and close it on top of the sponge, making sure that the membrane is still immersed in transfer buffer. Make sure nothing "sticks out" of the sandwich. Clamp the transfer sandwich unit closed, then lift it out of the transfer buffer tray and lock it.
4. Place the locked transfer sandwich unit in the transfer box with the black side of the sandwich facing the black side of the transfer box.
5. Transfer the proteins from the gel to the membrane at a constant 65 mA for 1 hour.

Part V: Western Blot Visualization

1. After one hour, remove the transfer module out of the transfer gel box. Open the sandwich and move the blot membrane into a large Petri plate. Cover with 30 mL of blocking/diluent buffer. Rotate at room temperature for 1 hour or, if necessary, store at 4°C overnight.
2. Pour the blocking solution off. Add 30 mL of the 1° anti-actin antibody in blocking/diluent buffer to the membrane. Rotate at room temperature for 1 hour or, if necessary, store at 4°C overnight.
3. Pour off the 1° antibody solution and cover the membrane with wash buffer. Rotate the membrane in 30 mL of wash buffer three times for at least 5 minutes each time. Pour off the wash buffer.
4. Add 30 mL of the 2° goat anti-rabbit antibody in blocking/diluent buffer to the membrane. Rotate at room temperature for 1 hour.
5. Pour off the 2° antibody solution and cover the membrane with wash buffer. Rotate the membrane in 30 mL of wash buffer three times for at least 5 minutes each time. Pour off the wash buffer.
6. Add 52.5 µL of X-phosphate (BCIP) and 52.5 µL of NBT to 15 mL of color substrate buffer in a foil-wrapped 50-mL tube. Invert 3 times to mix.
7. Add the NBT/X-phosphate mixture to the membrane and cover with foil. Check every 2 minutes or so, but be careful not to shake or disturb the membrane.

8. Stop the reaction when the bands on the blot are darkest but before too much background develops. Pour 10 mL of stop solution into the NBT/X-phosphate mixture to stop the membrane staining.

9. Photograph the membrane for a permanent record. Allow the membrane to dry. Glue the dry membrane and/or photograph into your notebook and label it (wells, standards, and actin) without writing on the membrane.

Data Analysis/Conclusion

Did any bands develop on the Western-blot membrane? If so, is there evidence of standard bands, known actin bands, and unknown bands containing actin? Give evidence and explanations for your statements and results. If some of the bands are missing, give several reasons for how that may have happened. If extra, unexpected bands are present, explain how they may have appeared. Recommend several ways to produce a blot that has darker protein bands and a lighter blue background. Explain how and why this type of blot might be used in food production quality control.

Thinking Like a Biotechnician

1. What may be a reason for the unknown samples not showing actin bands, while the known samples show actin bands?

2. Actin is one of the proteins found in high concentration in muscle tissue. Name a few others and the antibodies that would be needed to recognize them in tissue samples on a Western blot.

3. In your notebook, draw a schematic diagram to show what is attaching to what on the membrane during color development.

Laboratory 11k
Transformation of *Arabidopsis thaliana*

Inspired by a lab activity originally found at: The Woodrow Wilson Foundation website at woodrow.org. Developed with the help of Dr. Robert Creelman, Mendel Biological Solutions, Inc.; Bonnie Brayton, Mendel Biological Solutions, Inc.; Dr. Stan Gelvin, Purdue University; Christine Leung and Veronica Chiou, Biotechnology students, 2010.

Recommended for use only if the instructor has the time, interest, and funds to secure samples from a local source and to work on process development.

Figure 11.9. *Arabidopsis* **can be grown indoors under fluorescent lights. Its entire life cycle, from seed to flower and back to seed, takes about 2 months. This is one reason that** *Arabidopsis* **makes a good model organism. These plants are at various stages in their life cycle.**
Photo by author.

Background

Arabidopsis thaliana is a model organism in the plant genetics community. Its entire genome has been sequenced, and much of its growth and development are understood. It is also rather easy to transform *Arabidopsis*, using *Agrobacterium tumefaciens* (*A. tumefaciens*) and the Ti plasmid.

As the plant grows and flower buds appear, tiny ovules develop in the flowers. Scientists have had success dipping into, painting on, or spraying stems and young open flowers with *A. tumefaciens*/Ti plasmid broth culture. The *A. tumefaciens* infiltrates the plant tissue area and transfers Ti plasmid into some of the ovules. Transformed ovules are germinated on selection media into viable transformed plantlets and, when appropriate, transferred to potting soil (see Figure 11.9).

In this activity, *Arabidopsis* plants will be dipped in broth culture containing *Agrobacterium* transformed with a plasmid carrying two selection genes. One of the genes is the GUS gene, which codes for the enzyme for β-glucoronidase (β-gluc). β-gluc catalyzes the cleavage of X-gluc, a carbohydrate, from a white, colorless substrate to a blue product. Cells growing in the presence of X-gluc will turn blue if they are expressing the GUS gene.

The plasmid carries a second selection gene, the NPTII gene. NPTII stands for neomycin phosphotransferase. The NPTII gene produces the enzyme neomycin phosphotransferase, which degrades the antibiotic kanamycin. When kanamycin-sensitive cells (plant or bacteria) are transformed with the NPTII gene, they can survive in the presence of kanamycin, whereas untransformed cells die. Kanamycin resistance and X-gluc conversion give plant biotechnologists an assay to determine if foreign DNA has been taken up by "target" plant cells.

Purpose

Can *Arabidopsis* ovules be transformed with Ti plasmid carrying the neomycin phosphotransferase (NPT II) and beta-glucuronidase (GUS) genes?
To what degree do the genetically engineered plants express their new genes?

Materials

For Procedure Part I: Germinating Arabidopsis thaliana seeds

Arabidopsis thaliana seeds, wild type (Columbia)

1.7-mL reaction tubes and racks
Ethanol, 70%
Microcentrifuge
Micropipets and tips

Bleach, 30%
Dishwashing detergent
Deionized H$_2$O, sterile
0.1% agarose in dH$_2$O
Aluminum foil

Pasteur pipets and bulbs
Autoclave

Two sterile Petri dishes containing sterile seed germination media (80% MS):
- 80% Murashige and Skoogs Basal w/ Gamborg Vitamins (3.54g/L)
- 1% BD Bacto™ Agar (10 g/L)
- 0.3% sucrose (3 g/L)
- Parafilm®
- Grow lights (optimally 25 to 30 cm above the soil)

For Procedure Part II: Growing the *Arabidopsis thaliana* Seedlings

Plastic bucket
Potting soil
Vermiculite
Perlite
Lab scoops

Tri-pour beakers, 1 L
Aluminum foil
Six-cell planting trays
  (15 × 15 cm)
Forceps

Arabidopsis thaliana seedlings, wild type (Columbia), germinated on 80% MS germination plates
Plastic wrap

For Procedure Part III: *Agrobacterium* Inoculation of *Arabidopsis* - Floral Dip Method

LB broth base
Media bottles
Hot plate/stirrer
Autoclave
A. tumefaciens with GUS and NPTII-containing plasmid (pBI121 or other)
Shaking incubator

A. thaliana plants with unopened flower buds
Tubes, 15 mL conical, sterile
Sucrose
Silwett L-77 (available from Lehle Seeds, **biotech.emcp. net/arabidopsisLehle**)

Spectrophotometer and cuvettes
Glass beaker, 1 L, sterile
Plant tray, disinfected
Deionized H$_2$O, sterile

For Procedure Part IV: Testing Floral-Dipped *Agrobacterium* Inoculation of *Arabidopsis* for Transformation

Plastic sandwich bags
A. thaliana seeds with GUS and NPTII genes (positive control), available through **biotech.emcp.net/arabidopsis**
Reaction tubes, 1.7 mL

80% MS plates from Procedure Part I
NaH$_2$PO$_4$•H$_2$O
Na$_2$HPO$_4$, anhydrous
pH meter and buffers
X-gluc

DMSO (only to be used by the instructor)
Tubes, 15 mL conical, sterile
Microtiter plate, 16 well
Incubation oven
70% ethanol
Kanamycin sulfate

Procedure

Part I: *Arabidopsis thaliana* Seed Germination

1. Pour about 30 seeds in a 1.7-mL reaction tube.
2. Add 1 mL of 70% ethanol and agitate the tube for 5 minutes (loosens surface of seeds, removes fungi).
3. Spin seeds for 10 seconds in a microcentrifuge.
4. Remove the alcohol using a micropipet.
5. Add 1 mL of 30% bleach + 10 µL (0.01%) dishwashing detergent. Agitate for 20 minutes (use a rocker) and spin down.
6. Remove the bleach solution using a micropipet.
7. Using 1 mL of sterile water, wash the seeds for 30 seconds, five times. Spin seeds for 10 seconds in a microcentrifuge between washings and remove the water using a micropipet.
8. Add 1 mL of sterile 0.1% agarose to tube.
9. Wrap the tube in foil and stratify (pre-germination treatment) the seeds at 4°C for 2 to 3 days.
10. Use a Pasteur pipet (sterilized with bleach and rinsed with water) to suck up a few seeds at a time and place them on the 80% MS germination plates in 3 rows of five seeds.
11. Close and wrap the germination plates with Parafilm® (poke a few holes every inch or so, along the side for ventilation) and place in under grow lights at 22°C.
12. Monitor the germination for about a week, then transfer them to soil.

Part II: Growing the *Arabidopsis thaliana* Seedlings

1. Into a large plastic bucket, place approximately 2 L of potting soil, 1 L of vermiculite, and 1 L of perlite. Mix the soil with the scoop. This recipe will fill about five planting trays.
2. Transfer the soil mixture into three to four 1-L plastic tri-pour beakers. Cover them with aluminum foil and place them in the autoclave for 15 to 20 minutes at 15 to 20 psi. This soil must be used within a week, or algae will form on the surface and it will need to be resterilized.
3. Obtain clean planting trays. Make sure the trays have drainage holes at the bottom. Label the trays with the date that the seeds were sown, as well as the seeds' variety and your initials. Fill the trays to the top with the sterilized soil.
4. Fill clean planting trays with sterilized soil to the top.
5. Use clean forceps to make a small hole in the soil.
6. Gently remove a seedling from the plate and put it in the hole. Gently even out the soil without covering the seedling. Use a transfer pipet to add water to the tray wells until water drips from the bottom of each.
7. Get a tub reservoir that will fit the planting trays and fill the tub with enough water to cover the draining holes of the plant trays.
8. Place the planting trays in the tub and cover the whole growing chamber with plastic wrap. Secure the plastic in place to give the seeds a "greenhouse" environment.
9. Keep the trays under light. Be sure the soil stays moist!
10. Once the first sprout appears (within a week), open the plastic wrap to prepare the seedlings for being uncovered. Continue to keep the water at the same level. On the next day, remove the plastic completely.
11. Record the number of seedlings that survived the transplantation.
12. Each week, record the number of flowers and the number of flower buds per seedling.

Part III: *Agrobacterium* Inoculation of *Arabidopsis*—Floral Dip Method

1. Twenty-four hours in advance, prepare 200 mL of an LB broth culture of *A. tumefaciens* containing a plasmid with the GUS and NPTII genes. Incubate the culture at 28°C and 250 rpm for 24 hours.
2. Pick three plants that are ready to flower (no pods and mostly unopened flower buds). Use these for the floral dip/transformation. Select three more plants with unopened flowers as negative control plants.
3. Transfer 10 mL of cell culture to a 15-mL sterile, conical tube. At 3000X g for 8 minutes, spin down the *A. tumefaciens* cells into a pellet.

4. Prepare 1 L of filtered 5% sucrose solution.
5. Add 500 µL of Silwett L-77 to the sucrose solution.
6. Re-suspend the *A. tumefaciens* pellet in the sucrose/Silwett solution to a volume of 10 mL. The mixture should be cloudy and, if tested, the absorbance, using the sucrose solution as the blank, should be between 0.8 and 1.5 au.
7. Pour the *A. tumefaciens*/sucrose/Silwett mixture into a sterile 1 L beaker.
8. Tilt each of the three test plants over, and dip each opening flower on each plant into the *A. tumefaciens*/sucrose solution.
9. Placed dipped plants in a tray, laying them on their sides, for 24 hours. Move them to a dark cabinet. Do not expose to extreme light.
10. Stand the treated plants upright.
11. Once upright, place the plants back under the grow light. Water sparingly for two days, then water normally.
12. Re-dip/treat the plants 5 to 7 days after the first dip, and then repeat, if necessary, 5 to 7 days later.
13. Stop watering plants when the seed pods mature. Allow pods to dry, and harvest the seeds.
14. Take the three negative control plants and do steps 8 through 13, but dip them in sterile, deionized water instead of bacteria culture.

Part IV: Testing Floral-Dipped *Agrobacterium* Inoculation of *Arabidopsis* for Transformation

1. Harvested the seeds from dipped plants and untransformed negative control seeds (see Figure 11.10).

   a. After about 1 to 2 months, the *A. thaliana* will have tall stalks with pods of seeds. Once the pods begin to turn brown, cut the stalks near the bottom and place them in open plastic sandwich bags. This will break the pods and release the seeds.

   b. Store the bags in a safe place and keep them open until the stalks turn brown. This will prevent condensation from forming inside the bag. Once the stalks are brown, the bags can be sealed.

Figure 11.10.   **Collecting Arabidopsis seeds.**
Photo by author.

   c. When fully dried, transfer only the seeds to a 1.7-mL reaction tube and store them for later use.

2. Germinate several seeds from each treatment using the procedure in Part I.
3. While the seeds are germinating, prepare 100 mL of 0.2 M $NaH_2PO_4 \cdot H_2O$ solution and 100 mL of 0.2 M Na_2HPO_4 (anhydrous) solution. Combine 39 mL of the 0.2 M $NaH_2PO_4 \cdot H_2O$ solution with 61 mL of the 0.2 M Na_2HPO_4 solution to make 100 mL 200 mM sodium phosphate stock solution. Adjust solution to pH 7.0. Dilute the 200 mM sodium phosphate stock solution to 50 mM.
4. The instructor will dissolve 10 mg of X-gluc in 2 mL of DMSO in a 50-mL conical tube and then add 50 mM sodium phosphate solution up to 20 mL to make GUS staining solution. This is enough for 10 GUS-staining tests.
5. Place seedlings to be tested into separate wells of the 16-well plate. Use one row each for the negative control, positive control, and the test seedlings.
6. Add enough staining solution to cover the tissue completely (about 2 mL per seedling).
7. Incubate the 16-well plate at 37°C for 24 to 48 hours.
8. Remove GUS staining solution from the wells and add 70% ethanol to the wells.

9. Look for blue color (evidence of GUS presence and for β-glucoronidase activity) in the roots and the young leaves of the seedling. Record which plants show GUS activity.
10. To remove more green color so the blue color is more obvious, place the plate on an orbital shaker and do several one-hour ethanol washes of the tissue.
11. With the leftover seeds, germinate them on an 80% MS plate containing 50-µg/mL kanamycin sulfate (see Figure 11.9). Only seeds that are transformed will survive and germinate on kanamycin plates.

Conclusion

Discuss your group's results, as well as your classmates' results, and determine whether there is evidence that you succeeded in inserting new genes (transform) into *Arabidopsis* plants. Suggest methods by which the transformation efficiency could be improved. What is the value of being able to transform a plant, such as *Arabidopsis*? List and explain at least two reasons for developing a protocol such as this one.

12 Obtaining Molecules of Pharmaceutical Interest

Kevin Johnson is a Reagent Manufacturing Technician 4 at Illumina, Inc. Illumina is a leader in Next-Generation Sequencing (NGS) technology, which has significantly decreased the amount of time and money needed to sequence DNA and RNA for genomic applications. Illumina sequencing systems can determine sequences of up to 1 terabase in a single run making it possible to sequence the entire human genome for about $1000.

At Illumina, Kevin is responsible for manufacturing RNA and DNA reagent kits, and formulation and filling of reagent bulks needed in a high volume manufacturing setting. Prior to Illumina, Kevin was a Senior Manufacturing Technician at Affymetrix, Inc., where he worked on high-throughput filling systems that dispense reagents to create and read microarrays. Microarrays are used to study gene expression and genetic diversity. Gene targets for pharmaceutical research are often found using microarrays. Learn more about Affymetrix's GeneChip® arrays at biotech.emcp.net/affymetrix.
Photo by author.

The varied assortment of diseases and disease mechanisms requires that scientists look for preventions and therapies from a variety of sources. Many pharmaceuticals and other therapies have come from native sources such as plants, animals, fungi, algae, and bacteria. Scientists have learned how to isolate and test specific naturally occurring organic compounds for their potential medicinal value.

Another source of drug candidates is compounds made by other organisms in a laboratory situation. Molecular biologists have learned how to trick certain organisms into producing compounds that other organisms normally create. Over the past three decades, many new compounds have been produced in commercial quantities using recombinant DNA and genetic engineering techniques.

Recently, though, biochemists have applied long-standing organic chemistry practices to create many new small organic compounds that may be screened for pharmaceutical activity. These new drug candidates are synthesized by taking small molecules and attaching to them a few atoms or a new functional group. With the use of computers and robots, scientists can design and test thousands of new organic compounds created through combinatorial chemistry.

In the Chapter 12 lab activities you will learn one or more methods to:
• prepare and test plant extracts for antimicrobial action
• assay compounds of pharmaceutical interest
• synthesize new compounds through combinatorial chemistry
• screen new compounds using chemical tests
• screen samples for purity using melting point determinations
• purify an antibody of medicinal interest from a solution

Many of the organic chemistry techniques that you will learn are used in companies whose strategies are to create, purify, and test new compounds for their medical applications.

Laboratory 12a
Testing Plant Substances as Potential Medicines

Improved with suggestions by Mark Okuda, Bay Area Biotechnology Education Consortium.

Background

In nature, organisms are constantly battling for resources and survival. Plants compete with other plants for light and water. Fast growth, big leaves, and large root systems are advantageous characteristics in a crowded jungle. Many organisms have defense systems to combat the onslaught of foreign invaders. Some plants, such as rhododendrons, actually produce chemicals that drip from their leaves into the soil, killing competing plants around them.

All organisms are infected by viruses or threatened by bacterial disease. Numerous plants, fungi, and bacteria produce antimicrobial agents to battle microorganisms (microbes). Finding and isolating an antimicrobial molecule could lead to a potential therapeutic medicine and is not a trivial task. One might have to travel to distant places, such as the Brazilian rain forest, to collect samples. Once samples are collected, extraction techniques must be determined and samples processed. Then, samples can be tested for their ability to kill different microbes. When pharmaceutical researchers identify a potential antimicrobial agent, they must prove that it does not cause toxic effects in humans.

To test plant extracts for antimicrobial properties, technicians add extract-soaked filter paper disks to bacteria cultures spread on Petri plates. Plant extracts containing compounds effective against bacteria leave clear halos (from bacterial death or inhibited bacterial growth) around the soaked disks in the bacteria lawns. The extracts demonstrating these clear areas on Petri dishes are then further purified and screened for the specific ingredients causing the bacterial death. Isolated plant compounds that contain some antimicrobial activity may be used as antiseptics, astringents, or antibiotics.

Purpose

What plant materials, found locally, contain active ingredients that will inhibit the growth of bacteria?

Materials

Environmental Health and Safety Officer

Balance, weigh boat, lab scoops
Beakers, 100 mL, 250 mL
LB broth base
Hot plate/stirrer
Magnetic stir bar
Hot hands protector
Media bottles, 250 mL
Sterilizer/autoclave
LB agar base
Laminar flow hood and disinfectant
Glasses, safety, plastic
Bunsen burner and gas lighter
Inoculating loop, Ni/Cr wire or sterile plastic
Petri dishes, 100 × 15 mm, sterile
E. coli DH5alpha, available from G-Biosciences, #BTNM-0093 (stock plate)
Incubator, 37°C, shaking
Plant specimens, 3

Mortar and pestle
Pipet, 10 mL and pump
Plastic funnels, short-stemmed
Filter paper, 12 cm, medium-fast flow
Beakers, 100 mL
Syringes, 10 mL and sterile filter discs, 0.2 µm
Reaction tubes and rack, 1.7 mL
Filter paper disks, sterile (prepared using paper hole punch)
Methanol, absolute
Pipet, 1 mL and pump
Dry block heater/heat block
Forceps, fine-tipped, sterile
Deionized water, sterile
Ampicillin, 100 µg/mL, sterile
Cell spreader, glass or plastic, sterile
Gauze pads, sterile
Incubator oven, 37°C

Note: Methanol is highly flammable. Keep all containers of methanol away from flame. Methanol should be used with protective eye wear and behind a chemical fume hood. Use the smallest volumes of methanol possible for any given procedure.

Procedure

Part I: Pre-Lab Preparation

1. Two days prior to use, prepare 70 mL of LB broth and sterilize it in a 250-mL media bottle. The sterile broth will be used for the *E. coli* broth culture in Part I, step 4.
2. Two days prior to use, prepare 130 mL of LB agar and sterilize it in a 250-mL media bottle. Sterile LB agar plates will be used for the antimicrobial assay in Part III, step 1.
3. Pour six sterile LB agar Petri plates. Do this by liquefying the sterile LB agar in the microwave at 50% power. Using sterile technique, pour approximately 20 mL of sterile, liquid LB agar into each Petri plate. Close each plate. Let the agar solidify for 15 minutes. Let the plates sit in the laminar flow hood to "dry" for 24 hours.
4. Twenty-four hours prior to use, prepare an *E. coli* broth culture. Using sterile technique, add a colony of *E. coli* from the stock plate or tube culture to the sterile broth prepared in step 1. Incubate the broth culture, shaking at 250 rpm, at 37°C for 24 hours.

Part II: Preparing Plant Extracts

*Caution:
- Take care not to work with poisonous plants. Make sure plants are identified and known to be safe. Wear goggles and gloves when handling plant material.
- Alcohol-flame sterilization of instruments is used in this activity. Instructors should demonstrate how to safely alcohol-flame sterilize and use instruments.
- Prepare extracts 24 hours prior to use in Part III.

1. Using a mortar and pestle, grind up 2 g of plant tissue (leaves or bark) with 10 mL of deionized water. Let it sit for 3 minutes. Filter the sample through a 12-cm filter paper funnel. Filter-sterilize the filtered sample extract using a syringe filter, as demonstrated by the instructor. Collect 1 mL of extract into several 1.7-mL microtubes. Label the samples.
2. Repeat Part II, step 1, but replace the water with methanol as the extracting solvent. After the methanol extraction, place the 1.7-mL tubes with the 1 mL of methanol extract in a 65°C heat block (caps open) for 24 hours or more, if necessary, to evaporate the methanol. Reconstitute dry matter in the tube with 1 mL of deionized water.
3. For each of two other samples, repeat Part II, steps 1 and 2. There should be three different sets of sample tubes.
4. Using sterile forceps (that have been flamed in alcohol), drop three filter paper disks into a tube for each plant extract sample. If you need more extract to cover the disks, use extract from one of the duplicate tubes.
5. Prepare control disks, three each, of only methanol (+C) and only sterile distilled water (–C).
6. Prepare six positive control disks of 100-µg/mL ampicillin solution.
7. Allow the disks sufficient time to soak up enough extract to be saturated (overnight).
8. Close the tubes. Store all samples at 4°C until ready to use.

Part III: Setting Up Antimicrobial Plant Extract Assay

1. Do the following to each of the six Petri plates: Draw a "+" on each plate bottom to divide the plate into quadrants (four sections). Label the quadrants No. 1 through 4. Also, label the dish with your initials and the date.
2. Resuspend the cells of the bottom of the E. coli broth culture. Using sterile technique and a sterile pipet, transfer 1 mL of the E. coli broth (made in Part I) to the middle of each Petri dish. Sterilize a glass spreader (using alcohol and a flame) or use a sterile plastic spreader, and evenly spread the bacterial culture around the Petri plate. Quickly cover, and allow the culture to soak into the agar for at least 15 minutes.

3. Using sterile forceps, carefully place one sample extract disk into the middle of one of the quadrants, about 2 cm from the outer edge of the Petri dish (see Figure 12.1). Place one of the other sample disks into one of the other quadrants. Place a positive control disk with ampicillin in another quadrant of each plate. Place a control disk (either water only and/or methanol only) directly in the center of the plate or in a quadrant. Blot any excess liquid on a sterile gauze pad before placing each disk on the Petri dish. Keep all the methanol-extracted samples on the same dish and all the water-extracted samples on the same dish.

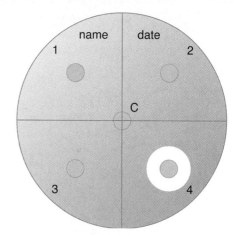

Figure 12.1. **Antimicrobial Screening.** With no antimicrobial agent, the *E. coli* bacteria grow in a lawn over the agar. Antimicrobial agents will diffuse out of disks, and kill or inhibit bacterial growth. A halo of no bacteria (No. 4) indicates that something is inhibiting the bacteria growth.

4. Repeat step 3 five more times so that you have three replicates of the methanol extraction and three replicates of the deionized water extractions for a total of six plates.
5. Make sure you have recorded exactly which plant extracts went with which solvent in each quadrant. Give everything a few minutes to "soak in."
6. Make sure that the disks are adhering well to the surface of the agar. For incubation, invert the plates and incubate at 37°C for 24 to 48 hours, until a bacterial lawn is seen covering most of each plate.
7. After incubation, examine the plates with the plant extract disks for zones of inhibition. This is a clear area formed around the disk by the inhibitory action of a substance(s) in the plant material (see Figure 12.1). Photograph or draw the plates, labeling any inhibition of bacterial growth.
8. Create a data table to collect and present data of all the replicates as well as the averages. Include descriptions of the bacterial lawn around each disk. Measure and record the diameter and clarity of any cleared areas around the disks. Give quantitative measurements of your observations.

Data Analysis/Conclusion

Evaluate the performance of each extract as a source of potential antimicrobial medicine. Did any show significant antimicrobial activity? Give evidence. Discuss possible errors in the experiment's design that could give false data. Discuss possible further experimentation. Make recommendations as to which extracts should be the focus of additional investigation as antimicrobial agents.

Thinking Like a Biotechnician

1. If an extract gives a negative result in the antimicrobial assay, does that mean that the extract is not an antimicrobial agent?
2. In preparing the sample disks, some of the methanol extractions smell like alcohol. Why is that a problem?
3. Each extract may have one or more compounds in it. What should be done to begin to identify the exact compound in an extract that is causing the antimicrobial action?

Laboratory 12b

Using the Spectrophotometer to Determine Caffeine Concentration

Modified by Josh Louie and Brian Quan, Biotechnology students, 2010.

Background

When you think of the compound caffeine, you probably think of coffee (see Figure 12.2). Coffee beans and the leaves of tea plants contain relatively high concentrations of caffeine. In the body, caffeine acts as a stimulant. Since caffeine affects physiological processes in the body, it is classified as a drug.

Due to its stimulant effect on cells and tissues, caffeine is an active ingredient in several over-the-counter and prescription medicine. In particular, many cold medications and some medications for migraine headaches contain caffeine. Caffeine speeds the body's uptake of other compounds in these medications and makes the medicine work faster.

Like all compounds in a medicine, the amount or concentration is important. Too much of a compound is costly and may be dangerous or deadly. Too little and the medication may be ineffective or could be dangerous as well.

Fortunately, caffeine has a distinct interaction with light, which a spectrophotometer can measure. Caffeine is a colorless molecule that produces a colorless solution. Caffeine molecules do not absorb light in the visible spectrum, but, instead, they absorb certain wavelengths of ultraviolet (UV) light. Therefore, a UV spectrophotometer (UV spec) may be used to study caffeine molecules in solution. The use of a UV spectrophotometer is introduced in the Chapter 7 labs.

An absorbance spectrum for caffeine may be determined by measuring the absorbance of a sample at wavelengths between 170 and 300 nm. Once a technician has determined the UV wavelength that gives the highest absorbance for caffeine (lambda$_{max}$), that wavelength is used to detect caffeine molecules in other solutions. A high absorbance value at caffeine's lambda$_{max}$ (ie, greater than 1.1 au) indicates a relatively high caffeine concentration.

Figure 12.2. Coffee beans are the seeds from coffee plants. They are picked, cleaned, dried, and then roasted. Even though roasted coffee beans are brown, caffeine is colorless and requires a UV spectrophotometer for quantitation.
© Jeremy Horner/Corbis.

Purpose

What is the absorbance spectrum for caffeine in solution?
What is the concentration of caffeine in different clear solutions?

Materials

Environmental Health and Safety Officer

Caffeine	Tubes, 15 mL, sterile and racks	Suspected caffeinated solutions
Caution: Do not ingest caffeine or any other laboratory chemical.	Pipets and pumps	
	UV/VIS spectrophotometer	
	UV spectrophotometer cuvettes	
Balance, weigh boats, lab scoops	Pasteur pipets, 9"	
	Pasteur pipet bulbs	

Procedure

Part I: Determining the Absorbance Spectrum for Caffeine

1. Prepare 10 mL of a 0.1 mg/mL stock caffeine solution (100 µg/mL caffeine in deionized water) in a 15-mL tube.
2. Dilute the stock solution in a 1:10 ratio. Make 5 mL of this dilution. Label it 0.01 mg/mL (10 µg/mL).
3. Dilute the stock solution in a 1:20 ratio. Make 5 mL of this dilution. Label it 0.005 mg/mL (5 µg/mL).
4. Measure the absorbance of each solution at different wavelengths, beginning at 190 nm. Prepare an appropriate blank for this application. Continue to make absorbance readings every 10 nm until you reach 320 nm. Record the data in a data table.
5. Which solution produces an absorbance spectrum with a well-defined lambda$_{max}$? Plot the data (the absorbance of each concentration of caffeine) as a three-line, line graph. Determine lambda$_{max}$ for the caffeine molecule. In the future, caffeine in solution will be studied at this wavelength.

Part II: Standard Curve for Caffeine Concentration of Unknown Solutions

1. Decide which dilution clearly showed lambda$_{max}$.
2. Make a serial dilution (such as five tubes in a 1:4 series) of caffeine in water using the dilution from step 1 (the new stock solution) as the starting solution. Record the concentrations of the new stock solution and the four dilutions in a data table.
3. Read the absorbance of the caffeine solutions from step 2 at lambda$_{max}$ (determined in Part I, step 5). Make a new data table to record the absorbance of these five standard, known caffeine solutions.
4. Plot the absorbance of the different concentrations of caffeine solutions on a line graph. Add a best-fit straight line to these data. (In Microsoft® Excel®, use "Add a trendline" and then select "Linear.")
5. From this graph, you will be able to estimate the concentration of caffeine in different beverages, either by drawing in each unknown's absorbance or by using the following equation:

$$y = mx + b$$

where y = the absorbance of the unknown sample
       m = the slope of the best-fit straight line
       x = the concentration of the unknown sample
       b = the y-intercept

Part III: Reading the Absorbance of Beverage Samples

1. Decide which solutions (unknowns) will be assayed. Select colorless samples, such as 5-Hour Energy® by Living Essentials, LLC, Mountain Dew® by PepsiCo, Inc., or a Vivarin® (GlaxoSmithKline, plc) tablet dissolved in 10 mL of dH$_2$O. If a solution is carbonated, it must be left out overnight to "go flat."
2. Make absorbance readings for each unknown sample. Determine an appropriate blank for each application. For each unknown to be tested, make dilutions in water until the absorbance reading measures between 0.5-1.0 au. In a new data table, record the dilution and absorbance readings that meet the absorbance criteria for each unknown.

Data Analysis

Using the best-fit straight line that shows the relationship between the absorbance and concentration of known caffeine solutions, estimate the concentration of caffeine in the unknowns. Multiply the concentration determined on the standard curve by any dilution factor to attain the concentration of the original undiluted unknown. Add these data to the data table.

Conclusion

In a short conclusion statement, report your estimation of each unknown's caffeine concentration. Compare your values with those of others in the class. Discuss the range and cause of variations in class results. Discuss the application of the UV spec in estimating the concentration of other molecules. How and when can this technique be used?

Thinking Like a Biotechnician

1. Why is it necessary for the carbonated drinks to "go flat" before taking readings?
2. Should the standard curve go through the "zero, zero" point? Why or why not?
3. Besides UV spectrophotometry, suggest some methods by which caffeine content in a sample might be determined.

Laboratory 12c

Synthesis of Aspirin, A Plant-Derived Pharmaceutical

This lab was developed with the assistance of Stephen Schram, San Mateo, California, 2003.

Background

In the late 1800s, salicylic acid, a compound that acted as a pain reliever, was extracted from willow plants. After initial use, however, the compound was found to irritate the stomach to such a degree that people could not take it.

Figure 12.3. Aspirin was one of the first synthetically produced medicines.

Photo courtesy of Bayer Historical Department/Archives, Leverkusen, Germany.

A German scientist, Felix Hoffman, first synthesized acetylsalicylic acid, a compound that was less irritating to stomach cells, by transferring an acetyl group ($-COCH_3$) to the salicylic acid molecule. Acetylsalicylic acid is the main ingredient in commercial aspirin (see Figure 12.3). This was one of the first examples of an organic synthesis of a pharmaceutical.

The synthesis reaction is simple: salicylic acid from willow trees (or another source) is combined with an organic compound, acetic anhydride (see Figure 12.4). To this day, aspirin is commercially produced in much the same way. Aspirin tablets contain acetylsalicylic acid, plus a few other ingredients to buffer the acidic aspirin.

$C_7H_6O_3$	$C_4H_6O_3$	$C_9H_8O_4$	$C_2H_4O_2$
salicylic acid	acetic anhydride	acetylsalicylic acid **aspirin**	acetic acid

Figure 12.4. Equation for Making Aspirin. The transfer of an acetyl group to salicylic acid produces the compound acetyl salicylic acid, which is less harsh to stomach cells. Do you see where the acetyl group has been added?

Purpose

Can acetylsalicylic acid (aspirin) be synthesized from its precursor, salicylic acid, in a reaction with acetic anhydride?

Materials

*These items are hazardous and should only be used in an operating chemical fume hood.

Environmental Health and Safety Officer

Balance, weigh boats/paper, scoops
Salicylic acid
Test tube, Pyrex®, 25 × 200 cm
Gloves, large
Glasses, safety, plastic
Hood, chemical fume
Acetic anhydride*
Pipets, 1 mL and 5 mL, Pyrex®
Pipet pumps, green and blue
Sulfuric acid, concentrated*
Pasteur pipets, 9" and bulbs
Graduated cylinders, 100 mL

Beakers, 250 mL
Hot plate stirrer (or a Bunsen burner)
Bunsen burner and lab gas lighter
Ring stand and Biuret clamp
Glass rods
Test tube holder (Stoddard)
Filter paper, 12.5 cm
Funnels, Pyrex® for 12.5 cm filter paper
Erlenmeyer flask, 125 mL
Pipets, 10 mL

Ethanol, 95%
Rubber stopper, #5, (25 × 200 cm tubes)
Watch glass, Pyrex®, 4" diameter
Tubes, 15 mL, sterile and racks
Tubes, glass, 13 × 100 mm and racks
Plug caps for 13 × 100 mm tubes
Pipets, 2 mL, and pumps
Ferric nitrate, nonahydrate, 1%

Procedure

Part I (Day 1): Synthesis of Acetylsalicylic Acid

Environmental Health and Safety Officer

- **Several of the compounds used in this activity are considered hazardous. Use the Safety Data Sheets (SDS) that are shipped with each product or available on-line to learn about the dangers of each reagent, how to protect users from exposure, and what to do if a user is exposed to a reagent.**
- **Do this procedure in a chemical fume hood. Do not inhale acid vapors.**
- **Wear goggles and gloves.**
- **The Instructor will add the sulfuric acid.**

1. Weigh 1 g of salicylic acid on a piece of weighing paper.
2. Put the salicylic acid into a large test tube.
3. Put on safety glasses and gloves.
4. In a chemical fume hood with the fan running, use a 5-mL glass pipet and pipet pump to measure 3 mL of acetic anhydride.
5. Add the acetic anhydride to the test tube containing the salicylic acid.
6. Gently, swirl the test tube to mix.
7. Before beginning this step, note the following safety precautions:
   Under the chemical fume hood with the fan running, use a glass 1-mL pipet to add 0.1 mL of concentrated sulfuric acid to the test tube. Swirl gently to mix.
8. Prepare a water bath by adding 60 mL of water to a 250-mL beaker. Using a Bunsen burner or, preferably, a hot plate, heat the water to boiling.
9. When the water bath is hot, clamp the reaction tube to the ring stand and place the tube in the boiling water. If you are doing this on a ring stand over a Bunsen burner, clamp the reaction tube to the ring stand.
10. Boil the mixture for 5-10 minutes, until the solution is clear. Stir the reaction mixture to make sure that the salicylic acid has dissolved.
11. With the clamp still holding the tube, cool the test tube under running water until it is cool enough to touch. Then, add 6 mL of ice water to the test tube. Hold the tube in a beaker of ice and water until a white crystals form (at least 20 minutes) in the tube. This is crude aspirin.
12. Fold a piece of filter paper into a cone. Put the filter paper in the glass funnel. Place a flask under the funnel. Pour the aspirin mixture into the filter paper lined funnel. Rinse the test tube with 5 mL of water. Pour the rinse water through the aspirin in the funnel. Rinse the aspirin twice with 5 mL of water. The liquid that has come through the filter is known as filtrate, and it can be discarded. Leave the filter paper funnel with crude aspirin in it to dry overnight.

Part II (Day 2): Removing Impurities

1. Scrape the crude aspirin from the filter paper into a clean large test tube. Add 7 mL of ethanol.
2. Place the tube in a 250-mL beaker about half filled with water. Place the beaker on a hot plate. Heat the water in the beaker to about 60°C until the aspirin dissolves. You may preheat the water in the beaker before putting in the tube of aspirin.
3. Add 15 mL of warm distilled water to the mixture in the test tube. If a solid forms, continue warming the beaker until it is completely dissolved.
4. Let the tube slowly cool to room temperature. If no crystals appear, gently scratch the inside of the tube with a glass rod.
5. Put a stopper in the test tube. Label the tube with your name. Let it stand at least 1 day in a cool place. Crystals of aspirin should begin to form in a few hours. If no crystals have formed after 24 hours, jar the test tube by flicking it with your finger.
6. Place the crystals in a filter or on filter paper, and wash them with 10 mL of cool distilled water. Set the filter paper and crystals on a watch glass to dry overnight. It may take 2 days. Store dry crystals in a 15-mL tube or some other container.
7. Determine the mass of the aspirin recovered/synthesized in the class. Determine the yield recovery based on the mass of the starting reagents. Record these values in your notebook.

8. Draw a picture of the aspirin crystals. Compare the crystals of chemically synthesized aspirin with those of commercially produced aspirin. Use a magnifying hand lens, if available. Conduct a ferric nitrate test on each product.

Test for salicylates by conducting a ferric nitrate test on the each of the prepared samples, following the procedure below. Compare these to positive controls (salicylic acid, acetylsalicylic acid) and negative controls (sodium chloride). Create a numerical system for ranking the color change compared with the positive and negative controls. Record all test results and descriptions in a data table.

Iron Testing for Salicylates

Mix 10 large crystals of the sample in 2 mL of dH_2O.
Add 250 μL of 1% ferric nitrate solution to the sample.
Observe the color, and compare to negative and positive controls.

9. Review a SDS for salicylic acid from either a chemical supply house or an Internet site. Study the information provided on the SDS. Find the melting point of pure salicylic acid.
10. Determine the melting point, compared with commercially produced aspirin (in the SDS), following the procedures in Lab 12d. Record melting-point determinations on the previous data table.

- Explain any discrepancies between the reported melting point and the observed melting point. Of what value are these data?
- Compare other characteristics described on the SDS, such as color and texture.

Conclusion

Discuss your success (yield and purity) at synthesizing aspirin (acetylsalicylic acid) from its precursor, salicylic acid. What mass of product was obtained? How does that compare to other groups? Discuss the results of the ferric nitrate test and what they might mean. Of what value are these data? Describe factors that could affect the success of the synthesis.

Thinking Like a Biotechnician

1. How is the salicylic acid/acetic anhydride reaction an example of combinatorial chemistry?
2. Give reasons for recrystallizing the aspirin. What is being removed with each wash? How does this affect the end product? How can you test your answer?
3. If it tested very pure, would it be safe to use your synthesized acetylsalicylic acid for medical purposes? Why or why not?

Laboratory 12d
Melting Point Determinations as a Quality Control Test of Purity

Background

The temperature at which a solid becomes a liquid is called the "melting-point temperature." Compounds have a particular, characteristic melting-point temperature that can be used to identify the compound and determine its purity. The closer a sample melts to the expected melting point, the more likely it is that the sample is pure.

Melting-point information can be obtained from several resources, including the Merck Index (Merck Publishing, Merck and Co., Inc.) and the SDS. In a quality control environment, there are instruments that will conduct a melting-point determination (see Figure 12.5). In our labs, it is easy to conduct a melting point determination using a capillary tube/melting-point apparatus (see Figure 12.6).

Purpose

How pure is chemically synthesized aspirin compared with commercially produced aspirin?

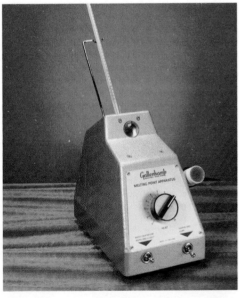

Figure 12.5. This instrument may be used to determine the melting point of a substance. A small amount of the sample to be tested is placed inside a tube. The tube is placed in the top of the apparatus and slowly heated while it is observed through the magnifying lens at the center right. When the solid-to-liquid transition is complete, the temperature is read from the mercury thermometer (yellow).
© Science Photo Library/Photo Researchers.

Figure 12.6. In this low-cost version of a melting point apparatus, a small number of crystals to be tested are added to a tiny capillary tube (closed at one end) suspended in oil. The oil is heated above 100°C. The technician, standing behind a fume hood shield, wearing safety goggles, can observe the temperature at which the crystals melt.
Photo by author.

Materials

Environmental Health and Safety Officer

Hood, chemical fume with protectie shield
Gloves, large
Glasses, safety, plastic
Bunsen burner and lab gas lighter
Test tube, Pyrex®, 25 × 200 cm
Synthesized acetylsalicylic acid samples from Lab 12d

Ring stand and Biuret clamp
Capillary tubes, 100 mm, open-ended
Pipets, 5 mL
Pipet pump for 5-10 mL pipets
Oil, mineral
Thermometer, mercury, –10°C to –260°C
Rubber bands

Lab mitts or other fire-resistant gloves
Additional samples to be tested including: commercial asprin, lab grade acetylsalicylic acid, lab grade salicylic acid, sodium chloride, etc

Procedure

Part I: Setting up the Melting-Point Measuring Apparatus

Environmental Health and Safety Officer

Safety Precautions:
- **The following procedures should only be conducted in a chemical flow hood with the protective shield in the "down" position.**
- **Wear goggles and lab mitts when boiling oil.**
- **Tie hair back.**

1. Set up a Bunsen burner apparatus ring stand with a **large** test tube clamped into place, so that the bottom of the test tube is in the hottest part of the flame during heating).
2. For each sample to be tested, start the Bunsen burner flame. Heat a capillary tube in the hot part of the burner until it melts, closing one end (see Figure 12.7). The Instructor will demonstrate. Turn off the flame.
3. Add a small amount of crystals of the substance to be tested to the open end of the capillary tube. Turn it over and tap the crystals down to the bottom of the closed end.
4. Using a rubber band to hold the capillary tube, secure the tube to the base of a mercury thermometer.
5. Using a pipet, carefully add 5 mL of mineral oil to the bottom of test tube.
6. Gently, place the capillary tube/thermometer in the test tube with the oil. Clamp the thermometer to the ring stand so that it will not fall over and break (see Figure 12.8).

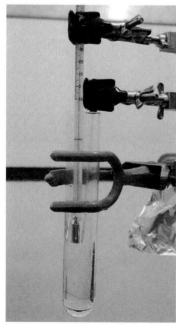

Environmental Health and Safety Officer

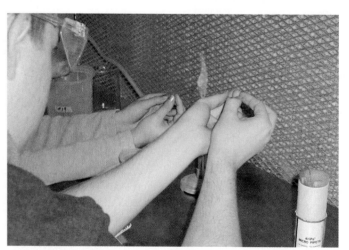

Figure 12.7. If you roll the end of a capillary tube in a flame, it will melt closed. It may take a few trials before a satisfactory closed end tube is made.
Photo by author.

Figure 12.8. The capillary tube is adjacent to the mercury thermometer (narrow tube to the right of the thermometer) for easy reading.
Photo by author.

Environmental Health and Safety Officer

Part II: Determining the Melting Point

1. Heat the test tube in a hot flame, watching the temperature until it gets within 15°C of its expected melting temperature (based on the reported MSDS value). Make sure that the oil does not boil over or splatter. There should be no water in or around the hot oil. This could cause splattering and possibly a fire or burns.
2. Lower the flame substantially to slow the heating rate so that there is a better chance of seeing when the crystals melt.
3. Watch to see the temperature (range) at which the crystals melt.
4. Record the melting temperature of the sample in a data table.
5. Repeat three times and average the results. Cool the oil back down to 20°C less than the expected melting temperature before doing another trial.
6. Repeat the procedure for each sample to be tested.

Conclusion

Analyze the results of the synthesis reactions. How close is the observed melting temperature to the expected temperature for each sample? Are the values close enough to conclude that the samples are the same? By what statistical method did you determine this? List some reasons why the values may be different than expected.

Thinking Like a Biotechnician

1. Why is the melting-point determination done in oil rather than water?
2. After the melting point test, when the capillary tubes cool, what should be visible inside of them?
3. What will happen if one test has twice as many crystals in the melting-point determination as another test?

Laboratory 12e

Testing a Protocol: Extraction of Salicin from Willow

Background

The main, active ingredient in modern-day aspirin is the compound, acetylsalicylic acid. Acetylsalicylic acid is made through an organic synthesis process where an acetyl group from acetic anhydride is added to salicylic acid.

Salicylic acid is produced by modifying salicin molecules. Salicin molecules are found, in nature, in the leaves and bark of many species of willow (eg, *Salix alba, Salix tetrasperma, Salix fragilis*) and a few species of poplar. Willow tissue may contain as much as 10% salicin. It has been reported in several sources that salicin or salicylic acid is easily extracted from willow bark and leaves using 80% ethanol as a solvent, and conducting a series of extractions and separations (for example, see biotech.emcp.net/salicin).

Figure 12.9. Salicin is reportedly extracted from a willow tree sample by grinding the plant tissue and placing the material in an ethanol solution. Photo by author.

In this activity, you will conduct a procedure for extracting salicin from willow tissue to see if, and how well, it works. The procedure is in the midst of process development and has shown some promise. It is the technician's task to try the procedure and to evaluate the product and yield. If time allows, improvements in the process to increase yield may be attempted.

Purpose

Can either salicin or salicylic acid be recovered from the extracts of willow bark using the proposed protocol?

Materials

*These items are hazardous and should only be used in an operating chemical fume hood.

White willow bark, shreds	Erlenmeyer flasks, Pyrex®,	NaOH, 0.1 *M*
Balance, weigh boats, scoops	250 mL, and rubber stopper	Acetylsalicylic acid
Mortar and pestle, 100 mL	Hood, chemical fume	Salicylic acid
Pipets and pumps	pH meter, electrode,	Sodium chloride
Ethanol, 95%	and buffers	Tubes, glass, 13 × 100 mm
Parafilm®	Hydrochloric acid, 1 *M*	and racks
Filter paper, 12.5 cm	Petroleum ether*	Plug caps for 13 × 100 mm tubes
Funnels, Pyrex® for 12.5 cm	Petri dishes, 100 × 15 mm,	Ferric nitrate, nonahydrate, 1%
filter paper	Pyrex®	Micropipet, P-1000 and tips

Procedure

Use the method below or a method that you have found from a different source (if approved by your instructor).

- **Several of the compounds used in this activity are considered hazardous. Use the Safety Data Sheets (SDS) that are shipped with each product or available on-line to learn about the dangers of each reagent, how to protect users from exposure, and what to do if a user is exposed to a reagent.**
- **Do this procedure in a chemical fume hood. Do not inhale acid vapors.**
- **Wear goggles and gloves.**
- **The Instructor will add the petroleum ether.**

1. Obtain a white willow leaf or bark sample.
2. Grind 3 g of plant tissue using a mortar and pestle with 15 mL of 80% ethanol solution (see Figure 12.9).
3. Allow the plant tissue-ethanol mixture to stand, covered with Parafilm®, for at least 24 hours.
4. Using a filter paper funnel, filter the solvent into a 250-mL flask and discard the solid.
5. Set the flask in a chemical fume hood with the fan running for approximately 1 week, or until all the ethanol has evaporated. Some crystals may be visible. Save some crystals for testing later.
6. Add 10 mL of deionized water to resuspend any compound on the bottom of the flask. Calibrate a pH meter. Add enough 1 M HCl to the solution to bring it to pH 4.0. (This should decrease the ionization of any salicylic acid that is present and make it readily dissolvable in petroleum ether).
7. Add 20 mL of petroleum ether. Use a rubber stopper to close the flask. With the flask in the chemical fume hood, shake (do not stir) the closed flask vigorously for 5 minutes.
8. Set the flask down and allow the mixture to separate into two distinct layers. The top layer should contain the uncharged salicylic acid.
9. Use a large volume pipet, such as a 50 mL, to remove the top layer and place it in a large Pyrex® dish. Allow the sample to have time to evaporate and for crystals to grow. This may take several weeks. Placing the sample in a chemical fume hood with the fan running can speed the process.
10. For crystals in either sample, determine the percent (%) yield. To do this, divide the volume of crystals by 3 g of willow tissue (starting sample), then multiple by 100.
11. Using the SDS for salicylic acid, from either a chemical supply house or an Internet connection, find the reported melting point of pure salicylic acid.
12. Test each sample for salicylates by conducting a ferric nitrate test on each of the prepared samples, following the procedure below. Compare these to positive (salicylic acid) and negative controls (sodium chloride).

Iron Testing for Salicylates

Mix 10 large crystals of the sample in 2 mL of dH_2O.
Add 250 µL of 1% ferric nitrate solution to the sample.
Observe the color and compare to negative and positive controls.

13. Determine the melting point of each sample, compared with a pure salicylic acid sample, following the protocol in Lab 12d.

Conclusion

Does it appear that salicin (salicylic acid) was extracted from willow using the procedures outlined above? What proof do you have? If so, what yield of salicylic acid did the procedure give? If there was little or no yield, propose modifications in the procedures.

Thinking Like a Biotechnician

1. Considering your experience with alcohol precipitation of DNA, why is the petroleum ether added to the watery salicylic acid solution?
2. Why might willow leaves contain large amounts of salicylic acid?

Laboratory 12f
IgG Purification from Porcine Serum

Developed by Catherine Su, with the assistance of Juan Afanador, SMBCP students.

Background

Plasma is the liquid portion of blood including the blood cells that are suspended in it. Serum is the part of plasma that does not include white or red blood cells or blood clotting factors such as platelets. Both serum and plasma are primarily water (up to 92%). Serum contains a collection of proteins many of which have important medical uses as antigens, antibodies and hormones. Serum also contains important inorganic compounds and electrolytes. Serum is most commonly used for clinical diagnostic tests of blood including the testing of nutrient, hormone or drug levels. Plasma, on the other hand, is usually used for is transfusions.

Of all of serum's organic material, Immunoglobulin G (IgG), is one of the most prominent making up almost 75% of all antibodies. IgG is a fundamental component of the immune system in that, like any other antibody, it detects antigens (components of allergens or other hazards) and triggers an immune response. IgG is particularly sensitive to fungi, bacteria and viruses particles and their antigenic regions. Due to IgG's recognition capabilities it is an important protein for use in medical biotechnology research and manufacturing.

IgG is a "Y" shaped antibody that has a total molecular weight of 150 kDa (see Figure 12.10). The antibody is composed of two sets of parallel strands that are known as chains. In each of these strands, there is a light chain (~25 kDa) and a heavy chain (~50 kDa).

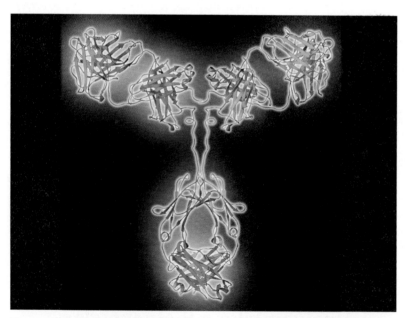

Figure 12.10. Computer Model of Immunoglobulin G (IgG) Immunoglobulin G (IgG) is the most abundant human antibody and is found in all body fluids. The Y-shaped molecule has two arms (top) that can bind to specific antigens, for instance bacterial or viral proteins. In doing this, they mark the antigen for destruction by phagocytes, the white blood cells that ingest and destroy foreign bodies. Antibodies can also kill some pathogens directly, and can neutralize toxins. © Science Photo Library/Photo Researchers.

PAGE visualization is an easy method of verifying the presence of antibodies such as IgG. The 150-kDa IgG antibody can be seen on a gel and, if it has been denatured by reducing agents (BME or DTT) or heat, the heavy and light chains can be resolved. Since other proteins could have similar molecular weights, protein purification by affinity chromatography is used to purify IgG from solution.

Affinity column chromatography is a method used to separate proteins based on the interactions between antigen and antibody, enzyme and substrate, or receptor and ligand. In IgG affinity chromatography, IgG binds to protein A conjugated onto resin beads packed in a column. After the IgG has bound to protein A, and contaminants have been washed away, an elution buffer with a very low pH is added to the column and elutes the IgG from the protein A resin beads, giving purified IgG from pig serum in eluted fractions. A protein A resin column, in 1 mL tips, for purifying small quantities of IgG, has been developed by PhyNexus, Inc. These Protein A Phytips are used in this activity.

Purpose

Can PhyNexus PhyTip® Protein A columns be used to purify measurable amounts of Immunoglobulin G (IgG) from porcine (pig) serum?

Materials

1X PBS Buffer, pH 7.4 (8g NaCl, 0.2 g KCl, 1.44g Na_2HPO_4, 0.2g KH_2PO_4 in 800 mL of dH_2O, adjust pH to 7.4, fill up to 1 L with dH_2O)
Porcine (Pig) Serum (G-Biosciences #BTNM-0063), 10 mL
Filter paper, 11 cm, medium-fast flow
Funnel, plastic
0.22-μm filter discs and syringe, 25 mL, Luer-lock
Centrifuge, clinical for 15 mL tubes
Centrifuge tubes, conical, capped, 15 mL
1X PAGE Running Buffer (see Lab 5e)
2X Sample Prep Loading Dye with BME (SPLD/BME), (see Lab 5e)
Protein sizing standard markers, (such as PAGEmark™ Tri-color protein ladder [G-Bioscience, Inc.])
Tube rack for 1.5-mL tubes
Reaction tubes, 1.5 mL, sterile
Micropipets, P-1000, P-200 and P-20 (or equivalents), and tips
Microcentrifuge
Dry/heat block, 90°C
LidLock, locking caps for 1.5-mL tubes
Gel box, vertical, for PAGE
PAGE gel, 10% TG/SDS, 10-well (NuSep® NN or equivalent)
Transfer pipets, 3 mL
PAGE gel loading tips
Coomassie Blue and destain (see Lab 5f or G-Biosciences LabSafe GEL Blue™ #786-35)
PhyNexus PhyTip® Protein A Columns #PTR 41-10-01 (48 tips, 1 mL volume)
Deionized water
Acetic acid, 0.15M
TRIS, 1M
pH paper, wide-range and narrow-range
Ethanol, 20%
Spectrophotometer, UV and cuvettes

Procedures

Part I: Preparing Porcine Serum Samples

1. Allow porcine serum thaw overnight in 4°C.
2. Fold filter paper into a cone, place in the funnel over a 15 mL tube.
3. Invert the container of thawed serum and dispense 10 mL of the serum into the filter.
4. Allow the 10 mL of serum to filter through. Keep the filtrate and dispense the filter paper.
5. Separate the filtrate into equal volumes (approximately 4 mL each) in two 15 mL tubes.
6. Spin in a balanced tabletop centrifuge for 5 minutes, at medium (about 3000xg) until blood particulate matter has pelleted, leaving a clear supernatant. Use the clear supernatant in the next step.

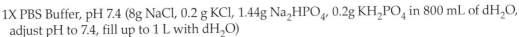

Environmental Health and Safety Officer

7. Using the 0.22 µm filter disc and syringe, filter-sterilize supernatant from the 15-mL tubes, into sterile 1.5 mL tubes, until there are four 1-mL samples of sterile, filtered serum. Label all samples. Keep on ice if being used the same day or store at -20°C until ready to use.
8. Using 1X Page Running Buffer as the diluent, prepare 1 mL of four diluted serum samples (1:10, 1:20, 1:40 and 1:80). Record how the dilutions were prepared in your notebook. Check your calculations with your supervisor.
9. Use the diluted samples to prepare 4 samples to run on a PAGE gel. Into labeled tubes, mix 40 µL of SPLD/BME with 40 µL of the each diluted serum sample. Change tips for each dispensing. Keep samples on ice if being used the same day or store at -20°C until ready to use.

Part II: Characterizing IgG by PAGE

1. Prepare a 10-well, 10% TG/SDS PAGE gel in a vertical gel box (see Lab 5f).
2. Using a LidLock, tightly cap prepared samples from Part I Step 9, heat samples on 90°C heat block for exactly 3 minutes. Quickly move to loading samples on to the gel.
3. Load 30 µL of samples 1:10, 1:20, 1:40 and 1:80 in to Wells 1-4 respectively. Change tips with each load.
4. Load 15 µL of samples 1:10, 1:20, 1:40 and 1:80 in to Wells 6-9 respectively. Change tips with each load.
5. Load 10 µL of protein sizing standard markers into Well 5 and 10.
6. Run the gel at 170 volts for 30-40 minutes or until the loading dye is in the bottom quadrant of the gel.
7. Stain the gel using Coomassie Blue stain and destain (see Lab 5f).
8. Observe the stained gel for bands of native (unreduced) IgG (at 150 kDA) and reduced IgG chains (at approximately 25 and 50 kDA). Are these bands visible? Are other bands visible? Which dilution resulted in sharp, easy to see (resolve bands)? Samples that have easily seen bands have protein amounts of at least 1 mg/mL.
9. Photograph and label your gel photograph with what was loaded in each well. Label all standard markers. Label sample bands that show the native (unreduced) IgG (at 150 kDA).
10. Determine if any of the 30 µL-load dilutions look like they have the native (unreduced) IgG (at 150 kDA) of approximately 1-10 mg/mL. Use that dilution (without loading dye) for the affinity chromatography column. Remember to factor in that the 15 µL loads have half of the protein of the 30 µL loads.

Part III: Purification of IgG using Protein A Affinity Chromatography (modified from PhyNexus procedure)

1. Obtain a PhyNexus PhyTip® Protein A column. The column is small enough to hold in your hand over a 1.5 mL collection tube or waste container. Once you start to use the tip, work quickly so the tip resin does not dry out.
2. Flush the PhyTip® Protein A column with 600 µL of deionized water to remove ethanol. Repeat 3 times. Discard the water flow-through. Repeat 3 times.
* If the column flows slowly, use a P-1000 set at 1000 µL to gently force air (creating pressure) at the top of the column. The tip fits snugly into the top of the column.
3. Equilibrate the PhyTip® Protein A with 600 µL of 1X PBS. Repeat 3 times. Discard the 1X PBS flow-through.
4. Prepare 1.2 mL of diluted pig IgG serum (the dilution that was determined best in Part II Step 10).
5. Add 400 µL of pig serum onto the top of the Protein A resin inside the PhyTip® column. Discard the flow-through. Repeat 3 times. The flow-through contains molecules that did not bind to the Protein A resin. The IgG in the serum should be bound to the Protein A resin.
6. Wash Protein A resin with 600 µL of 1X PBS, a total of 5 times. Discard each flow-through.
7. Elute the pig IgG off the resin, into a labeled, sterile 1.5 mL tube, by adding 600 µL of 0.15M acetic acid to the top of the column.
8. Add 70 µL of 1M TRIS to the eluted sample to bring its pH to between pH 6.0-6.5. Mix, gently but thoroughly by pipetting up and down. Use pH paper to check it. Add more 1 M TRIS, in 10 µL aliquots, if necessary. Change tips with each dispensing. Record the sample's final pH.

9. Determine the approximate protein (IgG) concentration of the eluted sample by diluting 100 μL of the elution with 900 μL of 1X PBS, then measure the absorbance at 280 nm as compared to a BSA standard sample curve (see Lab 7d).

10. Run diluted samples on another TG/SDS PAGE gel (as in Part II) to confirm the presence of the purified IgG (native protein and reduced chains). Photograph and label your gel photograph with what was loaded in each well. Label all standard markers. Label sample bands that show the native (unreduced) IgG (at 150 kDA) and heavy and light chains at approximately 50 and 25 kDA.

Part IV: Cleaning and Storage of PhyTip:

1. Clean the PhyTip® column with acid to remove remaining bound material. Add 600 μL of 0.15*M* acetic acid and discard the flow-through. Repeat 3 times.

2. Add 600 μL of deionized water to the column and discard the flow-through. Repeat 3 times.

3. Add 800 μL of 20% ethanol to the column and discard the flow-through. Add another of 20% ethanol, plug and seal the column. Store the column at 2-8°C. Columns may be re-equilibrated and used several times.

Data Analysis/Conclusion

Study the SDS PAGE and UV spectrophotometry results. Is there evidence of native or denatured IgG in any of the samples? If so, what is the approximate amount (mass or concentration) of protein in the diluted and undiluted samples? Does it appear that IgG may have been purified from other contaminant molecules in the serum? Explain. Discuss any technical errors that might have lead to unexpected results, including too little or too much IgG seen on the PAGE gels. What would you propose to do to get better purification and recover of IgG from the serum or off the column?

Thinking Like a Biotechnician

1. Why does 0.15*M* acetic acid elute (knock) the IgG off the Protein A column?

2. Describe how an affinity column chromatography might be used to purify other serum immunoglobulins such as IgA or IgE, separating them from IgG.

Extensions:
Kits for IgG purification are available from several vendors including G-Biosciences at **www.gbiosciences.com/PDF/Protocol/Pearl_IgG_Purification_Resin_Spin_Format.pdf** and Thermo Fisher Scientific at **www.thermofisher.com/order/catalog/product/89978**.

13 Making DNA Molecules

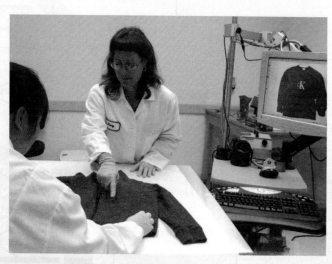

As a forensic scientist and biology unit supervisor for the Sacramento county district attorney's crime laboratory, Mary Hansen's work included identification and genetic marker typing of biological material derived from blood, semen, saliva, tissues, and hairs. The stability of DNA and the sensitivity of the typing methods have given law enforcement agencies the ability to solve current cases, cold cases, and cases involving "contact DNA," the DNA transferred when an individual's skin or mucosa makes contact with another person or object. The majority of the evidence examined is collected from victims of sexual assaults and homicides. Currently, Mary acts as a forensics consultant.
Photo courtesy of Mary Hansen.

The incorporation of new DNA and protein typing methods has had a major impact on several scientific disciplines. In forensic laboratories, for example, DNA sequencing and polymerase chain reaction (PCR) have helped reduce a large backlog of unsolved criminal cases and even helped to reverse the conviction of wrongly accused individuals. In other areas, including medicine, genetics, drug development, evolutionary studies, and environmental biotechnology, identifying differences between individuals and populations through DNA typing has become one of the foundations of research, development, and diagnostics.

In the Chapter 13 lab activities you will learn some basic DNA typing techniques, or in other words, how to identify DNA fragments. Specifically, you will learn how to

- synthesize DNA fragments, called oligonucleotides, that could be used as primers or, probes in DNA sequencing, PCR, microarrays or other DNA studies
- transfer DNA fragments to a Southern blot membrane for analysis purposes
- visualize DNA fragments produced during DNA synthesis or PCR
- use a "master mix"
- conduct and optimize a basic PCR reaction and use a thermal cycler
- use a database to gather information about data for use during a DNA investigation (bioinformatics)

Since DNA sequencing and PCR are modifications of DNA synthesis procedures, many of the methods used and the skills developed in these activities are similar to those used in sequencing and genomic studies. Using DNA or RNA fragments also are the foundation for searching for new genes and gene functions, as in microarray technology.

Laboratory 13a
DNA Synthesis *in Vitro*

Based on labs developed by Maureen Munn, PhD, University of Washington, Seattle, WA.
Modified by Luhua Zhang, Vidhan Mittal, Kate Stern, and Jacky Chan, Biotechnology students.

Note: This lab is recommended for use only if the instructor has the ability to have the required PCR primers and templates made.

Background

Oligonucleotides (short pieces of DNA) can be constructed in a test tube (*in vitro*) using a single-stranded DNA fragment as a template. A primer complementary to the 3' end of the template attaches and is used as the starting end of the oligonucleotide to be synthesized. With the appropriate concentrations of primer, dNTPs (A, C, G, T), polymerase, and other buffer reagents, the DNA polymerase can build an entire oligonucleotide fragment that is complementary to the template (see Figure 13.1). If any of the key ingredients are limited or missing, or the reaction is not conducted at the enzyme's optimum temperature of 37°C, the synthesis reaction will slow or stop.

Once a DNA synthesis reaction is complete, synthesis products may be run on a polyacrylamide gel to confirm the reaction (Lab 13b). The synthesized fragments separate on the gel based on differences in length of only a few nucleotides. Gels can be visualized through ethidium bromide (EtBr) staining or the gel bands may be transferred to a membrane for Southern blotting (see Labs 13c and 13d) and blot visualization.

In this activity, DNA strands of predictable lengths are built off a 60-base template DNA strand.

The template used has the sequence:

3'-ACATGCTGCTGCCGGTCACAAGGCAATTCCTAAAAAGGGAAGGAACCCCGAAGGCCTTTT-5'

The primer used is 32 bases long and has the following sequence:

5'-biotin-TGTACGACGACGGCCAGTGTTCCGTTAAGGAT-3'

Notice the biotin molecule, "tagged" to the 5' end, for visualization purposes.

Purpose:

Can DNA fragments (oligonucleotides) of different lengths be synthesized *in vitro*?
How does varying the availability of DNA nucleotide triphosphates (dNTPs) affect DNA synthesis strand development?

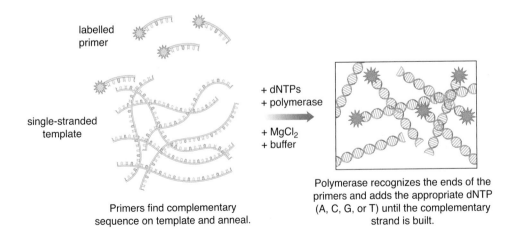

Figure 13.1. DNA Synthesis.

Materials

Reaction tubes, 1.5 mL and racks
Micropipets and tips
Lid locks, for 1.5-mL tubes
Water bath, 65°C
Floating rack (1.5-mL tubes)
Beaker, 400 mL
Thermometer, lab
No nucleotide mix (50 mM NaCl)
Microcentrifuge
Dry block heater/heat block, 37°C

DNA Synthesis Kit, G-Biosciences
#BTNM-0040
   DNA polymerase, 1.625 U/μL
   DNA template at 1.5 pmol/μL
   Biotin-tagged primer, 1.5 pmol/μL
   Reaction buffer
   Distilled water, sterile
   dNTPs for preparation of the
     dNTP mixes
   DTT, 0.1 M
   DNA Synthesis Stop mix (DNA loading dye)
   Sizing standard markers
     (32 bp, 45 bp, 60 bp), 0.038 pmol/μL

The template and primers are prepared at 1.5 pmol/μL with the following sequence:

Template DNA
3'-ACATGCTGCTGCCGGTCACAAGGCAATTCCTAAAAAGGGAAGGAACCCCGAAGGCCTTTT-5'

Primer
5'-biotin-TGTACGACGACGGCCAGTGTTCCGTTAAGGAT-3'

The DNA sizing standard markers are prepared at 0.038 pmol/μL, of each strand, with the following sequence:

32 bases (same as primer)
5'-biotin-TGTACGACGACGGCCAGTGTTCCGTTAAGGAT-3'

45 bases
5'-biotin-CAAGGAAGGGAAAAATCCTTAACGGAACACTGGCCGTCGTCGTAC-3'

60 bases
5'-biotin-TTTTCCGGAAGCCCCAAGGAAGGGAAAAATCCTTAACGGAACACTGGC
CGTCGTCGTACA-3'

Hypothesis

- Read the procedures and, in your notebook, create a flowchart of the experimental steps. Then, draw a sketch to represent the length of the DNA fragments that should be synthesized in each of the six nucleotide tubes.
- Draw a sketch to represent the distance that the different DNA fragments should run on a PAGE gel compared with the standard DNA size markers listed in the materials list. Although you will not be able to check them until you run the samples on a gel, blot it onto a membrane, and visualize it (Labs 13 b-d). When they are blotted and stained, you should be able to predict how they would run on a gel.

Procedure

Part I: Attaching the Primer to the Template (Annealing)

1. Label a natural-colored 1.5-mL tube with your lab group's initials (or your own initials if you have not been assigned to a group), and the letters AM (annealing mix). Add the following ingredients **in the order listed** to this tube and close the lid **tightly** (see Table 13.1). Check off each ingredient as you add it. Wrist-flick the tube to pool all reactants on the bottom. Place a locking cap on the top of the test tube after the last reagent is added.

Table 13.1. Annealing-Mix Tube Reaction Matrix

Ingredient	Volume (µL)
distilled water	12
reaction buffer	4
DNA template	2
biotin-tagged primer	2
total volume	**20**

65°C

2. To denature the primer and template molecules, place the AM tube, in a floating rack, in a 65°C hot water bath for 2 minutes. (This separates the DNA molecules and discourages random annealing.)

3. At the end of the 2-minute incubation, scoop up about 50 mL of the 65°C water into a 400-mL beaker. Place the AM tube, in its rack, into the beaker. Slowly, allow the AM tube to cool to 35°C or less for 15 minutes. Add a tiny bit of ice to the beaker to bring it to 35°C if it has not reached it after 15 minutes.

Part II: Preparing the Nucleotide Mixes

While the AM tube is cooling, the supervisor or a student group should prepare and label the "stock" nucleotide mixes in six different tubes, as follows (see Table 13.2):

Table 13.2. Stock Nucleotide Mix Preparation Matrix

Reagent	-dATP Mix (µL)	-dCTP Mix (µL)	-dGTP Mix (µL)	-dTTP Mix (µL)	Complete NTP Mix (µL)	No NTP Mix (µL)
dATP	–	30	30	30	30	–
dCTP	30	–	30	30	30	–
dGTP	30	30	–	30	30	–
dTTP	30	30	30	–	30	–
50 mM NaCl	–	–	–	–	–	120
Sterile Water	30	30	30	30	–	–

1. Label six 1.5-mL tubes (colored, if available) with your lab initials, NM (nucleotide mix), and then either 1, 2, 3, 4, 5, or 6. If colored tubes are available, pick all of the same color to help keep track of your tubes in the rest of the experiment. Put 2.5 µL of the corresponding (master) nucleotide mix into each tube (see Table 13.3). Close each tube tightly.

Table 13.3. Nucleotide-Mix Tube Ingredients

Tube No.	Mix
1	no nucleotide control mix (this is lacking all the nucleotides)
2	complete nucleotide mix (with dATP, dGTP, dCTP, dTTP)
3	missing dATP (but contains all the other dNTPs)
4	missing dCTP (but contains all the other dNTPs)
5	missing dGTP (but contains all the other dNTPs)
6	missing dTTP (but contains all the other dNTPs)

2. Give the tubes a "wrist-flick" or a quick spin in the centrifuge to pool the sample. Keep the tubes on ice until step 6.

37°C

Environmental Health
and Safety Officer

Part III: Synthesis Reaction

1. Add 2 µL of 0.1 *M* DTT and 4 µL of DNA polymerase to the annealing mix in tube AM. Change tips after each dispensing to avoid cross contamination. Give the tubes a "wrist-flick" or a quick spin in the centrifuge to pool the reagents. Keep the tube on ice until ready to use in the synthesis reactions.

2. A few minutes before starting the synthesis reactions, place the six nucleotide tubes into the 37°C water bath or a 37°C heat block for **at least 2 minutes.**

3. Add 3 µL of the AM mixture to each of the nucleotide tubes, No. 1 through 6. Pipet the mixture **directly** into the pooled NM solution in each reaction tube. **Change tips for each tube.** "Wrist-flick" the tubes to pool the reactants.

4. **Immediately,** place the tubes back into the 37°C water bath or heat block. **These samples must stay warm.** Incubate the samples at 37°C for **at least** 4 minutes (but not more than 10 minutes).

5. After incubation, add 4 µL of the DNA synthesis stop mix (DNA loading dye), to the tubes. Close the tubes tightly. Make sure the tubes are still labeled clearly. Spin to pool samples.

6. Put the tubes in a rack and freeze at –20°C until they are ready to use/run in the PAGE.

7. Confirm the presence of synthesis products by running the samples on a 10% TBE-urea gel (TBE stands for TRIS, boric acid, and EDTA) as described in the next activity. The sample fragments on the gel can be visualized through EtBr staining (15 minutes) or Southern blotting and visualization (Labs 13b, 13c, and/or 13d).

Thinking Like a Biotechnician

1. In this experiment, the type of dNTP in the reaction is varied so you can see the effect on strand synthesis. Make a prediction as to what negative consequences may result if the following key ingredients were varied.

   a) primer concentration
   b) DNA polymerase concentration

2. During the annealing reactions, the primer-template mixture is cooled very slowly from 65°C to 35°C. Describe what is happening in the AM tube during this period and what may happen if the AM tube is cooled too rapidly.

3. After all of the reagents are mixed together, what is the final concentration of template DNA in each of the synthesis-reaction tubes?

Laboratory 13b
Separating DNA Fragments on a PAGE Gel

Based on labs developed by Maureen Munn, PhD, University of Washington, Seattle, WA.
Modified by Luhua Zhang, Vidhan Mittal, Kate Stern, and Jacky Chan, Biotechnology students.

Note: This activity runs the DNA synthesis products, from the Lab 13a, on a PAGE gel.

Background

The DNA synthesis fragments produced in Lab 13a are too small to be separated and analyzed on an agarose gel. DNA fragments that are smaller than 500 nucleotides in length are best separated and visualized on a polyacrylamide gel (PAGE), as shown in Figure 13.2. PAGE gels used for small DNA fragments are similar to those used in protein analysis, but they are prepared with different buffers. These gels are also run at a higher voltage.

It is common to use TBE buffer to prepare and run PAGE gels for DNA synthesis or sequencing fragments. TBE withstands the higher voltage better than does the TAE buffer commonly used for horizontal gel electrophoresis.

TBE buffer can be prepared in the lab or purchased in a concentrated form (10X or 5X) from a supply house. TBE gels may be purchased prepoured and ready to use. In this activity, the pre-poured TBE gels contain urea. Urea is a denaturing agent that facilitates the separation of template and primer strands. Once the gels are rinsed, labeled, and loaded with sample, they are run for 20 to 30 minutes at 200 V. The fragments travel through the gel based on their size. Once the gels are stained, their sizes are determined by comparing their positions with standard fragments.

In this activity, the DNA fragments, from the DNA synthesis procedure (Lab 13a), will be run on a TBE-urea gel. In Labs 13c and 13d, the gel is blotted onto a membrane (Southern blotting) and run through a series of washes and stains. The fragments visualize on the membrane and can be further analyzed.

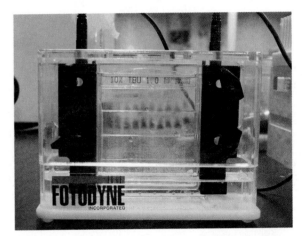

Figure 13.2. **Bromophenol blue (dark blue) and xylene cyanol (light blue) track the movement of the DNA synthesis fragments. The colorless DNA fragments are transferred to blotting membrane and "stained."** Photo by author.

Purpose

To prepare and load a DNA TBE-urea PAGE gel.
To separate DNA synthesis samples (oligos) on a TBE-urea PAGE gel for future study.

Materials

Environmental Health and Safety Officer

TBE buffer concentrate, 5X
Beaker, plastic, 1 L
Gloves, large
Glasses, safety, plastic
TBE-urea gel, 1.0 mm, 10%
Permanent lab marker pens
Gel box, vertical, for 10 × 10 cm PAGE

Pipets, transfer, 3 mL
Sizing standard markers, DNA synthesis, 0.038 pmol/µL (in DNA Synthesis Kit - Lab 13a)
Gel loading tips, PAGE
Power supply, 250 V
Lid locks, for 1.5 mL tubes
Dry block heater/heat block, 95°C

Procedure

Part I: Preparing Buffer

Environmental Health and Safety Officer

1. Prepare or purchase 1 L of 5X TBE buffer (recipe below)

5 X TBE Buffer: 1 L (concentrated buffer)

- 0.5 g of NaOH
- 54 g of TRIS base
- 3.7 g of EDTA, disodium salt (or 20 mL of 0.5 M EDTA solution)
- 27.5 g of boric acid

Measure dry ingredients. Place the TRIS in a clean 1 L beaker. Add 800 mL of distilled water, and stir to dissolve. Add EDTA, stir to dissolve. Add boric acid, stir to dissolve. Adjust to a final volume of 1 L by adding distilled water. Store at room temperature.

2. Prepare 500 mL of 1X TBE buffer by diluting the 5X TBE. Show the calculation of the dilution in your notebook.

Part II: Preparing the Gel

Environmental Health and Safety Officer

1. Obtain a prepoured, TBE-urea (10%) polyacrylamide gel, and a vertical minigel box. Wearing gloves and goggles, wash the outside of the gel by running tap water over it.
2. Gently, dry the gel cassette. Label the wells, and initial the gel cassette. If there is tape covering the bottom of the gel, pull it off.
3. Place the gel in the electrophoresis chamber **in the correct orientation,** labels facing the front of the gel box and the well side facing the internal buffer chamber.
4. Add enough 1X TBE electrophoresis buffer to the gel-box chambers to cover the wells and the bottom one-third of the gel.
5. Slowly, remove the comb from the top of the gel.
6. Using a transfer pipet or gel loading tips, rinse the gel wells with the 1X TBE buffer to remove the preservative. Rinse the equivalent of about 1 mL worth of buffer through each well. Be careful to not damage the fragile "fingers" that define the well. If any of them bend over, very gently take a gel-loading tip and straighten it out.
7. Place the top on the gel box and prerun the gel for 5 minutes at 200 V to remove preservative buffer from the wells.

Part III: Preparing the Samples

95°C

Note: Do this while the gel is preheating.
1. DNA **must be single-stranded** to be interpreted for this activity. To separate (denature) the template strands from the newly synthesized DNA strands, place the six sample tubes from the DNA synthesis procedure (Lab 13a) into the 95°C water bath or heat block for at least 3 minutes. Use lid locks to keep the lids of the tubes closed during heating.

Part IV: Loading and Running the Samples

1. If you are not an expert at loading a PAGE gel, practice with loading dye on Well No. 9 or 10.
2. After the 3 minutes of sample heating and 5 minutes of gel heating, **quickly** load each sample onto the gel. Load 10 µL of each sample into the wells, starting at Well No. 2. Into Well No. 8, load 10 µL of the DNA standards. All samples, plus the standards, must be loaded within 2 minutes to keep the strands from reannealing. Change tips every time.
3. Run the gels for at least 20 minutes at 200 V, or longer if there is time. At most, run the gels until the bromophenol blue dye is 4 cm from the bottom of the gel (just over halfway).
4. At the end of the run, turn off the power, and remove the gel. The gel can be stained with EtBr or it may be blotted to a membrane (Southern blotting in Lab 13c) for visualization (Lab 13d). Either method must be started immediately since the DNA fragments on the gel will begin to diffuse.

Thinking Like a Biotechnician

1. At the end of the gel run, blue bands can be seen near the bottom of the gel. What are the blue bands? Where are the DNA synthesis fragments?
2. If the samples are loaded on the gel too slowly, the template and primer pieces will reanneal. What is the size of the template-primer complex compared with the template alone or any of the synthesized fragments? Why is it important to consider the template-primer complex?
3. Why does the TBE buffer have to be diluted from 5X to 1X? What consequences are expected if the buffer is not correctly diluted to 1X?

Laboratory 13c
Conducting a Southern Blot

Based on labs developed by Maureen Munn, PhD, University of Washington, Seattle, WA. Modified by Luhua Zhang, Vidhan Mittal, Kate Stern, and Jacky Chan, Biotechnology students.

Note: This activity uses the PAGE gel from the last activity, upon which the DNA synthesis fragments were run.

Background

DNA on a gel is colorless and, therefore, not visible to the unaided eye. A DNA synthesis (or sequencing gels) can be stained with EtBr and photographed for analysis or probed with a radioactive marker. Alternatively, though, gels are transferred to nitrocellulose or a nylon membrane in a technique called blotting. When the sample being transferred is DNA, it is called a Southern blot. Blots are an easy way to handle (because they are less toxic), analyze, and preserve small DNA fragments. In addition, the visualization methods for Southern blots are more sensitive to low concentrations of DNA than EtBr.

In a blot, the gel is covered with a positively charged nylon membrane or nitrocellulose paper. Layers of absorbent filter paper are placed on top of the gel-membrane complex. Heavy weights or books are placed on top of the paper. After 20 to 30 minutes, capillary action carries the DNA fragments from the gel up to the membrane. Drying binds (cross-links) the DNA to the membrane. Cross-linking is faster and more complete if the membrane is exposed to ultraviolet (UV) light in a cross-linker for 20 seconds. At this point, the DNA samples are fixed onto the membrane, but are not visible.

The DNA fragments can be visualized by using an appropriate staining procedure, such as the one in Lab 13d.

Purpose

To conduct a Southern blot transfer of DNA synthesis fragments from a TBE-urea gel to a postively charged nylon blotting membrane.

Materials

DNA synthesis PAGE gel in the cassette (from Lab 13b)
Spatula or dinner knife, metal
Pipets, transfer, 3 mL
TBE buffer, 1X (from Lab 13b)

Pencil
Forceps, fine-tipped, stainless steel
Hybond N+ nylon membrane, GE Healthcare No.RPN82B

Beakers, plastic, 1 L
Filter paper, 12.5 cm
Plate, Plexiglass®, 10 × 10 cm
Textbooks, several, heavy
UV crosslinker (optional)

Procedure

1. Gather the necessary supplies for the blotting procedure.
2. Place the gel on the lab bench, with the longer plate of the cassette on the bench top.
3. Using the metal spatula or knife, gently pry the short top plate off, lifting it slowly so that the gel does not rip. If the gel sticks to both plates, squirt some buffer between the gel and the short plate to help it come off. Don't worry if the gel sticks to the short plate instead of the long one. It just means that the lanes will be reversed on the membrane. You will be able to determine the loading order based on the location of the standards.
4. With a pencil, not a pen, label the upper right-hand corner of the nylon membrane with initials. The membrane is delicate. Do not touch it with your hands. Only use forceps.
5. Make a sandwich directly on top of the exposed gel by stacking the following layers in the following order (see Figure 13.3):

   a) the nylon membrane
      (Dip the membrane in 1x TBE buffer, and lay it over the gel with the pencil mark facing down. Avoid trapping any air bubbles. Place it correctly the first time. If you try to reposition it, the DNA may smudge on it, and you will lose sample.)

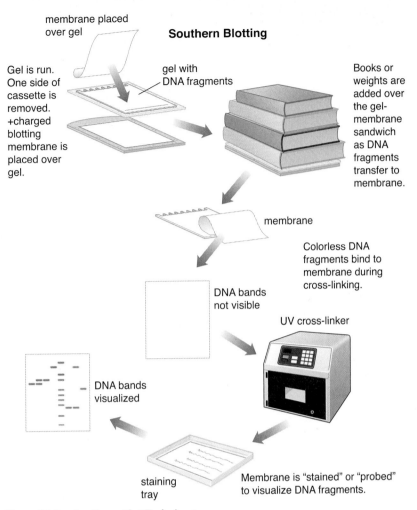

Southern Blotting

membrane placed over gel

Gel is run. One side of cassette is removed. +charged blotting membrane is placed over gel.

gel with DNA fragments

Books or weights are added over the gel-membrane sandwich as DNA fragments transfer to membrane.

membrane

Colorless DNA fragments bind to membrane during cross-linking.

DNA bands not visible

UV cross-linker

DNA bands visualized

staining tray

Membrane is "stained" or "probed" to visualize DNA fragments.

Figure 13.3. **Southern Blot Technique.**

b) five squares of dry Whatman filter paper or flat paper towel
c) a Plexiglas® plate
d) five heavy textbooks

Leave the blot alone for at least 20 minutes.

6. Carefully remove the book, plate, and Whatman paper from the top of the membrane. Using forceps, lift the membrane by the edges, gently removing the membrane from the surface of the gel. If the gel sticks, squirt a little 1X TBE buffer between the membrane and the gel. Don't worry if a small amount of gel remains stuck to the membrane since this will be washed off later.

7. Lay the membrane **DNA side up** (pencil mark up) on a dry piece of paper. Cross-link the DNA fragments to the membrane by drying overnight or exposing it to a 20-second UV exposure in a cross-linker.

Cross-linking Instructions

- Dip a piece of Whatman filter paper in 1X TBE buffer.
- Place the blotted membrane(s) on the wet Whatman filter paper, DNA side UP, in the UV cross-linker.
- Close the door.
- Irradiate the membranes with UV-254 light for 20 seconds. Depending on the model of cross-linker, this could be as easy as pressing the "start" button.

Conclusion

How does your blot look compared with others in the class? Is there evidence that the blot (transferring of molecules) was successful? Can you see DNA on the blot? If there is no visible DNA on the membrane, is there any evidence that the blotting (transfer of the DNA) was successful?

Thinking Like a Biotechnician

1. What may be the consequences of trapping a large air bubble between the gel and the nylon membrane during blotting?
2. Speculate as to why the cross-linker speeds cross-linking.

Laboratory 13d
Visualizing DNA on a Southern Blot

Based on labs developed by Maureen Munn, PhD, University of Washington, Seattle, WA.
Modified by Luhua Zhang, Vidhan Mittal, Kate Stern, and Jacky Chan, Biotechnology students.

Note: This activity "stains" the Southern blot membrane (from Lab 13c) that holds the DNA synthesis fragments.

Background

There are several methods of visualizing DNA on a Southern blot. In one technique, a complementary DNA probe, tagged with a radioactive label, finds its complement on the membrane and is visible as a spot on exposed x-ray film. Although this is a method commonly used in industry, there are disadvantages to using radioactive labels, not the least of which is the danger of exposure to radioactivity.

Another method of visualizing DNA bands on a membrane utilizes chromogenic agents. A chromogenic agent produces color. To use a chromogen, an enzyme complex is bound to the complementary DNA probe. The enzyme complex can cause a color change in a colored reagent when it is added to the membrane. The DNA that binds the enzyme complex turns color. In this activity, we will use an enzyme, alkaline phosphatase, which catalyzes a reaction between BCIP (5-Bromo-chloro-3-indolyl phosphate), and nitro blue tetrazolium (NBT), to produce a purple-blue color.

The alkaline phosphatase (AP) is attached to the DNA through a series of reactions that stack molecules on top of the DNA bands. After the AP is bound, NBT and BCIP are added. The AP changes the color of NBT to a bluish color. The colored molecules "stain" the DNA spot. On the blotted membranes, the DNA shows as blue bands where the AP has changed the color of the NBT.

In this experiment, visualization of DNA bands on the blot is possible because the primer used has a biotin molecule attached, or tagged, to it. During the visualization process, the biotin tag on the probe first binds a streptavidin molecule. Then, a second biotin molecule coupled to the AP enzyme is added to the streptavidin. The AP causes the colored reagent (NBT) to change to blue (see Figure 13.4). Any DNA band on the membrane, with a biotin-labeled primer attached, will turn a blue color from the staining procedure. Once colorized, the sizes of DNA synthesis products may be determined by comparing the distance their bands traveled on the gel/membrane to the distances the DNA standards of known length traveled.

DNA Fragment Visualization with AP

The biotin-tagged DNA fragment on the membrane is bound with streptavidin. Biotin-tagged alkaline phosphatase attaches to streptavidin. When NBT is present, AP converts it from yellow to blue. The blue NBT builds up on the DNA strand and makes it visible.

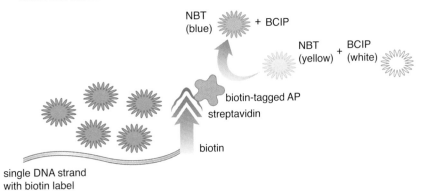

Figure 13.4. **Visualization of a Southern blot with biotin-tagged alkaline phosphatase.**

Purpose

To colorize the DNA synthesis fragments (oligonucleotides) on the Southern blot for the purpose of determining their size in bases.

Materials

*Note: Recipes for solutions follow the Materials list. Class volumes of each solution are prepared a few days prior to staining the membranes. Teams should share the work of stock-solution preparation.

Glasses, safety, and gloves
Blotted membrane (from Lab 13c)
Petri dishes, square, 100 × 15 mm, sterile
Graduated cylinders, 25 mL
Balance, weigh boats, scoops
Carboys, 5 L with spigot
Blocking solution*

Wash solution I*
Wash solution II*
Color substrate buffer*
Stop solution*
Forceps, fine-tipped, stainless steel
Micropipets and tips
Streptavidin, 1 mg/mL

Biotin-tagged alkaline phosphatase, 0.38 mg/mL
BCIP (X-PO$_4$)/NBT color 1.25/2.5 mL
Plastic wrap
Aluminum foil
Beakers, 50 mL
Filter paper, 12.5 cm

Reagents/Recipes (for staining 32 to 35 membranes)

Note: In your notebook, show all calculations for all solutions/reagents whether your group is preparing them or not.

Blocking Solution: 2 L needed
A 1-L recipe requires a sodium phosphate buffer at pH 7.2. Prepare the buffer by making 600 mL of 0.4 M Na$_2$HPO$_4$ and adding 0.4 M NaH$_2$PO$_4$ • H$_2$O (prepare 500 mL) until the pH is 7.2. Then, add salt and SDS to bring the concentration to 125 mM NaCl and 5% SDS (your instructor must add SDS in the chemical fume hood). Lastly, add deionized water to bring the final to 1 liter.

Wash Solution I: 2 L needed
Blocking solution diluted in a 1:10 ratio with deionized water

Wash Solution II: 2 L needed
A 1-L recipe equals 100 mM TRIS-HCl pH 9.5, 100 mM NaCl, and 10 mM MgCl$_2$.
Hint: Prepare 100 mL 1 M TRIS-HCl pH 9.5, and use it for the TRIS-HCl in the recipe. Then add other solutes and mix them together to equal a total volume of 1000 mL.

Color Substrate Buffer: 1 L needed
A 1-L recipe equals 100 mM TRIS-HCl, pH 9.5; 100 mM NaCl; 50 mM MgCl$_2$, 0.1 mM ZnCl$_2$.
Hint: Prepare 100 mL of 1 M TRIS-HCl, pH 9.5, and use it for the TRIS-HCl in the recipe. Then add other solutes and mix them together to equal a total volume of 1000 mL.

Stop Solution (TE Buffer): 2 L needed
A 1-L recipe equals 10 mM TRIS-HCl, pH 8.0, 1 mM EDTA.

Safety Precautions

- Wear goggles and gloves for the entire visualization procedure.
- Some of the solutions may be caustic.
- Use forceps to handle the membrane, and only touch it at the edges.

Procedure

Environmental Health and Safety Officer

1. Place the nylon membrane, DNA side up (ie, pencil mark up), in a staining tray. Pour the first solution listed in the staining/visualization matrix (15 mL of blocking solution) into the tray (see Table 13.4).
2. Swirl the tray for the entire wash time listed in Table I, making sure that the solution completely covers the membrane.
3. At the end of the wash time, pour the solution into a sink or trash beaker, using the forceps to hold the membrane in the bottom of the tray, holding the membrane near the edge only.

4. Repeat steps 1 through 3 for each of the other washes outlined in the matrix, using the solutions and times given. Rinse the graduated cylinders between each use with distilled water. Check off each box as you complete each wash step.

Caution:
- Do not let the membrane dry out between washes.
- Longer washes are better than shorter ones.
- For the mixed solutions*, mix the ingredients together, then pour on the side of the membrane. Tilt to cover the membrane.

Table 13.4. **Staining/Visualization Matrix**

Solution	Composition	Wash Time
blocking solution	15 mL blocking solution	5 minutes with swirling
streptavidin solution	10 mL blocking solution + 10 µL streptavidin*	5 minutes with swirling
wash solution I	20 mL wash solution I	5 minutes with swirling
wash solution I	20 mL wash solution I	5 minutes with swirling
biotin-tagged AP solution	10 mL blocking solution + 13.2 µL biotin-tagged AP*	5 minutes with swirling
wash solution II	20 mL wash solution II	5 minutes with swirling
wash solution II	20 mL wash solution II	5 minutes with swirling
wash solution II	20 mL wash solution II	5 minutes with swirling
color solution **Do not rinse.**	15 mL color substrate buffer + 52.5 µL NBT* + 52.5 µL BCIP	1 to 2 hours in the dark, covered, without swirling

5. After the color-substrate solution has been added, swirl one time only to mix, then cover the tray with plastic wrap. Next, cover the tray with foil to completely block out light. Make sure that it is easy to unwrap the top to check the color development. Put a label on the foil so it is distinguishable from other developing membranes.
6. Leave the tray in the dark spot to develop for 1 to 2 hours, checking the color development every 20 minutes or so. Do not leave the membrane in this solution for more than a few hours. When the DNA bands are visible, pour off the color-substrate solution, and pour in 25 mL of the stop solution. Swirl the tray for a few seconds, and then rinse twice with 50 mL of distilled water.
7. Place the membrane on a piece of filter paper to dry. When dry, glue the membrane, or a copy, into your notebook. Cover it with a small piece of plastic wrap and aluminum foil. Additional copies of the dry membrane can be made using a photocopier, photo-imaging system, or a digital camera.

Data Analysis

Label the top of the membrane to show the lanes and the contents of each lane. Write next to the membrane, not on it. Identify and label the DNA size standards. Determine which bands, in which of the lanes, represent synthesized oligonucleotides, primer-only strands, or primer-template complexes. Determine and record the length, in nucleotides, of the synthesized DNA fragment bands in each lane.

Conclusion

Review your hypothesis statements in Lab 13a. How well did your observed results match your expected results? Are there any extra bands present that were not expected? Explain. Are there any bands missing that should be present? Explain. Does the amount of color in each band support your hypothesis? Explain.

Thinking Like a Biotechnician

1. Each lab group's membrane is a replication of the DNA synthesis experiment. If one lab group had results different from the others, it was probably due to technician error. But, if all groups had the same unexpected results, a problem could exist in the shared materials, instruments, or procedures.
   Propose some reasons for the following:

   a. No groups had anything on their membranes except DNA loading-dye bands.
   b. All groups had sizing-standard bands visible on their membranes, but nothing else.
   c. All groups only had bands in one row higher than the 60-base standard and in one row at 32 bases.

2. If some of the six samples are shown to contain oligos, how might a technician determine the concentration of DNA remaining in the six sample tubes?

Laboratory 13e

Using PCR to Amplify Regions of Lambda Phage DNA

This lab was developed by Frank Stephenson, PhD, Applied Biosystems, Inc. and Maria Abilock, BABEC, for BABEC Member Teachers. It was modified for use in the San Mateo Biotechnology Career Pathway by Garrett Lew, Biotechnology student.

Note: Alternative kits and materials are listed under Materials for BABEC and non-BABEC users.

Background

Lambda bacteriophage is a virus that infects several species of bacteria, including *E. coli*. The genome of the lambda bacteriophage is approximately 48,500 base pairs (bp) in length, and the entire genome has been sequenced.

If a technician wants to study or use a particular section of the lambda genome, the polymerase chain reaction (PCR) can be used to recognize the section and amplify it. Since the DNA of the lambda virus is easily isolated, it is available from several biological supply vendors. By understanding some PCR basics, a technician can order primers that will recognize the region of interest and make several billion copies in a few hours. The PCR product can be used in further studies or tests.

PCR Basics

- A DNA strand is separated (denatured) by high temperature.
- At a lower temperature, primers recognize and bind (anneal) to each side of the region of DNA to be amplified or copied.
- At a third optimum temperature, *Taq* polymerase adds nucleotides [A, G, T, C (called dNTPs)] to the end of each primer and builds (extends) a strand complementary to each template.
- Two strands result, delineated by the primers on the ends.
- Each of the new strands is amplified again.
- An instrument called a thermal cycler manages the changes in temperature.

For a PCR reaction, two different primers must be designed to recognize the sequence just before and just after the region of interest. After primers bond to the template DNA, *Taq* polymerase builds the remaining region of interest from dNTPs in the reaction tube. For *Taq* polymerase activity, Mg^{2+} ions must be present, and the pH and temperature must be acceptable.

In this activity, genomic lambda DNA is probed to see how many amplification regions exist for the selected forward primer (P_F) and the reverse primer (P_R). After amplification in the thermal cycler, the PCR products are run on an agarose gel. The number of bands present in the PCR product tube represents the number of regions the primers recognized and amplified. A negative control will be prepared and run to ensure that there is no contaminant DNA present.

Purpose

How many regions of lambda DNA are amplified using the selected P_F primer and P_R primer?
What are the sizes of the PCR product(s)?
How does the concentration of template DNA affect the amount of PCR product?

Materials

Gloves and safety goggles

PCR tubes, 0.2 mL

Micropipets, P-100 and P-10, sterile, aerosol-plugged tips

Distilled water, sterile, nuclease-free

Taq polymerase, G-Biosciences #BTNM-0074

PCR buffer, 10X (comes with the polymerase)

MgCl$_2$, 25 mM

dNTP mix, 10 mM, G-Biosciences #786-443

Primers (from www.idtdna.com), see preparation instructions in Procedure Part I:

Forward primer = 5'-AAC-CTTCAACTACACGGCT-CACCT-3'

Reverse primer = 5'-ATGAAGGCGT-TTACGGCTTGTTGG-3'

Lambda DNA, diluted to 0.1 µg/mL and 0.1 µg/mL

Thermal cycler

Agarose, 2% in 1X electrophoresis buffer

Electrophoresis buffer, 1X TAE or 1X LB

DNA loading dye, 10X for TAE gels or 5X LB loading dye for LB gels

DNA standard markers, such as G-Biosciences DNAmark™ 1kb Plus Ladder

Gel box and power supply

Weigh boat 5.5" × 5.5"

Ethidium bromide, 0.5 µg/mL or 1X LabSafe Nucleic Acid Stain™

Photo-imaging system

Non-BABEC Users: The materials list above allows a class to conduct the lambda PCR procedure as written using individual ingredients, which is the preferred method for a first PCR activity when the goal is skill development. Similar, although not identical, kits, materials, and activities are available from several vendors and some biotechnology educational support groups.

BABEC Users: Members of BABEC may participate in the BABEC equipment loan program and materials support available for this activity.

Procedure

- Be sure to pipet a mixture up and down gently after adding a new reagent to ensure proper mixing. Change tips each time you measure and dispense any reagent.

Part I: Pre-Lab–Preparation of Reagents (for 16 lab groups)

1. On the day of use, prepare 200 µL of 0.25X *Taq* polymerase by diluting 50 µL of the stock *Taq* polymerase in 150 µL of sterile, distilled dH$_2$O. Keep on ice.
2. Prepare 200 µL each of 0.1 µg/mL and 0.1 ng/mL lambda DNA, using sterile, deionized water as the diluent. Label these tubes D$_1$ and D$_2$, respectively.
3. Prepare 100 µL of 10 µM forward primer (P$_F$). Use the mass on the sample and the molecular weight of P$_F$ as 7201.7 g/mol to make the calculation.
4. Prepare 100 µL of 10 µM reverse primer (P$_R$). Use the mass on the sample and the molecular weight of P$_R$ as 7454.9 g/mol to make the calculation.

Part II: Preparing PCR Reaction

1. Work in pairs. Obtain three 0.2-mL tubes. Using a fine-tipped permanent marker, label each tube with your lab initials and either "D$_1$," or "D$_2$" for the DNA samples or "–C" for the negative control.
2. Add the following reagents into each tube in the order listed (see Table 13.5). "Wrist-flick" samples to the bottom after each addition. Keep all reagents on ice.
3. Make sure the tubes are closed tightly. Give them a wrist-flick to pool the samples. Place each labeled tube into the thermal cycler. Record the tube position on the thermal cycler chart and in your notebook.
4. Record/copy the thermal cycling program shown on the thermal cycler. Explain what happens in each stage of the thermal cycling.
5. Run the thermal cycling program: 95°C for 2 min; then 94°C for 15 sec, 37°C for 15 sec, and 72°C for 15 sec for 25 cycles; 72°C for 7 min; 4°C for an infinite time period.
6. When the thermal cycling is completed, add DNA loading dye (5 µL for TAE or 10 µL LB depending on which electrophoresis buffer is used) to each PCR product tube. Store at 4°C until you are ready to run a gel.

Table 13.5. Lambda DNA PCR Reaction Matrix

Reagent	Lambda DNA, (D₁), (µL)	Lambda DNA, (D₂), (µL)	Negative Control (-C), (µL)
distilled water	26.0	26.0	31.0
10X PCR buffer	5.0	5.0	5.0
25 mM MgCl$_2$	3.0	3.0	3.0
10 mM dNTP mix	4.0	4.0	4.0
Taq polymerase 0.5x	2.0	2.0	2.0
Forward primer (P$_F$)	2.5	2.5	2.5
Reverse primer (P$_R$)	2.5	2.5	2.5
lambda DNA D₁ or D₂	5.0	5.0	—
final volume	**50.0**	**50.0**	**50.0**

Part III: Running PCR Products on Agarose Gel

1. Prepare a six-well, 2% agarose gel in 1X TAE buffer (review the procedure in Lab 4i).
2. Load the following samples into the gel.

   Well 1: nothing
   Well 2: 5 µL of 100-bp DNA standard markers
   Well 3: 25 µL of your Tube D₁ (lambda PCR product)
   Well 4: 25 µL of your Tube D₂ (lambda PCR product)
   Well 5: 25 µL of your Tube C (control-tube PCR product)
   Well 6: nothing

Environmental Health and Safety Officer

3. Draw a diagram of the gel in your notebook showing what was loaded into each well. Also, record the concentration of the gel and the type of buffer used.
4. Run the gel until the loading dye is 2/3 down the gel (15 minutes for a LB gel at 300 V or 45 minutes for a TAE gel at 115 V).
5. Stain the gel in either 1X LabSafe Nucleic Acid Stain™ or EtBr solution for at least 30 minutes. Rinse in deionized water. Visualize on a UV-light box and photograph it.
   Note: Only the supervisor is to use EtBr. Wear goggles and gloves where EtBr is in use.
6. Label the gel photo. Include labels for what was loaded in each well—the standard sizes, the primers, any primer bands (individual primer or primer-dimer), and the sizes of the PCR products.

Data Analysis/Conclusion

Is there evidence of PCR product? If so, how many PCR products per lane and what are the sizes in base pairs? How does template DNA concentration affect the results? Compare your results with those of fellow technicians, and compare replications of the experiment. Do other replications support your data? Are there any bands in the negative control sample? Explain. Describe any unexpected bands and any possible explanations for their presence. If your gel confirms the presence of PCR product, what are possible applications for this product? How is this kind of information or product utilized in research and industry?

Thinking Like a Biotechnician

1. A technician finds a long, white smear of DNA in a PCR product lane from about 500 bp down to 100 bp. What might be the cause of such a smear?
2. What might cause many bands at random positions in all lanes, including the control?
3. In this PCR protocol, a concentration of 25 mM MgCl$_2$ was used. How does one know that 25 mM MgCl$_2$ gives the best PCR product? Design an optimization of the MgCl$_2$ experiment that tests the effect of varying the concentration of MgCl$_2$ in the lambda PCR reaction.

Laboratory 13f

Extracting DNA from Human Cells for PCR and Sequencing

This lab is adapted with permission from Genetic Origins (www.geneticorigins.org), © Dolan DNA Learning Center, under the direction of David A. Micklos. This version is based on a modification developed for use by BABEC-member teachers and students by Frank Stephenson, PhD, Applied Biosystems, Inc., and Maria Abilock, BABEC. Alternative kits and materials are listed under "Materials for Non-BABEC Users" in Laboratory 13g.

Background

With a few precautions, DNA can be extracted from cells for PCR or DNA sequencing in much the same way as DNA is extracted from bacteria cells. Cells may be burst open and proteins precipitated out of solution (see Figure 13.5).

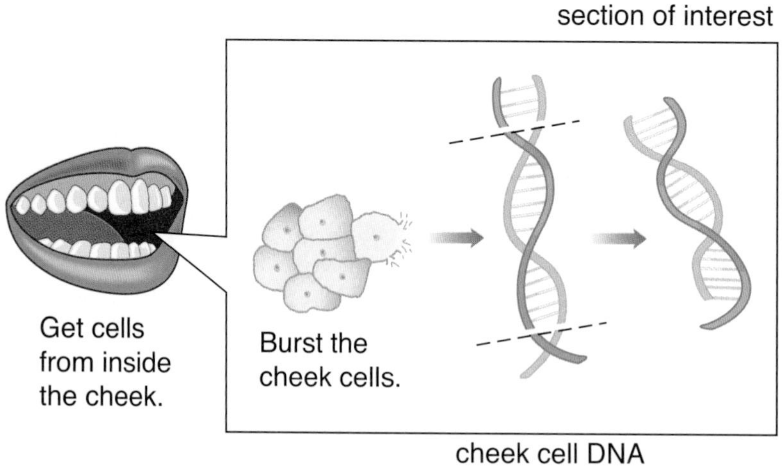

Figure 13.5. **Cheek Cell DNA Isolation.**

Ions that are released from the cell can interfere with Taq polymerase activity and inhibit the PCR reaction. To remove the ions out of the DNA sample, a step is added using the chelating agent, Chelex® (Bio-Rad Laboratories, Inc.) chelating beads. Chelating agents bind ions and remove them from solution. Although some ions are needed in PCR, the technician adds the desired ions at the an appropriate concentration when they are needed.

Purpose

To isolate human DNA from cheek cells for PCR and DNA-sequencing analysis.

Materials

Balance, weigh boats, scoops
Sodium chloride
Tubes, 50 mL, sterile and rack
Filtering flasks, 250 mL
Vacuum pump and "trap" jar
Pipets, 10 mL and pump

Paper cup
Micropipets and tips
Reaction tubes, 1.5 mL
  and rack
Permanent lab marker pens
Microcentrifuge

Chelex® resin beads
  G-Biosciences #BTNM-0024
Vortex mixer
Lid locks, for 1.5 mL tubes
Dry block heater/heat block,
  99°C

Procedure

Part I: Reagent Preparation

1. For a team of four, prepare 50 mL of 0.9% NaCl solution. In your notebook, record the calculation for this preparation and include a drawing of how it is prepared.
2. Filter sterilize the 50 mL of 0.9% NaCl solution using a filter flask and vacuum apparatus. Label the filter flask and store the solution at room temperature.

Part II: DNA Extraction and Preparation

Environmental Health and Safety Officer

- Do not eat or drink anything for at least 30 minutes before collecting a cheek-cell sample.
- To prevent possible disease transmission, discard all used cups and extra saliva after use.

1. Using a sterile pipet, transfer 10 mL of 0.9% NaCl (saline) solution into a paper cup. Place the 10 mL of saline in your mouth and vigorously swish for 30 seconds.
2. Expel the saline solution into a cup. Cells lining the inside of the mouth are in the saline solution.
3. Swirl to mix the cells in the cup, and transfer 1000 µL of the liquid into a 1.7-mL tube.
4. In a balanced centrifuge, spin your sample tube for 1 minute.
5. Carefully, pour off and discard the supernatant. **Careful! Do not disturb the pellet of cells.**
6. Add 30 µL of fresh 0.9% saline solution, and pipet in and out to resuspend the cell pellet. It is critical that all the cells in the pellet are resuspended.

99°C

7. Withdraw 30 µL of the cell suspension and add it to a previously prepared 1.7-mL tube containing 200 µL of 5% Chelex® resin beads. Shake well or vortex briefly to mix.
   Note: It is critical that the correct amount of Chelex® beads is used. When getting the 200 µL of Chelex®, invert the tube containing the Chelex® beads just before measuring to suspend them.
8. Secure the tube containing the cell suspension and Chelex® with a locking cap, and place the tube in a 99°C heat block for 10 minutes. During this time, the sample will boil and the cells will burst open, releasing their contents, including DNA. Transfer to ice for 1 minute.
9. Shake your tube well, or vortex briefly, and place the tube in a balanced centrifuge for 1 minute. The purpose of this step is to move all of the Chelex® resin beads to the bottom of the tube.
10. Using a new tip, extract 60 µL of the cheek-cell DNA sample and place it into a new, *labeled* tube. **Do not transfer any Chelex® beads with the DNA sample.**
11. Store your cheek-cell DNA sample at 4°C for up to 1 week for later use in PCR or DNA sequencing. Long-term storage should be at –20°C.

Thinking Like a Biotechnician

1. How could the purity and concentration of the check-cell DNA sample be determined?
2. Do these cheek-cell DNA sample tubes contain genomic DNA? Yes or no? Explain.

Laboratory 13g
DNA Typing by PCR-Genotype Determination of an Alu Insert

This lab is adapted with permission from Genetic Origins (www.geneticorigins.org), © Dolan DNA Learning Center, under the direction of David A. Micklos. This version is a modification developed for use by BABEC-member teachers and students by Frank Stephenson, PhD, Applied Biosystems, Inc., and Maria Abilock, BABEC. Alternative kits and materials are listed under "Materials for Non-BABEC Users."

Background

In this experiment, PCR is used to amplify a region (locus) of human DNA. The region of interest is called an "Alu insert." The Alu insert is a sequence of DNA of approximately 300 bp long. The sequence is called an Alu insert because it contains an Alu restriction-enzyme site.

Over millions of years, the Alu sequence has been copied and reinserted rather randomly throughout the primate genome. There are approximately 1.2 million copies of Alu in the human genome. These sections appear to have originated from DNA coding for ribosomal RNA.

The Alu sequence (300 bp in length) we are looking for, PV92, is one that has inserted itself into a particular region (noncoding regions) on chromosome No. 16. Primers may be designed to recognize a section (415 bp long) of PV92. Each person possesses two alleles for this particular Alu insert, one from each parent. This mutation (change in the genome at PV92) arose in some geographic region and people have carried it to other parts of the world. By genotyping the human population, scientists can propose theories for the origin of the PV92 mutation.

There are three possible genotypes an individual may have for the Alu locus. A person can have two Alu inserts (A+A+), one from each parent, so there are two chromosomes with the same alleles at the same locus (see Figure 13.6).

Individuals may have one chromosome with the Alu insert and one without it (A+A-), so there are two chromosomes with the different alleles at the same locus (see Figure 13.7).

Individuals may have two chromosomes with no Alu insert (A-A-), so there are two chromosomes with the same alleles at the same locus (see Figure 13.8).

On a gel, A+A+ individuals (homozygotes) will have a band only at approximately 715 bp (300 + 415). A+A- individuals (heterozygotes) will have bands at approximately 415 bp and 715 bp. A-A- individuals (homozygotes) will have bands only at approximately 415 bp.

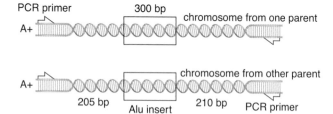

Figure 13.6. **A+A+ Alu Genotype.**

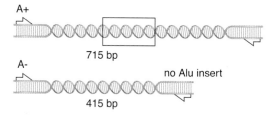

Figure 13.7. **A+A- Alu Genotype.**

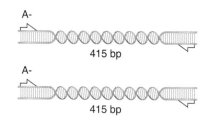

Figure 13.8. **A-A- Alu Genotype.**

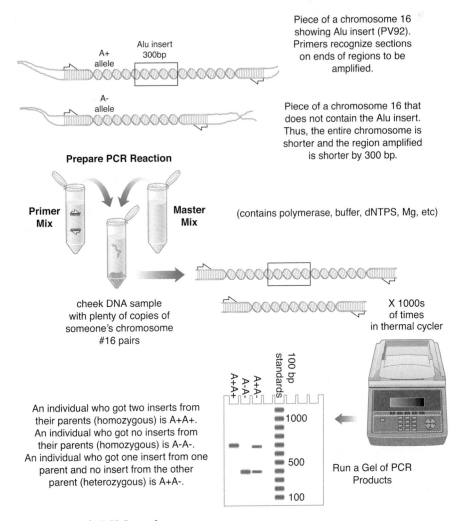

Figure 13.9. Alu PCR Procedures.

Piece of a chromosome 16 showing Alu insert (PV92). Primers recognize sections on ends of regions to be amplified.

Piece of a chromosome 16 that does not contain the Alu insert. Thus, the entire chromosome is shorter and the region amplified is shorter by 300 bp.

Prepare PCR Reaction

Primer Mix

Master Mix   (contains polymerase, buffer, dNTPS, Mg, etc)

cheek DNA sample with plenty of copies of someone's chromosome #16 pairs

X 1000s of times in thermal cycler

An individual who got two inserts from their parents (homozygous) is A+A+.
An individual who got no inserts from their parents (homozygous) is A-A-.
An individual who got one insert from one parent and no insert from the other parent (heterozygous) is A+A-.

Run a Gel of PCR Products

To find the Alu loci, primers are added that recognize the DNA on each end of the Alu locus to be amplified. The PCR duplicates the sections into billions of pieces in a few hours (see Figure 13.9). The fragments are run on a gel to be visualized and analyzed.

Purpose

What are your genotypes for this Alu (PV92) insert on chromosome No. 16?
What are the frequencies for each genotype within the class population?

Materials

Gloves and safety goggles
PCR tubes, 0.2 mL
Micropipets, P-100 and P-10, and sterile, aerosol-plugged tips
Distilled water, sterile, nuclease-free
Primer mix, 1000 µL (500 µL of each) primer at 1 µM (sequence from **biotech.emcp.net /geneticorigins_alu**, order from **www.idtdna.com**):

Forward primer =
  5'-GGATCTCAGGGT-GGGTGGCAATGCT-3'
Reverse primer =
  5'-GAAAGGCA-AGCTACC-AGAAGCCCCAA-3'
Master mix, G-Biosciences #786-449
Prepared cheek cell DNA samples (from Lab 13f)
Thermal cycler
Agarose, 2% in 1X electrophoresis buffer

Electrophoresis buffer, 1X TAE or 1X LB
DNA loading dye, 10X for TAE gels or 5X LB loading dye for LB gels
DNA standard markers/ladder, 100 bp
Gel box and power supply
Weigh boat 5.5"×5.5"
Ethidium bromide, 0.5 µg/mL or 1X LabSafe Nucleic Acid Stain™
Photo-imaging system

Non-BABEC Users: The materials list above allows a class to conduct the Alu PCR procedure as written using a commercial master mix. The procedures are modifications of a version originally found at biotech.emcp.net/geneticorigins_alu.

Similar, although not identical, Alu PCR kits, materials, and activities are available from several vendors (including G-Biosciences #305) and some biotechnology educational support groups.

BABEC Users: Members of BABEC may participate in the equipment loan program and materials support available for this activity.

Procedure

- Use new pipet tips for each transfer. Measure carefully.
- Do not touch the inside of the tube.

Part I: Setting Up the PCR Tubes

1. Obtain a sterile 0.2-mL PCR tube.
2. Using a fine-tip permanent marker, label the PCR tube on the top with your ID number.
3. Add 25 μL of master mix to the tube. What is in the master mix? What is the advantage of using a "master mix"?
4. Add 25 μL of the primer mix **directly into** the master mix in the bottom of the PCR tube.
5. Pipet up and down several times to mix the contents of the tube.
6. Give the PCR tube a quick "wrist-flick" to pool the mixture into the bottom of the tube.
7. Add 10 μL of your prepared cheek-cell DNA sample to your master-mix/primer-mix tube. **Take the DNA only from the top of the tube contents. Make sure there are no Chelex® resin beads contaminating your sample.**
8. Give the PCR tube a quick "wrist-flick" to pool the mixture into the bottom of the tube. Pipet up and down several times to mix the contents of the tube.
9. Again, give the PCR tube a quick "wrist-flick" to pool the mixture into the bottom of the tube.
10. Positive (+c) and (-c) negative controls should be made and run as space allows.
    The +control contains 25 μL master mix, 15 μL primer mix, 10 μL control DNA (from an individual with a known Alu genotype).
    The -control contains 10 μL sterile water, 25 μL master mix, 15 μL primer mix.

Part II: Running the PCR Reaction

1. Make sure the thermal cycler has been programmed for this Alu PCR reaction (see Table 13.6)

Table 13.6. **Alu PCR Thermal Cycle Program** (30 cycles)

Temperature (°C)	Time	Purpose of Step
95	10 min	polymerase activation and initial denaturation
94	30 sec/cycle	denaturation
60	30 sec/cycle	annealing
72	120 sec (2 min)/cycle	extension of strands
72	10 min	final extension
4	∞	storage

2. Put your PCR tube(s) in the thermal cycler. In your notebook, record the position of your tube(s) in the thermal cycler. Also, mark the position of your tube(s) on the thermal cycler diagram provided.
3. When all samples are in the thermal cycler, start the program. After the program is completed, the samples remain in the thermal cycler at 4°C until the next day.
4. Prepare a 2% agarose gel in 1X electrophoresis buffer for loading. Draw a diagram of the gel in your notebook showing what was loaded into each well. Mark the position of your sample(s) on the gel diagram. Also, record the concentration of the gel and the type of buffer used.

5. Add DNA loading dye (5 μL for TAE or 10 μL LB depending on which electrophoresis buffer is used) to the PCR tube(s). Cap the tube(s), and wrist-flick the dye to the bottom.
6. Mix the contents of the PCR tube by gently flicking the bottom of the tube with your fingers (a finger-flick). Give the PCR tube a quick "wrist-flick" to pool the mixture into the bottom of the tube.
7. Load 5 μL of DNA standards (100 bp markers) into Well 6 of the gel.
8. Load 25 μL of each sample into a well. Several individuals' samples may be run on one gel. Include a +c and -c sample.

Part III: Running the Gels

1. Plug the gel box into the power supply. Turn on the power supply and run the gel at 115 V.
2. Run the gel until the loading dye is approximately 2 cm from the bottom of the gel (15 minutes for a LB gel at 300 V or 45 minutes for a TAE gel at 115 V).

Part IV: Staining the Gels

Environmental Health and Safety Officer

1. Transfer the gel to a weigh boat.
2. Carefully, pour off the buffer, and add DNA stain to just cover the gel. Stain for 30 minutes. **Caution: Only the supervisor is to use EtBr. Wear goggles and gloves where EtBr is in use. Wipe spills immediately.**
3. Pour off the stain and save for future staining. Rinse the gel in distilled water.
4. Place the gel on a UV-light box. Observe the bands and determine their size in base pairs by comparing them with the DNA size standards.
5. Take a photograph of the gel using a photoimaging system.
6. Glue your photograph into your notebook. Label the gel photo with the type of gel and running conditions. Label the gel wells with what was loaded into each.
7. Identify your genotype for the Alu locus. Record this in the data section.
8. Make a data table to record the frequency of each genotype in the sample population. Does it appear that the Alu insert mutation is found more frequently in one ethnicity than another?
9. Compare these population frequency data with those reported at the Allele Server Internet site of the Dolan DNA Learning Center of Cold Spring Harbor Laboratory.

   - Go to **biotech.emp.net/bioservers**.
   - Click "Enter" under "Allele Server."
   - Click the question mark (?) at the upper right corner for directions on accessing data sets or entering your own group data. (Check with your instructor if you are unsure about the steps.)

10. Go to **www.bioservers.org/html/sad/sad.html** Click on "Manage Groups" Select Group Type "Reference" Pick 10 groups from the 7 continents and plot their Allele frequencies on a world map.

Thinking Like a Biotechnician

1. Why is the band for 415 bp so much darker than the band for 715 bp?
2. Considering the class's data and the data reported at the Allele Server, why are there so few of one genotype compared with the others?
3. Although Alu PCR gives you genotype information about one human locus, it is not very valuable in distinguishing between individuals. This is because it only has three possible genotypes. A more useful DNA fingerprinting locus is D1S80. Use the Internet to learn about D1S80 and how it is used in DNA fingerprinting. Create a half-page fact sheet about D1S80 and its use.

Laboratory 13h
Confirming the Amylase Gene Using PCR

Background

The pAmylase 2014 (pAmy2014) plasmid is a recombinant plasmid containing the amylase gene. It is used to transform *E. coli* cells into amylase producers. It is believed that the pAmy2014 plasmid (see Figure 13.10) was constructed by inserting the amylase gene from the bacterium *Geobacillus stearothermophilus* into an existing plasmid (pUC57).

After a transformation of *E. coli* cells with pAmy 2014, the plasmid DNA can be extracted out of the transformed cells using a mini-prep protocol (Labs 8f or 8g). Confirmation of the plasmid as pAmy 2014 may be done through restriction digestion (Lab 8b). In addition, the presence of the amylase gene on pAmy 2014 (or in the source DNA from the original bacterium) may be confirmed through PCR.

To conduct a PCR reaction to recognize the amylase gene, primers are designed to recognize a specific, unique region (in this case, a 388 bp section) on the target DNA. Using a thermal cycling protocol and a master mix of *Taq* polymerase, dNTPs, and buffer, the target amylase DNA region may be amplified. The amplified DNA is visible on an agarose gel as a band at 388 bp.

The amylase gene PCR protocol used in this activity was developed using a known sample of pAmylase 2014. The primers were designed to recognize the 388 bp section of the plasmid's amylase gene. Theoretically, the amylase PCR protocol developed for pAmy 2014 should also recognize the same sequence in the original amylase gene in DNA extracted from the original source bacterium, *Geobacillus stearothermophilus* (also called *Bacillus stearothermophilus*). *Geobacillus stearothermophilus* is a rod-shaped, Gram-positive bacterium, It prefers warm temperatures and thrives in soil and hot springs. In this activity, DNA from the bacteria will be extracted and the genomic DNA will be tested by PCR for the presence of the amylase gene.

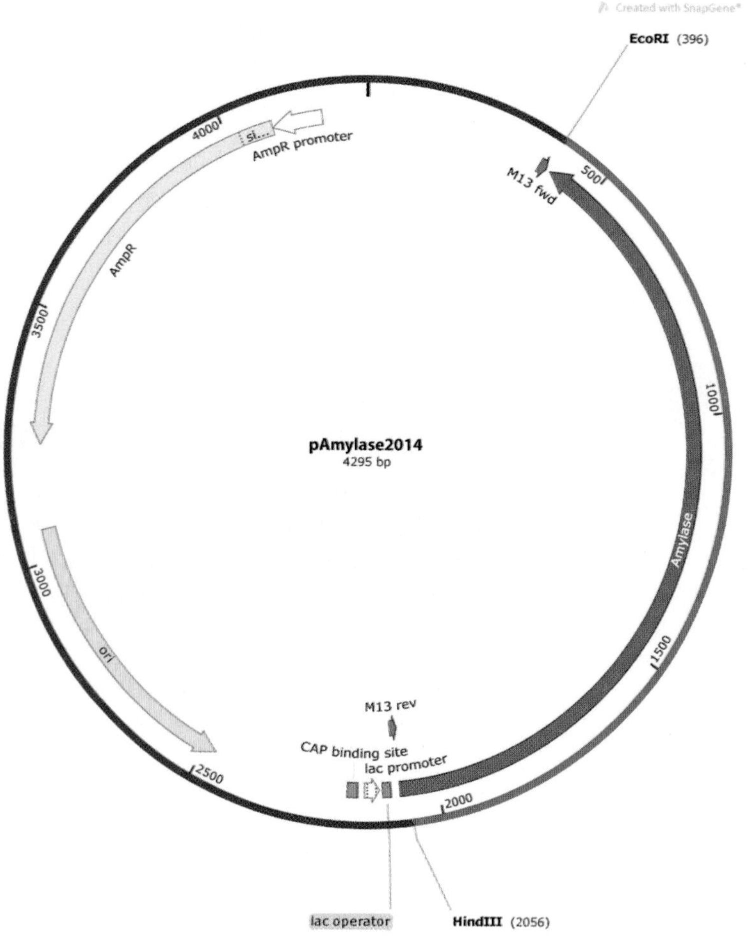

Figure 13.10. pAmylase2014 Plasmid. pAmylase contains the amylase gene. In cells, the amylase gene is transcribed and amylase is produced. Starch clearing occurs on Luria Bertani (LB) starch agar plates around colonies that are transformed with pAmylase2014. An AmpR gene is also part of pAmylase2014. The AmpR gene allows a second way to detect that the plasmid got into cells, since only E. coli cells transformed with the AmpR gene will grow on ampicillin agar.

Purpose

Using the PCR protocol developed for amylase gene amplification in pAmylase2014, can a 388 bp sequence of the amylase gene be recognized in extracted *Geobacillus stearothermophilus* DNA?

Materials

Gloves and safety goggles
Reaction tubes, 1.5 mL and racks
Geobacillus stearothermophilus, stock sample (plate or tube)
Tryptic soy agar plates
Tryptic soy broth, sterile
Media bottles, 250 mL
Bunsen burner
Lab gas lighter
Inoculating loop, Ni/Cr wire
Incubator, 58°C, shaking
DNA extraction kit, genomic DNA such as G-Biosciences XIT™ Genomic DNA from Gram Positive Bacteria kit #786-339
Microcentrifuge, high-speed
UV spectrophotometer and UV-cuvettes, 50 μL or G-Biosciences Nucleic dotMETRIC™ Assay
Distilled water, sterile, DNase-free
PCR tubes, 0.2 mL

Micropipets, P-100 and P-10, and sterile, aerosol-plugged tips
0.2 μg/μL pAmylase2014
PCR Master Mix, 2X, G-Biosciences #786-449
Forward primer, 10 μM,
  5'-GTCACGACTTCGG-
  GATGATCCATATCAAGG-3',
  www.idtdna.com
Reverse primer, 10 μM,
  5'-CTCAATATCTTCAA-
  GCCATTCAAGCCGCCC-3',
  www.idtdna.com
Thermal cycler
Agarose, 2% in 1X electrophoresis buffer
Electrophoresis buffer, 1X TAE or 1X LB
DNA loading dye, 10X for TAE gels or 5X LB loading dye for LB gels
DNA standard marker such as G-Biosciences DNAmark™ 1kb Plus Ladder
Gel box and power supply
Weigh boat 5.5" × 5.5"
Ethidium bromide, 0.5 μg/mL or 1X LabSafe Nucleic Acid Stain™
Photo-imaging system

Safety Precautions

- Use sterile technique for the cell culture steps, including a laminar flow hood, if available.
- Dispose of all biohazards appropriately.
- Gloves and goggles are required when using EtBr.
- Only the instructor should use EtBr.

Procedure

Part I: Pre-Lab (2 days prior to Part II)

1. Use a stock plate or tube of *Geobacillus stearothermophilus* to streak a few tryptic soy agar plate cultures to use as stock plates for the class. Incubate upside-down for 24 hours at 55°C. Parafilm® the plates and store at room temperature until the start of Part II.
2. In a 250-mL media bottle, prepare 100 mL of sterile tryptic soy broth.
3. Using a colony from the stock plate, start an overnight culture of *Geobacillus stearothermophilus* in the tryptic soy broth. Incubate for 24 hours at 55°C, shaking at 250 rpm.
4. Using a commercially available gDNA extraction kit, such as G-Biosciences *XIT*™ Genomic DNA from Gram Positive Bacteria kit #786-339, extract the *Geobacillus stearothermophilus* gDNA.
5. Estimate the concentration of the extracted sample through UV spectrophotometry or using a nucleic acid colorimetric dot assay.
6. Prepare two samples of the gDNA that are thought to have a concentration of 0.1 and 0.01 μg/μL, respectively. Using sterile dH$_2$O as the diluent, prepare 4 μL of each sample. Label these diluted samples D1 and D2, respectively.
7. Prepare 4 μL of the 0.1 μg/μL pAmylase2014 from the 0.2 μg/μL pAmylase2014 stock sample using sterile dH$_2$O as the diluent. Label this tube +C.

Part II: PCR Reactions

1. Label four 0.2-mL PCR tubes "D1," "D2," "+C," and "-C," respectively.
2. Using a micropipet with a fresh aerosol-plug tip each time, add PCR reagents in the order listed on the reaction matrix (see Table 13.7), adding one reagent directly into the other.

Table 13.7. **Amylase Gene PCR Reaction Matrix**

Reagent	Volume (µL) Tube "D1"	Volume (µL) Tube "D2"	Volume (µL) Tube "+C"	Volume (µL) Tube "-C"
nuclease free water	15	15	15	19
Promega master mix	25	25	25	25
DNA sample (from D1, D2, or +C	4	4	4	0
forward primer, 10 µ	3	3	3	3
reverse primer, 10 µM	3	3	3	3

3. Pool each 50-µL sample with a 2-second centrifuge spin.
4. Program to the thermocycler to run the Amylase Gene PCR program (see Table 13.8).
5. After the cycles are complete, PCR reactions can be refrigerated at 4°C or prepared for electrophoresis.

Table 13.8. **Amylase Gene PCR Program.**

Temperature (°C)	Time	Purpose of Step
95	120 sec	initial activation
95	30 sec	denaturation
60	45 sec	annealing
72	45 sec	extension of strands
72	5 min	final extension
4	∞	storage

Part III: Analysis of PCR Products

1. To prepare the samples for electrophoresis, add DNA loading dye (5 μL for TAE or 10 µL LB depending on which electrophoresis buffer is used) to each tube.
2. Load and run samples (25 µL of each) in the first four wells of a 2% agarose gel in 1X electrophoresis buffer. Run 5 µL of 1 kbp DNA sizing standards in Lane 5.
3. Immediately after running, stain the gel in DNA stain for 30 minutes. Rinse the gel in dH$_2$O and photograph it using an imaging system.
4. Glue the gel image into your notebook and label it. Label the wells and the sizing standards pieces, and identify the PCR product bands on the gel. Also, identify any excess primer bands on the gel.

Data Analysis/Conclusion

Discuss how well the PCR protocol amplified a 388-bp band from the positive control (pAmylase2014 sample). Is there any PCR product in the unknown samples (diluted *Geobacillus stearothermophilus* gDNA samples)? If yes, what is the size of this PCR product(s)? Did either of the dilutions amplify better than the other? What can be concluded from the bands in the unknown sample lanes?

Thinking Like a Biotechnician

1. When the gel of the PCR products is run, a 388-bp band of lighter intensity is seen in the negative control sample. List three ways this unexpected result could occur.
2. When the gel of the PCR products is run, the only bands seen anywhere on the gel are in the sizing standard sample. Which reactant or ingredient missing in the PCR reaction could yield this result if accidentally left out of the PCR reaction tubes?
3. When the gel of the PCR products is run, a bright smear of DNA bands is up high on the gel near the well. Explain how this unexpected result could occur.

Laboratory 13i
Optimizing a PCR Reaction

Background

The goal of PCR is to recognize a specific section of DNA and then make billions of copies of it, and no other fragments, in a short time. Many variables affect the success of a given PCR protocol. Since each PCR reaction is unique, each reaction has specific optimum conditions to produce the maximum amount of the "cleanest" PCR product.

In the early stages of PCR process development, optimization experiments are conducted to determine the ideal conditions for each variable used in the amplification. Having each reactant at an "optimum" concentration and volume, as well as choosing the "best" cycling times and temperatures and the "right" number of cycles ensures that the amplification proceeds efficiently producing a maximum yield of DNA product.

Each variable in the PCR protocol must be tested separately to measure its effect on product yield. These include:

- Primer length and sequence
- Primer concentration
- Template concentration
- *Taq* polymerase type and concentration
- Deoxynucleotide (dNTP) concentration
- Magnesium chloride concentration
- PCR Reaction buffer ingredients and concentration
- Thermal cycling times and temperatures
- Number of thermal cycles

The protocol in Lab 13h is based on using a commercially available PCR Master Mix. But, is that Master Mix and the other variables in the reaction optimized to produce the brightest single band of PCR product, with no other extra bands in the samples or the negative control?

In this experiment, the goal is to optimize, one of the reagent variables for the Lab 13h Amylase Gene PCR reaction. Using the individual reagent ingredients in Lab 13e (Lambda DNA PCR) and the basic PCR protocol in Lab 13h, optimize one reagent variable to produce, visualize, and quantify the 388 bp PCR product on a 2% gel and using a nucleic acid indicator.

Purpose

How does varying _____ (add the variable to be tested) affect PCR product yield?

General Procedure

- Read through the entire Lab 13e and Lab 13h procedures in the lab manual, the results of those experiments, and this entire sheet before your start to do the lab procedure design. Confirm with the supervisor the volume and concentration of stock reagents that are available for you to use.
- Select a reagent variable to optimize and test. Consider the importance of the reagent variable, what concentration and or amount was used in Lab 13e and how you might varying that to form 4 variations of the reagent to test.
- Create/type/and turn in a lab sheet proposal to your supervisor for approval. Include a/an:
  - Title
  - Purpose Question
  - Materials List
  - Procedures (step by step, short and easy to understand so that anyone can follow them to conduct the PCR experiment, with all reagent quantities and concentrations)
  - Reaction Matrix that shows what reagents at what volume and concentration will be mixed in each 50-μL PCR reaction tube.
  - Hypothesis statement of what you think might happen during the reaction and what will be seen on the gel.

- Have your proposal reviewed and approved by your supervisor.
- With an approved proposal, conduct the entire PCR optimization protocol and run PCR products on a 2% agarose gel (as in Labs 13e and 13h).
- Print up the completed lab sheet including a labeled gel diagram. Label the samples loaded, standard marker bands, PCR product, primer, primer/dimer, any whole plasmid, and any random or unexpected bands.
- Include a REE/PE/PA conclusion in your lab report.

14 Biotechnology Research and Applications

Kamrun Zargar, PhD
Biofuels Pathways, Fuel Synthesis
Joint BioEnergy Institute (JBEI)
Emeryville, CA

Dr. Kamrun Zargar studies microbes living in extreme environments such as hot springs, salty or acidic lakes, or in the deep ocean. He thinks these extreme microbes may be the key to finding hotter burner biofuel molecules. Kamrun studies the unique compounds made by anaerobic bacteria living in the sludge of hot springs in Yellowstone Park. He is looking for compounds with aromatic carbon rings that burn even hotter than known bioalcohols. His work requires use of a sterile, anaerobic biosafety hood, pictured here. Kamrun grows bacterial cultures and isolates compounds of interest from the growth media. He uses analytical instruments including LCMS (Liquid Chromatography coupled to Mass Spectrometry) and GCMS (Gas Chromatography coupled to Mass Spectrometry) to identify, isolate and quantify volatile compounds in the anaerobic cell cultures. Kamrun is also interested in the chemical interactions between different extreme microbes in their local ecosystems.

Photo by author.

Throughout this lab manual, methods of recognizing and characterizing biological molecules or reactions have been presented. DNA extractions and preparations, DNA gel analysis, DNA synthesis, and PCR are essential for DNA identification, fingerprinting, sequencing, and genomics. Similarly, protein extraction and preparations, PAGE, ELISA, Western blots, protein assays, spectrophotometry, and chromatography are necessary for proteomic work.

All of these molecular biology procedures and biotechnologies are applied when scientists study medicine, the environment, biofuel production, biodefense, and animal health care. The research techniques are similar from one application to another. PCR and electrophoresis, for example, are used in virtually every lab. It is not uncommon to have a scientist or technician engineering plants at an agricultural biotech facility, then move to a biotechnology company whose focus is medical biotechnology. The skills are transferable.

In the following activities, you will learn how some biotechnologies are applied in the field of environmental biotechnology. Specifically, you will learn how to do the following:
- conduct an assay to measure chromium ion assimilation by the bioremediation bacterium, *Shewanella oneidensis* MR-1
- set up and run an assay to measure the activity of an enzyme important in biofuel production
- test a species of bacteria to measure its ability to metabolize oil as a potential bioremediation of oil spills
- isolate a naturally occurring insecticide (bioinsecticide) and test its effectiveness

As you continue your training in biotechnology and gain experience in the laboratory, you will have the opportunity to apply the techniques you have learned to many applications that may contribute to products or processes that clean the environment and improve the quality of life for all of us.

Laboratory 14a
Biofuel Enzyme Assay

Inspired by a protocol from Worthington Biomedical at: biotech.emcp.net/Worthington-biochem. Modified by Arun Asundi, Biotechnology student, 2010.

Background

With the need to develop alternate fuels, bioethanol production from cellulostic biomass is a process that is receiving a lot of attention. The process is a complicated one and has several chemical and enzymatic steps. See biotech.emcp.net/biofuelprocess for a diagram describing the process.

One enzyme that is used in the conversion of cellulose to ethanol is cellulase. As one of the first steps in bioethanol production, cellulase breaks down cellulose to glucose. Then glucose is fermented to ethanol.

Several decomposition fungi make cellulase. Two known cellulase-producing fungi are *Aspergillus niger* and *Trichoderma viridae*. Each species' cellulase is slightly different in its structure and activity. Determining which cellulase from which species works best (producing the most glucose in the shortest amount of time) would be important for scientists optimizing cellulostic biofuel production.

Purpose

What is the difference in activity (glucose production) of two different samples of cellulase?

Materials

Deionized water
Tubes, 50 mL, sterile and racks
Cellulase, *Aspergillus niger*
Cellulase, *Trichoderma viridae*
Cellulase, from other sources, (if available)
Glucose
Balance, weigh boats, lab scoops
Pipets and pumps

Tubes, 15 mL, sterile and racks
Cellulose, microcrystalline, 25 g, G-Biosciences #BTNM-0023
Acetic acid, 0.05*M*, *Use gloves and goggles*
Incubator, 37°C, shaking
Centrifuge, 15-mL rotor
Glucose test strips

Reaction tubes, 1.7 mL and racks
Micropipets and tips
Benedict's solution
Hot plate/stirrer
Beaker, 250 mL
Culture tubes, 13 × 100-mm
Peg rack, for 13 × 100-mm tubes
Test tube holders, Stoddard

Procedure

Day 1

Part I: Pre-Lab

1. For each brand of cellulase, prepare 5 mL of 4 mg/mL cellulase in deionized water.
2. Prepare a set of glucose standards (glucose in deionized water). Using a 1:2 serial dilution and starting at 200 mg/dL, prepare 4 mL of seven samples of decreasing concentration.

Part II: Setup of Experimental Trials

1. In labeled 15-mL conical tubes, prepare cellulase assay sample tubes (A and T) and a negative control (–C) assay tube by adding the reagents listed in Table 14.1 to each tube. Add the samples in the order they are listed. *Wear gloves and goggles.*
2. Cap the tubes and invert 5 times to mix.
3. Place samples in a test tube rack in a 37°C shaking incubator (300 rpm). Incubate for 24 hours.

Table 14.1.   Cellulase Activity Assay Reaction Matrix

Reagent	Tube A (cellulase from *Aspergillus*)	Tube T (cellulase from *Trichoderma*)*	-C (negative control)
dH$_2$O	0	0	I mL
0.05 *M* acetic acid	4.0 mL	4.0 mL	4.0 mL
cellulase (4 mg/mL)	I mL	I mL	0
cellulose	200 mg	200 mg	200 mg

* or cellulase from a different source

Day 2

Part III: Glucose Assay

1. After 24 hours, place the samples on ice for 2 minutes to cool to room temperature.
2. Spin the tubes in a centrifuge at about 3000 × g for 5 minutes. The supernatant contains glucose from the degradation of the cellulose samples.
3. Pipet the supernatant into labeled 15-mL tubes. Make sure the sample that is transferred is clear and does not contain fragments of the cellulose fibers.
4. Test the supernatants from the cellulase assay samples (including the negative control) for glucose using the glucose test strips. Follow the directions on the glucose test strip package. Record the concentration of glucose in each sample in a data table. Affix all test strip test results in your notebook.
5. Conduct a Benedict's solution aldose (glucose) assay on each supernatant sample and on each of the glucose concentration standard samples following the steps below:

   Aldose Assay
   a. Place 2 mL of the solution to be tested into a 13x100-mm tube. Include a tube with only deionized water as a negative Benedict's test sample.
   b. Add 2 mL of Benedict's solution to the sample.
   c. Mix by gently vortexing for 1 to 2 seconds.
   d. Heat in a boiling water bath (100 mL of boiling water in a 250-mL beaker) for 2 minutes.

6. Using test tube holders, remove the tubes from the hot water bath and set up the glucose standard tubes (of known concentration) and the negative Benedict's control tube in a peg rack. Record the difference in colors observed in these standard tubes.
7. Compare the results of the Benedict's test cellulase sample tubes with the known glucose standard samples. Create a data table to record the colors observed and any sample concentration estimations that can be made.

Data Analysis/Conclusion

Is there evidence of cellulase activity in any of the cellulase assay samples? Give evidence for your statement. Did one cellulase appear to have significantly better activity than the other? If so, how much more? Describe any of the procedural steps that might have affected the results of the experiment. What one thing might be changed in the next trial of this experiment to increase the amount of glucose produced by the cellulase activity?

Thinking Like a Biotechnician

1. How might cellulose synthesis be increased in "biofuel" plants (the source biomass)?
2. Lignin is a plant compound that acts like a glue-like filler that hardens between cellulose fibers in plant cell walls. Removing lignin exposes more cellulose for processing. Propose a "biotech" method for removing lignin from cellulostic biomass.
3. Design a variation of this experiment to test the ability of each of the enzymes on cellulose in a grain product such as oatmeal.

Laboratory 14b
Bioremediation of Metal Contamination

Developed and modified by Xijia Sun, Selina Shen, and Ryo Kasagi, SMBCP students.

Background

Bioremediation occurs when an organism or biological system corrects an environmental problem. An example of bioremediation is when bacteria or fungi remove toxic chemicals from soil or water polluted during petroleum spills.

Shewanella oneidensis MR-1 (for "metal-reducing") is a species of bacteria that may have significant economic and environmental value due to their ability to bioremediate. In aerobic or anaerobic conditions, *S. oneidensis* can enzymatically reduce a variety of compounds, removing them from the surroundings.

Due to its potential to clean environments of metal contamination, *Shewanella oneidensis* MR-1 is being studied to assess the extent to which it can remove chromates, sulfates, or nitrates, and heavy metals such as iron, arsenic, lead, and perhaps even uranium from soil and water contaminated by agriculture, mining, and other industrial processes.

Purpose

How well can *Shewenella oneidensis* reduce the amount of potassium chromate present in a broth culture?

Materials

LB agar base
LB broth base
Beakers, 400 mL
Media bottles, 500 mL and 125 mL
Hot plate stirrer
Autoclave, autoclave tape
100 × 15-mm Petri dishes
Laminar flow hood
Inoculating loops, sterile, plastic
Shewanella oneidensis MR-1 (different samples are available from the

American Tissue Culture Collection, for example, ATCC #700550 or ATCC #BAA-1096)
Incubator oven, 30°C
Tubes, 50 mL sterile, conical
Tubes, 15 mL sterile, conical
Potassium chromate, G-Biosciences #BTNM-0064
Micropipets, P-1000, P-100, P-10 and sterile tips
Pipets, sterile 1 mL, 5 mL, 10 mL
Incubator, shaking, 30°C

Spectrophotometer, Spec 20D+
1,5-Diphenylcarbazide, 99%, 25g, G-Biosciences #BTNM-0028
Acetone
Centrifuge, for 15 mL tubes
Culture tubes, 13 × 100-mm
Peg rack, for 13 × 100 mm culture tubes
Plug-type caps, for 13 × 100 mm culture tubes
NaOH, 1 M
HCl, 1 M

Procedure

- Wear goggles and gloves when using chemicals.
- Use sterile technique throughout the procedure. Use a laminar flow hood, if available.
- Dispose of all biohazards appropriately.

Pre-Lab: Media and Reagent Preparation

1. Two days in advance of the Part I procedure, prepare 250 mL of sterile LB agar and pour 3 to 4 LB agar plates for use as stock plates. Also prepare four bottles of 250 mL of sterile LB broth for the class to use in Part I.
2. One day in advance of the Part I procedure, streak *Shewanella oneidensis* MR-1 bacteria onto the LB agar plates and incubate upside down at 30°C for 24 hours.
3. Prepare enough potassium chromate stock solution for multiple replications of the experiment. 20 mL of sterile 0.5 M stock solution of K_2CrO_4 is a good amount for a class of 32 students working in 16 pairs. Filter-sterilize the 0.5 M K_2CrO_4 stock solution.

Part I: Shewanella Potassium Chromate/LB Broth Cultures

1. Using sterile technique, prepare 3 mL of 0.1 M (100 mM) solution from the 0.5 M K$_2$CrO$_4$ stock solution in a sterile, 15-mL conical tube, using sterile LB broth as the diluting solvent.
2. Using sterile technique, prepare 10 mL of 1.0 mM solution from the 0.1M K$_2$CrO$_4$ solution in a sterile, 15-mL conical tube, using sterile LB broth as the diluting solvent.
3. Obtain six 15-mL, sterile, plastic conical tubes and label them as follows:

| 0 mM | 0.01 mM | 0.05 mM | 0.1 mM | 0.5 mM | 1.0 mM |
| K$_2$CrO$_4$ | K$_2$CrO$_4$ | K$_2$CrO$_4$ | K$_2$CrO$_4$ | K$_2$CrO$_4$ | K$_2$CrO$_4$ |

4. Add the specified amounts of 1.0 mM K$_2$CrO$_4$ solution to each of the labeled tubes as shown on the reaction matrix below (see Table 14.2). Mix well without foaming.

Table 14.2. **Potassium Chromate Preparation Matrix**

Final Concentration of K$_2$CrO$_4$ Desired (mM)	Volume of 1.0 mM K$_2$CrO$_4$ to be added (mL)
0	0
0.01	0.03
0.05	0.15
0.1	0.3
0.5	1.5
1.0	3.0

5. Add sterile LB broth up to the 3-mL graduation in each of the six tubes.
6. From the stock plate of *Shewanella oneidensis* MR-1, inoculate a large *Shewanella* colony into all of the tubes. Use a new inoculating loop for each transfer. Make sure the colony is well distributed throughout the broth solution.
7. Incubate the six culture tubes in a 30°C shaking incubator at 220 rpm for 48 hours.

Part II: Diphenylcarbazide Test for Potassium Chromate

1. Turn the spectrophotometer on and allow it to warm up for 15 to 20 minutes.
2. In an operating chemical fume hood and using a 125-mL glass media bottle, prepare 15 mL of 1% diphenylcarbazide solution in 50% acetone.
3. Remove the culture tubes from the 30°C incubator. Centrifuge the tubes for 10 minutes to pellet the bacteria cells. Do not disturb the pellet. The supernatant should be a clear, yellow broth.
4. Carefully pipet the supernatant from the 15-mL tubes and transfer each sample to a labeled 13 × 100-mm tube.
5. Prepare a negative control tube to use to compare the color change in the sample tubes, −C = 3 mL of 1.0 mM K$_2$CrO$_4$ mixed with LB broth (no bacteria added).

Diphenylcarbazide Test

6. Add 25 μL of 1 M NaOH into each of the 13 × 100-mm tubes.
7. Add 500 μL of the diphenylcarbazide solution to each of the 13 × 100-mm tubes.
8. Add 40 μL 1 M HCl into each of the 13 × 100-mm tubes.
9. Cap the tubes with plug caps. Shake the tubes until thoroughly mixed. Hexavalent chromium reacts with diphenylcarbazide under acid conditions to form a red-violet color. In a data table, record the color change in each tube (5 = bright magenta, 0 = clear, yellow).
10. Quickly, record the absorbance of each sample at 540 nm using the −C tube as a blank. Repeat using dH$_2$O as a blank. Record the absorbance data in a data table.
11. Collect data from other groups and determine the average values for each concentration tested. Plot the average absorbance data for each set of controls on two separate line graphs comparing absorbance to concentration of K$_2$CrO$_4$ in the samples.

Data Analysis and Conclusion

Compare the color and absorbance values of the bacteria-treated samples in each concentration of K_2CrO_4. Which samples showed evidence of bioremediation? What was the relative amount of bioremediation in samples with increasing concentrations of K_2CrO_4? Did the results support what you expected? Explain. Which negative control best demonstrated the difference in potassium chromate concentration after bacteria incubation? Explain why.

Did any of the samples give data that did not seem "right" or as expected? Explain what may have led to confusing or contradictory results.

Propose some practical applications of the data that was collected. Describe how bioremediation tests similar to this one might be used "in the field."

Thinking Like a Biotechnician

1. How can you tell if the *Shewanella* broth cultures in Part I, step 7, have a high-enough concentration of cells in them?
2. If all tubes are equally colored magenta at the end of the diphenylcarbazide test, what should you conclude?
3. Use the Internet to learn what effect chromium has on plants, both positive and negative.

Laboratory 14c
Bioremediation of Oil Contamination
Developed with the assistance of Hanna Evensen and Kiana Woodward, SMBCP Students

Background

Petroleum-based or nonpetroleum-based oil contamination of fresh or marine waters and soils is a serious threat to our environment. Spilled oil harms living things in several ways. The oil itself can be toxic. Many oils kill plants or animals directly after it has been ingested and some oils contaminate food sources poisoning animals in a food chain. Oils can also coat organisms affecting how they thermoregulate or other biological processes.

In an oil spill, the immediate response is to try to contain the spill and minimize the amount of area affected. Once a spill is contained, then efforts to clean up the oil are used. One strategy is to use bioremediation to remove oil from contaminated areas. Some bacteria have been found to thrive in "oily" environments and have shown the ability to "eat up" chemicals in oil. One particular bacterium, *Pseudomonas putida*, has been shown the ability to use compounds in oil and other aromatic hydrocarbons as a food source (genome.jgi.doe.gov/psepu/psepu.home.html). The efficiency of bacterial bioremediation may be affected by several factors including bacteria strain, culture concentration, water source, other nutrients, aeration of the culture, etc.

In this investigation, *Pseudomonas putida* is grown with aromatic hydrocarbons (refined motor oil) in an aqueous solution to test their ability to remove oil in a simulated aquatic environment.

Purpose

How does the aeration of a *Pseudomonas putida* culture affect its ability to degrade measurable amounts of oil in a culture?

Materials

Pseudomonas putida, LB agar plate, stab, or glycerol culture
Incubation oven, 30°C
Culture tubes, 50 mL, sterile, capped, conical
Tube rack, for 50-mL capped conical culture tubes

LB agar plate, (prepared following procedure in Lab 4e)
LB broth, 125 mL, sterile, in 250 mL media bottle (prepared following procedure in Lab 4e)

Aged, sterile tap water (left overnight in an open beaker, moved to media bottle for autoclaving)
Refined motor oil
Orbital shakers
Metric ruler

Procedure

Part I: Preparation of Stock LB Broth Culture

1. Streak a LB agar plate with a loopful of *Pseudomonas putida* and incubate upside-down in a 30°C incubator for 24 hours.
2. Use a colony from the overnight plate culture to inoculate the 125 mL of LB broth in the 250 mL media bottle. Place in an orbital shaker and incubate overnight at 250 rpm and 30°C. The culture should be cloudy with an O.D.600nm of approximately 0.6 au. Store it at 4°C for up to 2 days.

Part II: Preparation of Experiment Oil/Culture Tubes

1. Label 9 sterile, capped 50-mL tubes with identification initials and a tube number corresponding to a treatment and a replication. Prepare tubes for three repetitions of the samples to be tested in different amounts of aeration (A1, A2, A3 tubes = 300 rpm, B1, B2, B3 tubes = 150 rpm, C1, C2, C3 tubes = 0 rpm).
2. Add the following reagents to each tube in the order given in the reaction matrix. Use a sterile pipet or sterile micropipet tip (if using a micropipet) for each reagent dispensing. Make sure the overnight bacterial culture is fully suspended before taking a sample.

Table 14.3. Oil/Culture Tube Reaction Matrix

Reagent	Volume (mL)	Comments
Aged tap water	15	
LB broth	2	
Overnight Pseudomonas putida Broth Culture	2	Make sure that the culture is well suspended before sampling. Cap and invert tube before adding oil.
Refined Motor Oil	1	Cap and invert tube before moving to orbital shaker.
Total	**20**	

3. Once the experimental culture tubes are set up quickly make observations of the tubes, as a group, considering the factors listed in Table 4.4. Then, move the tubes quickly to a rack in one of three 30°C incubators (O rpm, 150 rpm, or 300 rpm).
4. After one week's incubation, return to the lab and take the tubes out of each incubator. Again, make observations of the tubes, in groups, considering the factors listed in Table 4.4.
5. Allow them to sit for 30 minutes and make observations of the tubes, in groups, considering the factors listed in Table 4.4
6. Allow the tube contents to settle or separate overnight and describe the samples and record observations in a data table similar to Table 4.4. Measurement of the oil layer is done with a metric ruler up against the outside of the tube. Measurements should be done at eye-level.

Table 14.4. The Amount of Oil in Oil/Bacterial Cultures with Different Amounts of Aeration

A tubes = 300 rpm, B tubes = 150 rpm, C tubes = 0 rpm

Sample	Turbidity/Cloudiness (0->10)	Emulsion/Oil Droplets in Solution (0->10)	Depth of Oil Layer on Top (mm)	Comments
A1				
A2				
A3				
A tube Average				
B1				
B2				
B3				
B tube Average				
C1				
C2				
C3				
C tube Average				

Data Analysis/Conclusion

Discuss evidence that the *Pseudomonas putida* culture were able to degrade measurable amounts of oil in a culture. Was there any significant difference in the amount of oil degradation in tubes with different amounts of aeration? Give evidence. Identify any technical errors that may have led to erroneous data. How might techniques be improved to achieve more reliable data? Make recommendations for procedural changes to increase oil degradation in samples.

Thinking Like a Biotechnician

1. In one replicate tube of a treatment, all of the oil has disappeared but the color of the culture is different from the replicates. How do you explain these results?
2. A small amount of LB broth is added to each culture tube. Explain why LB broth is added to the tubes and why it is added in such small amounts.

Laboratory 14d
D-Limonene as a BioInsecticide

Developed and modified by David Shao and Chris Zou, Biotechnology students.

Background

D-limonene is a hydrocarbon found in the rind of oranges and other citrus fruits. It has a strong orange scent and has been used as an ingredient in fragrances (see Figure 14.1). Currently, it is being used by some extermination services as a "natural" insecticide as an alternative to some of the chemical insecticides that are known to be dangerous to animals.

D-limonene, like most hydrocarbons, is not very water-soluble. To isolate it from citrus rinds, citrus rind slush is prepared and then steam-distilled. During steam distillation, water is boiled off and a concentrated limonene mixture is left in the boiling flask.

The orange rind slush, limonene concentrate, and the steam distillate can be tested for insecticidal properties by exposing wingless fruit flies to the samples and measuring the number of fly deaths.

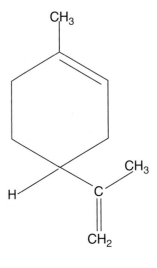

Figure 14.1. **D-limonene.**

Purpose

Can an insecticidal compound be isolated from orange rinds?

Materials

Part I: Preparation of Drosophila melanogster cultures

Drosophila melanogster, wingless
Drosophila medium, instant
Cups, paper, 8 oz
Tap water
Vials, sterile, plastic, 125 mL with vented tops
Sterile plastic netting or several sterile cotton swabs on wooden sticks
Funnel
Paintbrushes, small

Part II: Preparation of Orange Rind Slush

Orange
Cheese grater
Plate, plastic
Balance, weigh boat, lab scoops
Blender
dH$_2$O
Media bottle, 250 mL

Part III: Steam Distillation of Orange Rind Slush

Chemical fume hood with adjacent water faucet and sink
Distillation apparatus kit or components such as Fisher Science Education # S04534
Hot plate
Tubing, clear plastic
Ring stands and clamps
Rubber stoppers (2) with connecting glass tube
Beakers, 250 mL
Safety goggles
Orange slush
Pipet, 10 mL and pump
Tubes, 15 mL sterile, conical and racks

Part IV: Bioinsecticide Activity Assay

Petri dishes, 150 × 15 mm
Whatman filter paper, 12.5 cm
Compass and pencil
Pipet, 2 mL and pump
Samples to test for bioinsecticide activity from the distillation (deionized water, orange slush distillate, concentrated limonene sample from flask)
Drosophila melanogster, wingless, cultured in Part I

Procedure

Part I: Preparation of replicate Drosophila melanogster cultures upon culture arrival

1. Pour an equal amount of tap water and instant media into the bottom of the 125-mL flask to make about 40 mL of wetted media.
2. Let it sit for a minute or two. Make sure it's not too dry or too wet. Adjust as necessary.
3. Add a piece of sterile plastic netting to stick up out of the media so the flies have something to crawl on. Sterile cotton swabs on wooden sticks may be used as an alternate if netting is not available.
4. Place the "stock" flies' vials on their sides in the refrigerator for 5 minutes. This will temporarily cool the flies, slow them down, and prevent them from running away when trying to transfer them to the new cultures. Tilt the vials or bottles of new media at an angle.
5. After 5 minutes, take the flies out of the refrigerator and pour several through the funnel onto the side of the new media vials or bottles. Don't let the flies fall into the new media because they may drown. Use the paintbrush to move flies if necessary.
6. Quickly cap the vial or bottle. Leave the vial on its side until the flies become active, then set them upright. Store at room temperature in dim light until ready to use in each assay.
7. Repeat the process to transfer flies to new media about every two weeks.

Part II: Preparation of Orange Rind Slush

1. Place the cheese grater on top of a plate.
2. Grate the peel off the orange using the cheese grater. Apply only enough pressure to remove the rind and not the pith. Grate until there is only pith left as the outer layer of the orange.
3. Use scoops to scrape the grated rind into a blender.
4. Add 100 mL of dH$_2$O into the blender and blend until it is completely liquefied.
5. Pour the orange slush into a media bottle.
6. Label the bottle and store at 4°C for later use.

Figure 14.2. **Distillation Apparatus.**
Photo by author.

Part III: Steam Distillation of Orange Rind Slush

Wear goggles. Procedure should be done in a chemical fume hood with the protective shield in the down position.

1. Set up distillation apparatus as shown in Figure 14.2 in a chemical fume hood.
2. Add 100 mL of the orange slush into the round bottom flask.
3. Make sure the tubing is secure and turn on the sink faucet to make sure cold water is running through both the tubing and the condenser of the distillation apparatus.
4. Place a beaker at the end of the condenser to catch the distillate.
5. Lower the chemical fume hood protective shield to protect the user.
6. Turn on the hot plate and set to "High" or "10" to bring the sample to a boil.
7. As soon as it boils, lower the temperature setting to about medium-high or "7" to prevent it from boiling over.
8. Record the start time and the amount of orange slush used.
9. Allow it to slowly boil for 1 to 1.5 hours. During this time water vapor will rise, condense on the condenser, and drip into the collection beaker. This is the distillate.
10. Turn off the hot plate when there is only about 10 mL of sample left in the bottom of the flask. Allow to cool to room temperature.
11. Record the stop time. Use a 10-mL pipet to collect the sample (limonene concentrate) in the bottom of the flask. Transfer it to a labeled 15-mL tube. Record the amount of limonene concentrate collected. Store at 4°C.
12. Record the total amount of distillate collected. Collect 10 mL of the distillate (watery) sample. Transfer it to a labeled 15-mL tube. If there is an oily layer on top of the distillate, collect the 10-mL sample by pipeting the top of the oily layer. Store at 4°C.

Part IV: Bioinsecticide Activity Assay

1. Cut a filter paper to fit flat on the bottom of a Petri dish. Repeat with three others so there are four dishes with filter paper liners.
2. Use a compass and a pencil to draw a ring encircling the center of the filter paper at about 4 cm from the center. A circular sample of test material will be added on this line.
3. Use a 2-mL pipet to withdraw 2 mL of a sample to be tested (start with the limonene concentrate) on the pencil line, dispensing the sample slowly and equally over the entire line circle. Try to keep the sample from spreading toward the center of the plate (where the flies will be placed).
4. Repeat the dispensing of test liquids on the other three filter paper inserts in the other three plates (one for the orange slush, one for the distillate, and one for the deionized water).
5. Chill the fly vial for 5 minutes. Pour ten chilled wingless flies into the center of each filter paper inserts in each of the three plates.

6. Watch the flies as they begin to warm up and walk from the center out. When flies walk across the circles that have an effective bioinsecticide sample on them, the flies will stop and die.
7. On a data table, record the number of flies that reach the circle on each plate and die. Record the number of flies that reach the circle on each plate and do not die. Record the number of flies that did not reach the circle on each plate. Explain why you think they did not walk to the sample(s).
8. Repeat steps 1 through 7 three times and average the results. Create a bar graph to show the summary results.

Data Analysis/Conclusion

Is there evidence of bioinsecticide activity in any of the samples? Give evidence for your statement. Did one sample appear to have significantly better bioinsecticide activity than the others? If so, how much more? Describe any of the procedural steps that might have affected the results of the experiment. Suggest methods for increasing the insecticidal properties of any of the samples.

Thinking Like a Biotechnician

1. Use the Internet to find commercially available D-limonene. Where can you get some? How much does it cost? For what applications do the vendors claim D-limonene may be used?
2. Suggest a method for confirming that any sample actually contains D-limonene.